W9-DEW-281

discover Stampin' Up!

getting started

24 stampin' kits
Each kit includes the stamps, ink, and card stock you need to create dozens of cards and other projects.

stamps

28 holidays
Commemorate your favorite holidays: Valentine's Day, Easter, Halloween, Christmas, and more.

54 seasons
Stop here for a selection of images that celebrate the seasons: winter, spring, summer, and fall.

64 occasions
Find something for every occasion–birthdays, graduations, baby and bridal showers, weddings, and more.

90 sentiments
Select from a variety of sets with coordinating messages and images, including thank you, get well soon, and inspirational.

107 growing up
Celebrate the stages of a child's life with a selection of stamp sets devoted to babies, kids, and teens.

121 flowers
Pick a stamp set from this garden of floral images, and watch your projects blossom.

135 nature
Appreciate the beauties of nature with images inspired by leaves, seashells, animals, birds, bugs, and more.

150 vintage
Try art trends, such as photo realistic or pencil sketch, in an assortment of images, including scenery, antiques, and collectibles.

163 frames, borders & backgrounds
Add to and accentuate your artwork with our frame, border, and background stamps.

177 say it with stamps
Say what you mean and mean what you say with these greetings, verses, titles, and alphabets. Also try our personalized stamps.

paper, ink, albums & more

198 accessories
Stampin' Up! offers a full line of accessories. You'll find templates, adhesives, embellishments, and more–all designed to help you be creative.

1

Follow these four steps for easy stamp assembly:

[1] Trim rubber close to image. Make straight cuts.

[2] Match rubber to correct blocks. Trim and apply labels.

[3] Apply rubber, matching position of rubber with label.

[4] Apply label with stamp set name to the end of box.

In this catalog, you'll find stamp sets you can't find anywhere else! Renowned within the stamping industry, our exclusive images earned the 2005 *Creating Keepsakes'* Readers' Choice Award for best rubber stamps—for the fourth year in a row! Our stamp sets offer deeply etched images on foam-backed rubber that ensure sharp and clear stamped images.

By allowing you to assemble the stamps, Stampin' Up! passes the savings to you and gives you the freedom to position your stamps to suit your stamping style.

Note: Stamps in this catalog are shown at actual size.

2

There's no limit to the number of projects you can create with only one stamp set, such as the Flower Filled set shown here. Select a set and let it spark your imagination!

Our stamps are sold in sets, which ensures versatility for all of your stamping projects. With each set, you can create cards, scrapbook pages, home décor, gift packaging, place-card holders, napkin rings, calendars, door hangers, mini books, and more. Notice the array of projects we have created with the same set, Flower Filled (page 56).

Stampin' Up! offers rubber stamps in a variety of styles: bold, line art, contemporary, vintage, and more. With nearly 400 sets in this catalog, there's something to appeal to everyone.

Note: You will find a list of Stampin' Supplies for each project in this catalog beginning on page 241.

3

If you're looking for an easy way to stamp your projects, nothing's faster than our Stampin' Around® wheels. Because many wheels are designed to complement images in our stamp sets, you can use the wheel and stamp set together to create beautifully coordinated projects. With cartridges available in Stampin' Up!'s exclusive colors, wheeled images also coordinate with our other products, such as card stock, eyelets, and more. Turn to pages 238-239 to see all of our Stampin' Around wheels.

Our Stampin' Around Wheel Guide (page 225) makes it easy to align wheeled images without worrying about crooked lines or overlapping images. This convenient tool works with standard and jumbo wheels.

4

With all the images Stampin' Up! offers, you're sure to find countless combinations of stamp sets and accessories that work together to create a pleasing, consistent feel. These combinations simplify the project-making process—you can choose a theme, select its coordinating products, and plan your project. Here, we present projects to demonstrate one of our favorite styles.

When you want to combine stamps with other stamps and accessories on a project, look for products with a similar style. Our stamp sets are designed to coordinate with other image sets, verses, and alphabets. You'll build a wonderful collection of stamps and be amazed by the incredible looks you can achieve.

Note: To help you find coordinating products, we've placed *don't miss it!* suggestions throughout the catalog that list stamp sets and their coordinating accessories.

5

Bold Brights

 glorious green

 green galore

 gable green

 yoyo yellow

 only orange

 real red

 pink passion

 pixie pink *new!*

 orchid opulence

 lovely lilac

 brilliant blue

 tempting turquoise

Earth Elements

 chocolate chip

 close to cocoa

 creamy caramel

 more mustard

 pumpkin pie *new!*

 really rust

 ruby red

 cameo coral

 summer sun

 old olive

 garden green

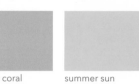 not quite navy

6

These products are available in
Stampin' Up!'s exclusive colors:

- Stampin' Write® journalers
- Stampin' Write markers*
- Classic Stampin' Pads® and refills*
- Craft Stampin' Pads and refills*
- 8-1/2 x 11 card stock*
- 12 x 12 card stock*
- Stampin' Pastels® and refills*
- Stampin' Around standard cartridges*
- Stampin' Around jumbo cartridges
- Boxes, cards, and tags (pages 212–214)
- Spectrum pads (page 222)
- Watercolor Wonder™ Crayons (page 223)
- Eyelets (page 229)
- Buttons (page 230)

Products can be found on pages 198–201
unless otherwise noted.

*Available in all color families.

Use the Color Coach®
(page 199) to create fun
color combinations.

Stampin' Up!'s large collection of accessories is based
on a foundation of four color families along with neutral
colors to enhance them. Because most of our products
are formulated to go together, we take the guesswork
out of color coordination. Each color is organized into
one of our families: Bold Brights®, Earth Elements®, Rich
Regals®, and Soft Subtles®. The colors within each group
are designed to complement each other.

Once you have selected your color scheme, you have
a full range of coordinating products from which to
choose. We offer an array of accessories and embellishments designed to enhance your stamped projects.

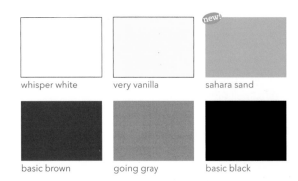

whisper white   very vanilla   sahara sand

basic brown   going gray   basic black

Rich Regals

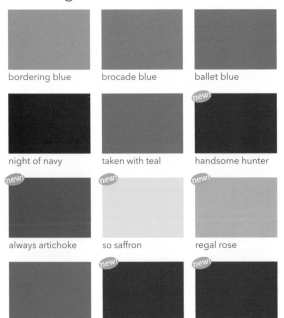

bordering blue   brocade blue   ballet blue

night of navy   taken with teal   handsome hunter

always artichoke   so saffron   regal rose

rose red   bravo burgundy   elegant eggplant

Soft Subtles

perfect plum   pale plum   pretty in pink

blush blossom   apricot appeal   barely banana

certainly celery   mellow moss   sage shadow

bashful blue   almost amethyst   lavender lace

aloha

To a fabulous purse-on!

wish-shoe a happy day!

Babies are bits of stardust blown from the hand of God. —Larry Barretto

8

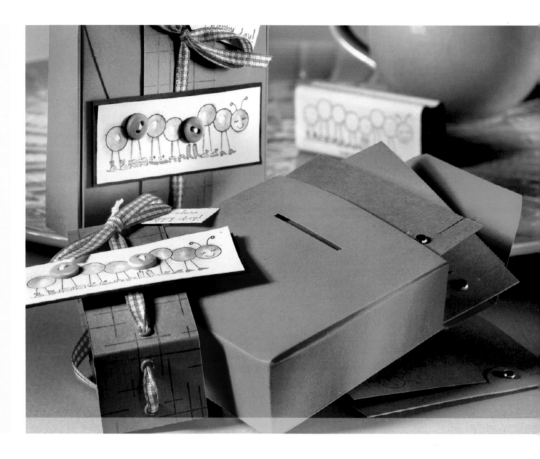

Create a cute stationery set by filling our Bloomin' Box (page 212) with some hand-stamped cards.

Cardmakers have long appreciated Stampin' Up!'s diverse product line, but cards aren't the only projects you can create with our products. In addition to cards, you can create scrapbook pages, home décor, wrapping paper, books, journals, and other unique projects. Whatever you envision, Stampin' Up!'s stamp sets and accessories help you transform your creations from the ordinary to the extraordinary. Whether you're creating cards or three-dimensional items, you'll find everything you need to make your projects truly unique and memorable. And if you need project ideas, this Idea Book & Catalog includes more than 500 full-color samples you can duplicate!

Stampin' Up! is a national sponsor of Ronald McDonald House Charities® (RMHC®)—and we're pleased to offer this exclusive stamp set to all of our customers! We'll donate $2 from the sale of each **Sweet & Sassy** set (shown at right and on page 137) to RMHC, an organization committed to improving the lives of children and their families throughout the world. When you buy the set, you make a difference in the lives of children and families served by RMHC.

9

Label the spine of your linen albums (shown on page 204) with Hodgepodge Hardware® pieces (shown on page 229).

You may not realize it now, but your friends and family will be forever grateful to you for preserving your memories. Explore the variety of options Stampin' Up! provides to help you capture any theme or occasion and preserve your memories so that your family will enjoy reminiscing and poring over your albums in the future.

Combine your passion for stamping with your desire to preserve memories by introducing rubber stamping into your scrapbooking. You can use any of our stamp sets to create scrapbook pages with personalized elements, such as titles, accents, and journaling pieces. Stampin' Up!'s color families make it easy to coordinate these accents with your photos.

In addition to our stamp sets, we have a range of scrapbooking products, including Simply Scrappin'® kits, Designer Series papers, and more. Scrapbookers will also appreciate these products:

- Our alphabet sets can be used to create titles in any color, and you'll never run out of letters.

- Our *Write Me a Memory*® Journaling Fonts CDs make your computer journaling look handwritten and stylish.

- While any stamp set can be used on your scrapbook pages, stamps such as our Flexible Phrases sets (page 191) are especially suited for scrapbooking.

With Stampin' Up!'s products, your pages will always be original and unique.

Note: While most of Stampin' Up!'s products are safe for your scrapbooks, our Stampin' Memories symbol identifies those that were specifically created for and are the best choice for scrapbooking.

ITS

TOOL TIME

Every time dad pours
on his tool belt, Zach
is right behind him.
He loves helping out
with Dad's projects.

2005

Vacation

We enjoyed our trip to HAWAII
so much! We had been looking forward to
this trip for a long time. We spent 2
wonderful weeks together.

A WALK IN

THE PARK

11

12

You'll love how easy it is to create hand-stamped, framed art. Use any stamp set and color palette to create custom home accents for any season or occasion.

With Definitely Decorative® stamping, you can create custom interiors at a fraction of the cost usually required to update home furnishings. Customize your home décor by stamping walls, fabrics, and other furnishings to give them an entirely new look.

Two-Step Stampin'

Create a single multicolored image with Two-Step Stampin'®—simply layer one image over another for fast and easy stamping with amazing results. The Two-Step Stampin' logo marks these sets in the catalog.

Step 1: Stamp the base image in a light color.

Step 2: Stamp the outline image in a darker color.

13

Create a wish list of products you would like to earn when you host your own workshop.

Earn free products by hosting a Stampin' Up! workshop, a stamping event where you open your home and invite your friends to enjoy an exciting demonstration provided by a Stampin' Up! demonstrator. When you host a workshop, you'll see new project ideas, learn different stamping techniques, and have fun with people you enjoy. To thank you for being a hostess, you'll receive a free Idea Book & Catalog from your demonstrator. Based on the sales of your workshop, you can also earn:

- Free stamp sets available only to hostesses (select from the sets on pages 15–23 based on your workshop sales).

- Free Stampin' Up! products of your choice (see chart for details).

- Free Hostess Appreciation Special (shown in the current mini catalog).

14

Hostess Benefits

net workshop total	hostess sets			hostess awards
	[level] 1	[level] 2	[level] 3	free merchandise totaling up to:
$150.00 – $199.99	choose 1	–	–	$15.00
$200.00 – $249.99	choose 1	–	–	$20.00
$250.00 – $299.99	choose 1	–	–	$25.00
$300.00 – $349.99	choose 1 OR	choose 1	–	$35.00
$350.00 – $399.99	choose 1 OR	choose 1	–	$40.00
$400.00 – $449.99	choose 1 OR	choose 1	–	$45.00
$450.00 – $499.99	choose 1 OR	choose 1	–	$50.00
$500.00 – $549.99	choose 2 OR choose 1 OR –	– choose 1 –	– – choose 1	$60.00
$550.00 – $599.99	choose 2 OR choose 1 OR –	– choose 1 –	– – choose 1	$65.00
$600.00 – $649.99	choose 2 OR choose 1 OR –	– choose 1 –	– – choose 1	$75.00
$650.00 – $699.99	choose 2 OR choose 1 OR –	– choose 1 –	– – choose 1	$85.00
$700.00 – $749.99	choose 2 OR choose 1 OR –	– choose 1 –	– – choose 1	$95.00
$750.00 +	choose 2 OR choose 1 OR –	– choose 1 –	– – choose 1	$100.00 plus 15% of amount over $750.00

No shipping and handling amounts are charged on hostess benefits.

Pocket Full of Posies [set of 4]
105511

[level **1**]

Around the Block [set of 4]
105483

[level **1**]

Birthday WISHES

Timeworn Trim [set of 4]
105505

[level **1**]

grateful

joy

wish

always

Small Script [set of 4]
105414

[level **1**]

Flowers of

gratitude

bloom forever

in the heart.

Flowers of Gratitude [set of 4]
105495

[level **1**]

joy

The Winders 12·04

boo!

love

celebrate

joy

Say It Simply [set of 4]
105477

[level **1**]

16

winter
wonder

peace

Too **cute** for words

you are

Made from Scratch [set of 4]
104956

[level **1**]

3 sheets
Tempting Turquoise

3 sheets
Certainly Celery

2 sheets
Whisper White

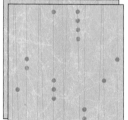

I took these pictures of Ella when she was 8 months old. She was just so happy that day. She played with her toys and had so much fun!

ELLA

February 2005

17

Simply Scrappin' **Island Blossoms**
105802

[level **1**]

Simply Scrappin' Kits contain 18 sheets of coordinating materials to create quick and easy, yet distinctive, scrapbook pages. Combine with Stampin' Up!'s alphabet stamp sets for personalized page titles. See pages 208–211 for our full line of Simply Scrappin' Kits.

Provençal [set of 4]
105000

[**level 2**]

try this

Turn a paper clip into an eye-catching embellishment. The tools in the Crafters' Tool Kit (shown on page 228) will help you sew the clip to the page.

18

You're just my style!

You're just my style!

You're just my style!

sassy

Haute Couture [set of 7]
104810

[level **2**]

thanks

THE AMEN OF NATURE IS ALWAYS A FLOWER. —EMERSON

THE HEART THAT GIVES ALSO GATHERS.

SPREAD YOUR LOVE EVERYWHERE YOU GO. —MOTHER TERESA

Reverse Prints [set of 3]
105425

[level **2**]

celebrate!   bundle of joy wish big!

Along the Same Lines [set of 4]
104824

[level **2**]

don't miss it! This set coordinates with the Nice & Narrow set shown on page 71.

Oh, My Word [set of 6]
104957

[level **2**]

much appreciated

My

FaVoRitE

HAT

From the collection

January 2005

you're
an
original!

Most angels are not invisible
and they usually
leave their wings at home.

hatty birthday!

always
in
step!

thanks-
you're an
angel!

you're
an
original!

*foot note

you're
an
original

thanks for
your support

thanks for
your support

knit
happens

Fashion Statements [set of 12]
105421

[level **3**]

Nature's Secret [set of 6]
105416

[level **3**]

22

GIRLS WITH **ATTITUDE**

Sassy SheLby

GrooVy GretcheN

Summer 2004

Definitely Decorative **Island Blossoms** [set of 12]
105260

[**level 3**]

Stampin' Kits make a perfect gift. They offer all one needs to start a fun and creative new hobby.

Our Stampin' Kits help you start stamping in one easy step. Each preselected kit includes basic stamping supplies, such as a stamp set, ink pads, card stock, and envelopes, so you can create the projects shown here, plus dozens more of your own design. The optional Step It Up products and accessories allow you to expand your creative options and enhance your stamping projects.

If these kits aren't exactly your style, you can create kits of your own by ordering items individually, using our recommendations as a guideline. Simply follow the SIP principle, which stands for **S**tamps, **I**nk, and **P**aper. Once you select a stamp set, ink pad(s), and coordinating card stock or paper, you have what you need to get started! Your Stampin' Up! demonstrator can help you select the items that are right for you.

Create Your Own Custom Kit

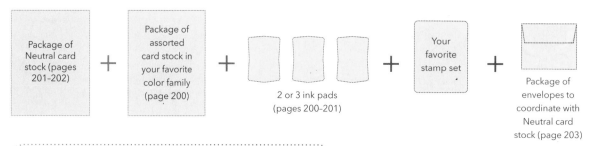

Package of Neutral card stock (pages 201–202)

+

Package of assorted card stock in your favorite color family (page 200)

+

2 or 3 ink pads (pages 200–201)

+

Your favorite stamp set

+

Package of envelopes to coordinate with Neutral card stock (page 203)

Note: We have provided page numbers for your convenience in selecting the accessories. The two bottom samples shown for each kit use Step It Up products as well as kit items. Kits do not include adhesive or scissors. For a great selection of these products, turn to pages 220–221.

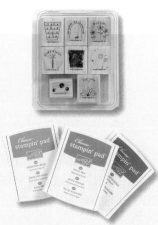

Loads of Love Stampin' Kit
105738 **$49.25**

....

[p. 29]   Loads of Love Stamp Set
[p. 200]   Earth Elements Card Stock (8-1/2 x 11)
[p. 201]   Very Vanilla Card Stock (8-1/2 x 11)
[p. 201]   Basic Brown Classic Stampin' Pad
[p. 200]   Ruby Red Classic Stampin' Pad
[p. 203]   Very Vanilla Medium Envelopes

Fun Filled Stampin' Kit
105736 **$51.20**

....

[p. 64]   Fun Filled Stamp Set
[p. 200]   Rich Regals Card Stock (8-1/2 x 11)
[p. 201]   Whisper White Card Stock (8-1/2 x 11)
[p. 201]   Always Artichoke Classic Stampin' Pad
[p. 201]   Brocade Blue Classic Stampin' Pad
[p. 201]   Rose Red Classic Stampin' Pad
[p. 203]   Whisper White Medium Envelopes

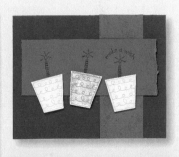

stampin' kits

25

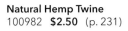

Step it up

Loads of Love Accessories Stamp Set
105349 **$16.95** (p. 29)

Natural Hemp Twine
100982 **$2.50** (p. 231)

Stampin' Pastels
105542 **$24.95** (p. 199)

Step it up

Slit Punch
104388 **$4.95** (p. 218)

Vintage Brads
104583 **$7.95** (p. 229)

Black Gingham Ribbon
104832 **$6.95** (p. 232)

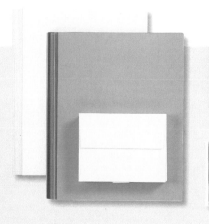

Tag Time Stampin' Kit

105735 **$61.20**

[p. 28]	Tag Time Stamp Set
[p. 200]	Bold Brights Card Stock (8-1/2 x 11)
[p. 201]	Whisper White Card Stock (8-1/2 x 11)
[p. 200]	Tempting Turquoise Classic Stampin' Pad
[p. 200]	Real Red Classic Stampin' Pad
[p. 200]	Gable Green Classic Stampin' Pad
[p. 203]	Whisper White Medium Envelopes

Heartfelt Thanks Stampin' Kit

105737 **$63.20**

[p. 125]	Heartfelt Thanks Stamp Set
[p. 200]	Soft Subtles Card Stock (8-1/2 x 11)
[p. 201]	Whisper White Card Stock (8-1/2 x 11)
[p. 201]	Pretty in Pink Classic Stampin' Pad
[p. 201]	Certainly Celery Classic Stampin' Pad
[p. 201]	Perfect Plum Classic Stampin' Pad
[p. 203]	Whisper White Medium Envelopes

stampin' kits

26

Step it up

Bold Brights Petal Cards & Tags
105069 **$6.95** (p. 212)

Clear Buttons
105447 **$4.95** (p. 230)

Turquoise Grosgrain Ribbon
102119 **$5.95** (p. 232)

Step it up

Celery Grosgrain Ribbon
105373 **$5.95** (p. 232)

Silver Brads
104336 **$6.95** (p. 229)

Collage Stampin' Memories Kit
105739 **$63.65**

....

[p. 196]   Collage Alphabet Stamp Set
[p. 205]   Heirloom Timeworn Collection Paper (12 x 12)
[p. 200]   Rich Regals Card Stock (12 x 12)
[p. 202]   Kraft Card Stock (12 x 12)
[p. 201]   Always Artichoke Craft Stampin' Pad
[p. 200]   Creamy Caramel Craft Stampin' Pad
[p. 201]   Basic Black Stampin' Write Journaler

Use the Stampin' Memories kit to create a theme album. Turn to page 204 to see our complete line of albums.

stampin' kits

27

Step it up

Aged to Perfection Stamp Set
105410 **$22.95** (p. 161)

Pockets & Pieces Assortment 1
105067 **$8.95** (p. 213)

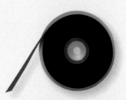

Antique Brass Hodgepodge Hardware
105531 **$26.95** (p. 229)

Chocolate Grosgrain Ribbon
105374 **$5.95** (p. 232)

GOOD LUCK

TO:

FROM:

best witches!

CELEBRATE!

happy shower!

too cute!

Tag Time [set of 14]
105453 **$26.95**

don't miss it! These stamps are sized to fit on our Tag Sheets and Metal Edge tags, shown on pages 214–215. This set is also sold as part of a kit on page 26.

always

forever

cherish

happy shower!

a little something

happy spring

Festive Four [set of 4]
105451 **$11.95**

thought you could use a little pickup!

Loads of Love!

wishing you loads of holiday cheer!

merry christmas!

Loads of Love [set of 7]
104606 **$19.95**

don't miss it! This set is sold as part of a kit on page 25.

driving by with a birthday "Hi"!

just moved!

happy harvest

eggstra special easter wishes!

friends for the long haul

Loads of Love Accessories [set of 12]
105349 **$16.95**

Stampin' Around **Time for a Tree**
104524 **$5.95** *(Wheel only. Handle and ink cartridges sold separately. See pages 200-201, 225.)*

Stampin' Around **Tailgating**
105519 **$5.95** *(Wheel only. Handle and ink cartridges sold separately. See pages 200-201, 225.)*

holidays

29

© 1990-2005 STAMPIN' UP!

Year-Round Fun II [set of 28]
103913 **$28.95**

Just a little note to let you know how much your kindness means to me.

May this holiday find you surrounded by those you love.

Thanks!

Sketch It [set of 12]
103311 **$34.95**

holidays

30

May this holiday find you surrounded by those you love.

KISS ME   LOVE YOU   BE MINE   HUGS

Sweet Talk [set of 6]
103967 **$9.95**

Mon Ami [set of 4]
104877 **$14.95**

Stampin' Around **Love Swirls**
102254 **$5.95** *(Wheel only. Handle and ink cartridges sold separately. See pages 200-201, 225.)*

holidays

31

Loving Hearts [set of 7]
103728 **$19.95**

32

Stampin' Around **All Heart**
104069 **$5.95** *(Wheel only. Handle and ink cartridges sold separately. See pages 200-201, 225.)*

Smitten [set of 6]
103883 **$17.95**

hoppy Valentine's day!

a little toucan of my friend-ship!

here's a treat 'cause you're so sweet!

HAPPY VALENTINE'S DAY!

you're fin-tastic!

to

from

Toucan of My Love [set of 6]
103945 **$19.95**

Happy Hearts [set of 6]
100319 **$14.95**

Create a unique box by trimming the top approximately 1/2-inch above the score line. When you assemble it, fold the top edges inside the box. This box is sold on page 212.

try this

holidays

33

Happy SPRING!

Spring Fling [set of 4]
104020 **$11.95**

May God's everlasting love bring you never-ending joy.

Easter Blessings

Never-Ending Joy [set of 6]
105038 **$17.95**

Bitty Boos Too [set of 12]
105355 **$16.95**

coltin and mallorie could hardly wait to go to the pumpkin patch to pick out their pumpkins this year. coltin was on the hunt for the biggest pumpkin he could carry and mallorie was looking for the roundest one she could spot.

october 2004

Carved & Candlelit [set of 6]
104225 **$14.95**

holidays

35

TRICK
* OR
TREAT
*

Trick or Treat [set of 4]
100028 **$11.95**

Halloween Backgrounds [set of 4]
104028 **$11.95**

36

Stampin' Around **Spooky Spiders**
100351 **$5.95** *(Wheel only. Handle and ink cartridges sold separately. See pages 200-201, 225.)*

Stampin' Around **Happy Jacks**
100267 **$5.95** *(Wheel only. Handle and ink cartridges sold separately. See pages 200-201, 225.)*

One ... **Spooky** Night

Home Is Where the Haunt Is [set of 6]
105412 **$14.95**

Happy Halloween! From our web to yours.

Web Wishes [set of 6]
104614 **$21.95**

Creeping by just to say hi!

Happy Halloween! From our web to yours.

37

Stampin' Around Jumbo **Spooky Skyline**
105521 **$7.95** *(Wheel only. Handle and ink cartridges sold separately. See pages 200-201, 225.)*

Happy Holidays

Frosty [set of 4]
101826 **$16.95**

> Mix a variety of ribbon on your project for a fresh, fun look.
>
> **try this**

Crazy for Christmas [set of 4]
100126 **$19.95**

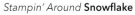

Stampin' Around **Snowflake**
101233 **$5.95** *(Wheel only. Handle and ink cartridges sold separately. See pages 200-201, 225.)*

holidays

38

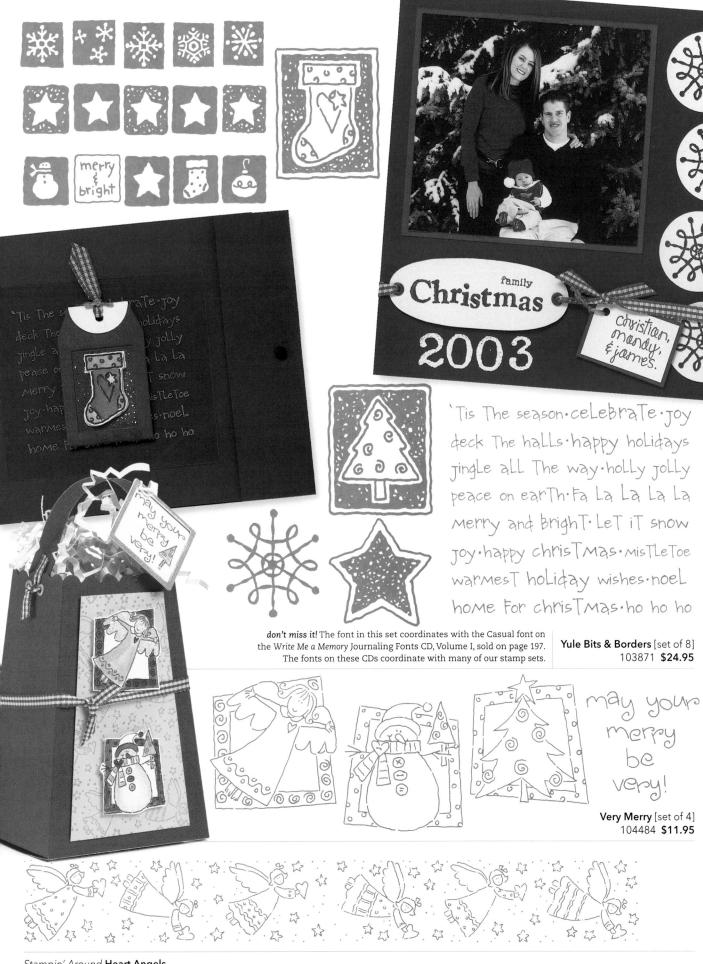

'Tis The season·ceLebraTe·joy
deck The haLLs·happy holidays
jingLe aLL The way·holly joLLy
peace on earTh·Fa La La La La
merry and brighT·LeT iT snow
joy·happy chrisTmas·misTLeToe
warmesT holiday wishes·noeL
home For chrisTmas·ho ho ho

don't miss it! The font in this set coordinates with the Casual font on the *Write Me a Memory* Journaling Fonts CD, Volume I, sold on page 197. The fonts on these CDs coordinate with many of our stamp sets.

Yule Bits & Borders [set of 8]
103871 **$24.95**

may your
merry
be
very!

Very Merry [set of 4]
104484 **$11.95**

holidays

39

Stampin' Around **Heart Angels**
103150 **$5.95** (Wheel only. Handle and ink cartridges sold separately. See pages 200-201, 225.)

Santa Post [set of 6]
104111 **$14.95**

40

happy holidays

to:

from:

Holiday Woodcuts [set of 6]
100006 **$19.95**

Stampin' Around **Gingerbread Man**
101829 **$5.95** *(Wheel only. Handle and ink cartridges sold separately. See pages 200–201, 225.)*

Sparkling Season [set of 6]
100335 **$19.95**

don't miss it! This set has a coordinating Simply Scrappin' kit on page 210.

Tie ribbon through a clip to make a nice box closure. Scraps of ribbon are perfect for projects like this.

try this

holidays

41

Stampin' Around **Funky Firs**
104102 **$5.95** *(Wheel only. Handle and ink cartridges sold separately. See pages 200-201, 225.)*

Stampin' Around **Candy Cane Craze**
100398 **$5.95** *(Wheel only. Handle and ink cartridges sold separately. See pages 200-201, 225.)*

Flaky Friends [set of 8]
101850 **$24.95**

Create a custom accent by wheeling an image on our twill tape. Use brads to hold the tape in place.

try this

Stampin' Around **Star**
101638 **$5.95** *(Wheel only. Handle and ink cartridges sold separately. See pages 200-201, 225.)*

Stampin' Around **Many Mittens**
100417 **$5.95** *(Wheel only. Handle and ink cartridges sold separately. See pages 200-201, 225.)*

*Carols in the frosty night,
Holly boughs and candlelight,
Children's faces shining bright—
How sweet the joys of Christmas!*

Christmas Carolers [set of 2]
103843 **$17.95**

Holiday Print [set of 1]
100313 **$16.95**

holidays

43

CAROLS IN THE CHILLY NIGHT,
SNOWFLAKES, HOLLY, CANDLELIGHT,
CHILDREN'S FACES
SHINING BRIGHT—
BRING JOY TO ALL AT CHRISTMAS!

Merry Minstrels [set of 4]
105357 **$17.95**

Holiday Wishes [set of 6]
100426 **$22.95**

Stampin' Around **Gifts Galore**
103195 **$5.95** *(Wheel only. Handle and ink cartridges sold separately. See pages 200-201, 225.)*

holidays

44

Happy Winter [set of 4]
100789 **$11.95**

Ornament Elements [set of 8]
105347 **$24.95**

Use the fine tip of a 2-Way Glue Pen to add glitter exactly where you want it.

try this

holidays

45

Stampin' Around **Pine Bough**
101088 **$5.95** *(Wheel only. Handle and ink cartridges sold separately. See pages 200-201, 225.)*

PEACE BE UNTO YOU

May peace be more
than a season...
May it be a way of life.

PEACE BE
UNTO YOU

Peace Be unto You [set of 4]
105335 **$17.95**

May the
holiday spirit
find a home
in your heart.

Holiday Spirit [set of 6]
103532 **$19.95**

holidays

46

Stampin' Around **Only Ornaments**
103543 **$5.95** *(Wheel only. Handle and ink cartridges sold separately.* *See pages 200-201, 225.)*

May your season be touched with the simple grace of His love.

Merry Christmas

For unto us a child is born, unto us a son is given...

—Isaiah 9:6

Madonna and Child [set of 4]
105343 **$18.95**

Angels descending from above, echoes of mercy, whispers of Love.

Let the heavens rejoice and the earth be glad

holidays

47

It's easy to create a complementary background by repeatedly stamping a smaller image from a stamp set. Use the same color ink as the card stock for a subtle tone-on-tone effect, or stamp with a different color for dramatic results.

try this

Renaissance Angels [set of 5]
105158 **$22.95**

Now abide
faith, hope, love,
these three;
but the greatest
of these is
love.

1 Corinthians 13:13

O Christmas star
forever bright,
shine into our hearts
tonight-
Remembering
the holy birth,
His love and hope,
His peace on earth.

Peace & Love [set of 6]
104377 **$22.95**

VERY
MERRY

HAPPY HOLIDAYS HAPPY HOLIDAYS
HAPPY HOLIDAYS

HO HO HO

TO

FROM

holidays

48

DO NOT
OPEN 'TIL
CHRISTMAS!

Holiday Tag Team [set of 14]
104105 **$26.95**

Wishing you the happiest of holidays.

don't miss it! Create custom holiday wrapping paper with one of the three jumbo wheels on this page and our white wrapping paper (page 216). Complete the gift by adding a tag using the Happiest of Holidays set.

Happiest of Holidays [set of 4]
104417 **$14.95**

Stampin' Around Jumbo **Swirling Stars**
104425 **$7.95** *(Wheel only. Handle and ink cartridges sold separately. See pages 200-201, 225.)*

Stampin' Around Jumbo **Woodcut Holly**
104423 **$7.95** *(Wheel only. Handle and ink cartridges sold separately. See pages 200-201, 225.)*

Stampin' Around Jumbo **Poinsettia**
104424 **$7.95** *(Wheel only. Handle and ink cartridges sold separately. See pages 200-201, 225.)*

holidays

49

Cruisin' by with a Christmas hi!

A time for joy,
a time for hope,
a time to wish
all good things.

'Tis the SEASON

The Walkers

A time for joy,
a time for hope,
a time to wish
all good things.

2004

MERRY Christmas

holidays

'Tis the Season [set of 6]
104419 **$19.95**

don't miss it! This set has a coordinating Classy Brass® embossing template on page 227.

To:
From:

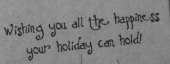
Wishing you all the happiness
your holiday can hold!

HOLIDAY
Greetings

Wishing you all the happiness
your holiday can hold!

Sleigh Full of Toys [set of 7]
104375 **$19.95**

Glory to God in the highest,
and on earth,
Goodwill to men.

believe

Glory to God in the highest,
and on earth,
Goodwill to men.

holidays

51

the love of
beautiful things is
heavenly
homesickness.

Glory to God in the highest,
and on earth,
Goodwill to men.
© 2005 STAMPIN' UP!

Heavenly Heralds [set of 4]
105435 **$17.95**

joy!

THINK of CHRISTMAS-
Think of SNOW-
THINK of Santa-
* Ho! ho! Ho!

merry!

Merry [set of 8]
105152 **$22.95**

wishing you
sweet holiday
memories

Sweet Holidays [set of 6]
104032 **$16.95**

wishing you
sweet holiday
memories

Stampin' Around **Holiday Sweets**
104157 **$5.95** *(Wheel only. Handle and ink cartridges sold separately. See pages 200-201, 225.)*

Merry Minis [set of 28]
105433 **$29.95**

Have yourself a merry little Christmas!

Happy Holidays

Sending a little wish for a lot of joy!

Little Holiday Wishes [set of 12]
104462 **$16.95**

holiday Postcard

Stampin' Around **Candy Cane Christmas**
103296 **$5.95** *(Wheel only. Handle and ink cartridges sold separately. See pages 200-201, 225.)*

Warm Winter Wishes

May the beauty
of the season
bring you joy
and warm memories
to cherish
throughout the year.

The world
in solemn stillness lay...

Snowflakes [set of 6]
101589 **$21.95**

Solemn Stillness [set of 6]
103771 **$28.95**

seasons

54

Stampin' Around **Star Studded**
104061 **$5.95** *(Wheel only. Handle and ink cartridges sold separately. See pages 200-201, 225.)*

cold twigs-
warm hearts!

The chill of
winter
is warmed by
friendship.

Christmas is
a time of cheer
with wishes for
a bright
new year!

cold twigs-
warm hearts!
© 2004 STAMPIN' UP!

© 2004 STAMPIN' UP!

© 2004 STAMPIN' UP!

friendship

winter

holiday

It's Snow Time [set of 12]
104093 $29.95

seasons

55

Stampin' Around **Snowman Fun**
101927 **$5.95** (*Wheel only. Handle and ink cartridges sold separately. See pages 200-201, 225.*)

Happy Belated Birthday

don't miss it! See more samples made with this set on page 3.

Flower Filled [set of 9]
105180 **$24.95**

seasons

56

brrrr...

Bundle Up [set of 7]
104816 **$19.95**

much appreciated

Stampin' Around **Twinkle**
104893 **$5.95** *(Wheel only. Handle and ink cartridges sold separately. See pages 200-201, 225.)*

57

Always on My Mind [set of 6]
105487 **$28.95**

For best results, sew the edge of the
card stock before assembling the box.

try this

Sparkling Summer [set of 11]
104163 **$24.95**

You can emphasize different words in a title or journaling by mixing alphabets as shown in the page above.

try this

The best things
in life
are not free,
but priceless.

Love returned
is the
true reward
of love given.

Seaside Sketches [set of 6]
103555 **$27.95**

don't miss it! This set coordinates with
the Simply Scrappin' Kit on page 209.

The best things
in life
are not free,
but priceless.

Some like it HOT...

Some Like It Hot [set of 9]
105431 **$24.95**

seasons

59

Window on the World [set of 7]
103941 **$19.95**

Little Layers II [set of 8]
100030 **$19.95**

don't miss it! This set coordinates with Little Layers (page 67) and Little Layers Plus (page 65), and a coordinating Classy Brass® embossing template on page 227.

Stampin' Around **Swirl Fun**
100622 **$5.95** *(Wheel only. Handle and ink cartridges sold separately. See pages 200-201, 225.)*

*Joy is not
in things,
it is in us.*
—Richard Wagner

I love watching you play. I have been amazed as you have grown and I have watched you discover the world around you. It brings me such happiness watching you find such joy in the little things.

Summer
memories

*Joy is not
in things,
it is in us.*
—Richard Wagner
© 2004 STAMPIN' UP!

*Wishing
you
happiness.*

don't miss it! This set coordinates with the Simply Scrappin' Kit on page 209.

Summer by the Sea [set of 6]
104243 **$28.95**

Little Somethings [set of 12]
101635 **$16.95**

Fall Whimsy [set of 6]
100130 **$14.95**

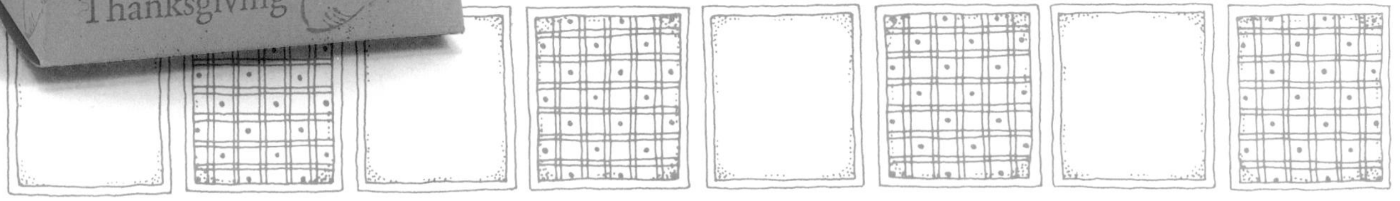

Stampin' Around **Pindot**
102604 **$5.95** *(Wheel only. Handle and ink cartridges sold separately. See pages 200-201, 225.)*

Stampin' Around **Acorns**
100360 **$5.95** *(Wheel only. Handle and ink cartridges sold separately. See pages 200-201, 225.)*

seasons

62

A Tree for All Seasons [set of 4]
102744 **$11.95**

try this

For a softer look, use a stamping sponge to apply ink to only part of your background stamp before stamping. (See Smile card.)

Sweet Seasons [set of 4]
104024 **$27.95**

seasons

63

for you

bloom

make a wish

for you

i'd rather be shopping!

wishes

don't miss it! This set is sold as part of a kit on page 25, and has a coordinating Classy Brass® embossing template sold on page 227.

Fun Filled [set of 8]
105461 **$16.95**

Bat Mitzvah

APR 2005

Bar Mitzvah

Mazel Tov

Bat Mitzvah

L'Chayim [set of 9]
105499 **$28.95**

Little Layers Plus [set of 8]
105454 **$19.95**

congratulations!

It All Adds Up [set of 4]
105054 **$19.95**

66

Stipple Celebrations [set of 14]
104483 **$28.95**

Stampin' Around **Lovely Ladybugs**
101965 **$5.95** *(Wheel only. Handle and ink cartridges sold separately. See pages 200-201, 225.)*

Little Layers [set of 8]
103049 **$19.95**

don't miss it! This set has a coordinating Classy Brass®
embossing template on page 227.

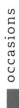

occasions

67

don't miss it! This set has a
coordinating Classy Brass® embossing template on page 227.

Shapes & Shadows [set of 12]
104014 **$29.95**

THANK YOU

FROM THE HEART

HOORAY FOR YOU!

HAPPY BIRTHDAY

GET WELL SOON

THANK YOU

HAPPY BIRTHDAY

GET WELL SOON

friend

FRIEND·TO·FRIEND

THANKS SO MUCH

Nice & Easy Notes [set of 8]
103039 **$26.95**

Happy
Birthday

Best
Wishes

Happy
Birthday

Thank
You

Thinking
of
You

Simple Wishes [set of 4]
101167 **$11.95**

happy everything!

happily ever after

'tis the season

celebrate you!

happy new baby!

thinking of you

just because i care...

thank you

Greetings Galore [set of 8]
104477 **$28.95**

January 2004

JAMES

Mini Medleys [set of 12]
104467 **$16.95**

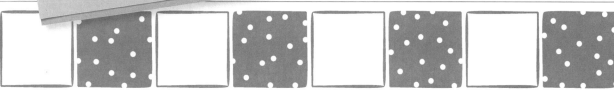

Stampin' Around **Polka Dot Blocks**
104099 **$5.95** (*Wheel only. Handle and ink cartridges sold separately. See pages 200–201, 225.*)

70

Favorite Teddy Bear [set of 15]
103361 **$29.95**

Stampin' Around **Paw Tracks**
101090 **$5.95** *(Wheel only. Handle and ink cartridges sold separately. See pages 200-201, 225.)*

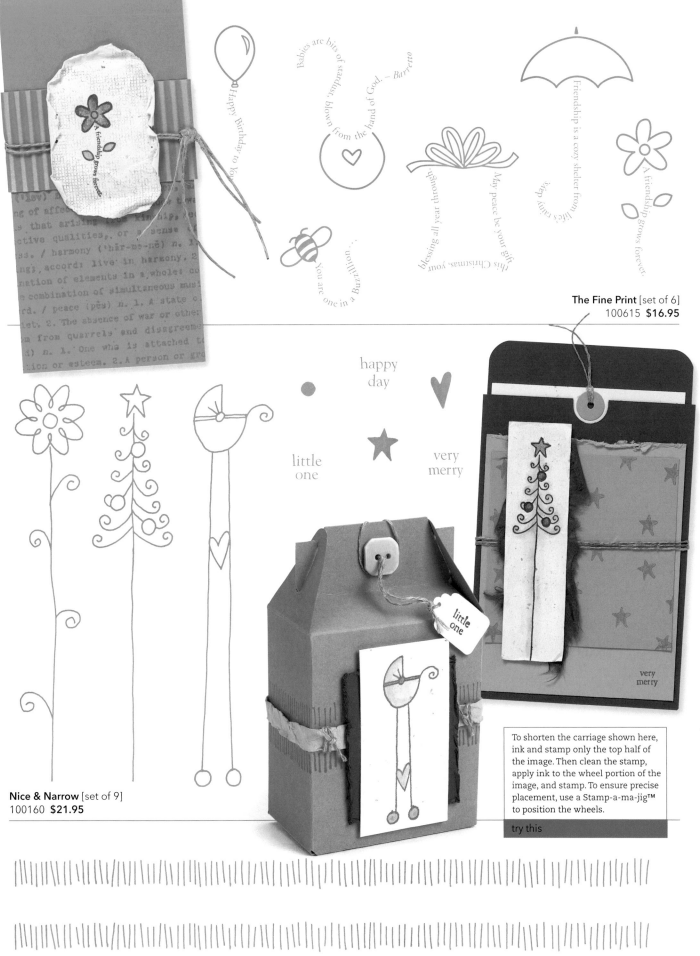

Babies are bits of stardust, blown from the hand of God. – Barretto

Happy Birthday to You.

Friendship is a cozy shelter from life's rainy days.

May peace be your gift this Christmas, your blessing all year through.

A friendship grows forever.

You are one in a Buzzillion.

The Fine Print [set of 6]
100615 **$16.95**

happy day

little one

very merry

Nice & Narrow [set of 9]
100160 **$21.95**

little one

very merry

To shorten the carriage shown here, ink and stamp only the top half of the image. Then clean the stamp, apply ink to the wheel portion of the image, and stamp. To ensure precise placement, use a Stamp-a-ma-jig™ to position the wheels.

try this

occasions

71

Stampin' Around **Double-Line Stitched Plaid**
101100 **$5.95** *(Wheel only. Handle and ink cartridges sold separately. See pages 200-201, 225.)*

elebrate! celebrate! celeb
te! celebrate! celebrate! c
lebrate! celebrate! celeb
rate! celebrate! celebrate
elebrate! celebrate! celeb
! celebrate! celebrate! ce

thank you thank you tha
you thank you thank you
nk you thank you thank
ou thank you thank you
ank you thank you than!
u thank you thank you t

love joy peace love joy p
oy peace love joy peace
ve joy peace love joy pea
peace love joy peace love
ce love joy peace love jo
joy peace love joy peace

my friend my friend my
friend my friend my fri
d my friend my friend m
iend my friend my friend
y friend my friend my f
d my friend my friend m

Mini Messages [set of 8]
103796 **$16.95**

don't miss it! Mini Messages and Figures of Speech (opposite) are designed to fit perfectly on our Metal Edge tags, shown on page 215.

To Someone Special...

hello...

Thinking of You

Happy Birthday to You...

hello

Best Wishes

Welcome Baby!

Miss You...

Thank You

Feathered Friends [set of 8]
102680 **$26.95**

happy holidays happy holidays happy holidays happy holidays

good for you! good for you! good for you! good for you! good for you!

to have and to hold to have and to hold to have and to hold to have and to hold

FROM THE HEART FROM THE HEART FROM THE HEART FROM THE HEART

just a little some thing just a little something just a little something just a

celebrate you! celebrate you! celebrate you! celebrate you! celebrate you!

just a little some thing just a little something just a

friend

thank you thank you thank you thank you thank you thank you

itsy bitsy baby itsy bitsy baby itsy bitsy baby itsy bitsy baby

Figures of Speech [set of 8]
103935 **$21.95**

birthdays are good for you- the more you have, the longer you live!

when it's dark enough, you can see the stars.
-Ralph Waldo Emerson

a little bit of thanks for a whole lot of nice!

your kindness touches my heart.

kindness

when it's dark enoug you can se the stars
-Ralph Waldo Emerso
© 2002 STAMPIN' UP!

© 2002 STAMPIN' UP!

Quick & Cute [set of 8]
103236 **$16.95**

 Happy Holidays For the Bride

Just a note   Make a wish!   I'm sorry

Hang in there! For you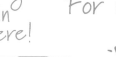

You light up my life!   You did it!

Wedding Wishes Get well soon! Just Because

 Welcome, baby!

You're sweet!

Mini Mates [set of 28]
104465 **$29.95**

Use markers to create multicolored images such as the one on the Just for You box.

try this

Just for You
to: _____
from: _____

Tags & More [set of 8]
101380 **$19.95**

occasions

74

Date
Time
Place
For
RSVP

It's a Shower

Happy Birthday

It's a Shower

Something to Celebrate [set of 9]
104016 **$24.95**

sweet

friends

she's here

surprise!

smile

dream

congrats

good luck

celebrate

good times

he's here

noel

shop!

joy

smile
© 2003 STAMPIN' UP!

Good Times [set of 28]
104466 **$28.95**

occasions

75

Simply Sweet [set of 4]
100337 **$19.95**

Sketch an Event [set of 8]
102032 **$21.95**

Create an interesting focal point by layering a photo on offset pieces of card stock.

try this

DATE:

TIME:

PLACE:

FOR:

IT'S a PARTY!

HAPPY BIRTHDAY!

It's a Party [set of 6]
103769 **$19.95**

Let's Party [set of 4]
100148 **$11.95**

occasions

77

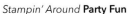

Stampin' Around **Party Fun**
100358 **$5.95** *(Wheel only. Handle and ink cartridges sold separately. See pages 200–201, 225.)*

happy
birthday
today-
happy
times
all
year!

Birthday Best [set of 4]
105455 **$12.95**

Simple Somethings [set of 4]
104482 **$11.95**

PARTY

for: Melanie

on: September 6th

at: 7:00 P.M.

together!
laugh
friend!

Stampin' Around **Hot to Dot**
104312 **$5.95** *(Wheel only. Handle and ink cartridges sold separately. See pages 200-201, 225.)*

congratulations!

babies are the best gift of all

pursenally, you're the best!

da dum dee dum...

thanks for everything!

finally!

happy holidays

thanks for everything!

a birthday wish for my friend... may the happy never end!

a birthday wish for my friend...

Framed Greetings [set of 14]
104034 **$28.95**

best wishes

for baby

thank you

thinking of you

happy holidays

happy birthday

miss you

friends

Little Hellos [set of 8]
104478 **$19.95**

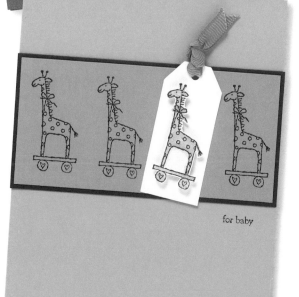

for baby

occasions

79

Happy Birthday

Thinking of you

Thank you

Simple Sketches [set of 12]
102771 **$28.95**

Happy Birthday

Thinking of you

Congratulations

to:
from:

Thank you

Merry Christmas

A Greeting for All Reasons [set of 14]
100999 **$28.95**

Sending
happy thoughts,
for a
happy occasion!

Happy Occasions [set of 4]
105467 **$14.95**

Stampin' Around Jumbo **Leaves & Swirls**
105524 **$7.95** *(Wheel only. Handle and ink cartridges sold separately.
See pages 200-201, 225.)*

Stampin' Around Jumbo **Adoring Hearts**
105523 **$7.95** *(Wheel only. Handle and ink cartridges sold
separately. See pages 200-201, 225.)*

Stampin' Around Jumbo **Baby Rattle**
105522 **$7.95** *(Wheel only. Handle and ink cartridges sold separately. See pages 200-201, 225.)*

occasions

HOPE YOUR DAY IS THE HAPPY-FACE KIND!

HAPPY BIRTHDAY!

YOU MAKE ME SMILE!

Smile [set of 6]
102654 **$14.95**

CeLeBRaTe!

82

Perfect Party [set of 9]
103029 **$24.95**

TRaVeRS

Stampin' Around **Party**
102671 **$5.95** *(Wheel only. Handle and ink cartridges sold separately. See pages 200-201, 225.)*

a
HAPPY
HELLO!

WISHING
YOU a
SeaSON
OF
HAPPY
SMILES!

a
HAPPY
HELLO!

WISHING
YOU
MANY
HAPPY
SURPRISES!

Smile Some More [set of 6]
104057 **$14.95**

> When using a corner rounder (shown on page 218), try a combination of round and straight corners on your project.
>
> try this

Have a
Happy
Birthday!

Surprise!

Have a
Happy
Birthday!

Surprise! [set of 4]
104118 **$14.95**

Surprise!

© 2004 STAMPIN' UP!

Stampin' Around **Splat**
104063 **$5.95** *(Wheel only. Handle and ink cartridges sold separately. See pages 200-201, 225.)*

occasions

83

Warm and Wonderful Birthday Greetings

Happy Birthday Greetings [set of 1]
100311 **$16.95**

84

Sweet Treats [set of 3]
100180 **$17.95**

birthday!

Stampin' Around **Whimsical Blossoms**
100268 **$5.95** (Wheel only. Handle and ink cartridges sold separately. See pages 200-201, 225.)

A princess is what you were meant to be, 'cause being sweet comes naturally!

Happy Birthday

Happy Birthday

Pretty Princess [set of 7]
103767 **$22.95**

The tassel was worth the hassle!

The tassel was worth the hassle!

Class of

Congratulations

Tassel Time [set of 9]
101581 **$24.95**

occasions

85

Special Day [set of 1]
104213 **$16.95**

Happily Ever After [set of 6]
104305 **$16.95**

Add a fun accent to a box by grouping tags.

try this

Wishing You a Lifetime of Love

You are Special

You are Special

Life's Special Moments [set of 5]
105266 **$22.95**

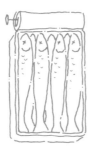

happy birthday!

.oops! iT's a hare pasT your birThday!

happy birThday!

...From some oF your closesT Friends!

hand sTamped

oops! iT's a hare pasT your birThday!

we may noT be Tadpoles anymore buT aT leasT we haven'T croaked!

i know how much women your age enjoy a new FloraL moo-moo!

Birthday Banter [set of 11]
103814 **$24.95**

occasions

87

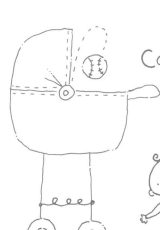

Congratulations on your sweet new arrival!

bundle of boy!

cuddle bug · bundle of joy
butterfly kisses · ma-ma
cutie patootie · peek-a-boo
nighty-night · sweet pea
hugs & kisses · whaaaaaa!
tickle toes · lullaby baby
too cute · da-da · cutie pie

for baby

yeah, it's a girl!

Baby Talk [set of 7]
105065 **$22.95**

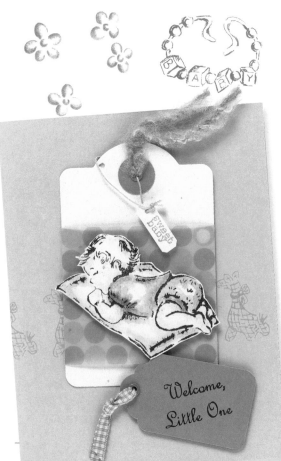

bundle of boy!

Welcome, Little One

Date:

Time:

Place:

For:

RSVP:

A new little baby
to cuddle and love,
a bundle from heaven
to think the world of!

Welcome,
Little One

Welcome, Little One [set of 7]
103905 **$19.95**

occasions

88

you're invited

baby boy

Congratulations on your Swell News!

You Grow Girl!

Happy Waiting!

Swell News [set of 6]
105475 **$16.95**

To create the greeting on the Congratulations card, hold the tag in place and stamp the greeting once. Then, attach the tag with Stampin' Dimensionals, aligning the word on the tag with the words on the card.

try this

Congratulations on your Swell News!

God could not be everywhere, and so He created mothers!

Maternal Instincts [set of 2]
103959 **$17.95**

God could not be everywhere, and so He created mothers!

occasions

89

You're Fabulous!

Bubble Queen!

Bubble Queen [set of 6]
105513 **$21.95**

you're the cat's meow!

meow!

for you

party

Cool Cat [set of 6]
104970 **$14.95**

sentiments

Stampin' Around Jumbo **Cool**
105032 **$7.95** *(Wheel only. Handle and ink cartridges sold separately. See pages 200-201, 225.)*

aloha

Do the Hula [set of 7]
105473 **$26.95**

birds of a
feather...
party
together!

just
beakause

just
beakause

Just Beakause [set of 9]
105171 **$24.95**

sentiments

91

Stampin' Around **Island**
105449 **$5.95** *(Wheel only. Handle and ink cartridges sold separately. See pages 200-201, 225.)*

don't miss it! This wheel coordinates with the
Island Blossoms hostess set on page 23 and the
Island Blossoms Simply Scrappin' Kit on page 17.

TO ERR IS HUMAN—
TO REALLY MESS UP
REQUIRES
A COMPUTER

HOME IS
WHERE YOU
HANG YOUR
@

LIFE
BYTES!

HOPE YOUR
BIRTHDAY
IS
GLITCH FREE!

Computer Quips [set of 7]
105256 **$19.95**

HOPE YOUR
BIRTHDAY
IS
GLITCH FREE!

Of all the gifts
life could send—
the best is
knowing
you're my friend!

one of a kind!

92

thanks a bunch!

happy bird-day to you!

love
ya
bunches

one of a kind!

Love Ya Bunches [set of 6]
105462 **$17.95**

© 1990–2005 STAMPIN' UP!

Celebrate in Style!

Celebrate

Celebrate in Style!

wish-shoe a happy day!

To a fabulous Purse-on!

Celebrate in Style [set of 7]
105057 **$19.95**

Well behaved women rarely make history. ~L. T. Ulrich

hats off!

Boa Babe!

Well behaved

Going Out in Style [set of 7]
104820 **$19.95**

sentiments

93

Stampin' Around Jumbo **Millinery**
104895 **$7.95** *(Wheel only. Handle and ink cartridges sold separately. See pages 200-201, 225.)*

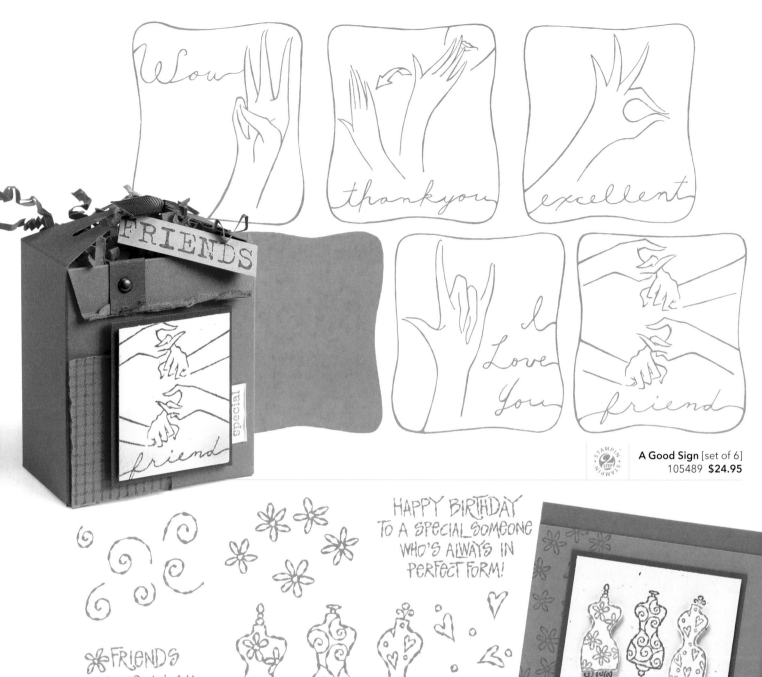

Wou

thankyou *excellent*

I Love You *friend*

A Good Sign [set of 6]
105489 **$24.95**

HAPPY BIRTHDAY
TO A SPECIAL SOMEONE
WHO'S ALWAYS IN
PERFECT FORM!

✻FRIENDS
COME IN ALL
SHAPES AND SIZES,
NEED NO ✻
✻ ALTERATIONS,
AND NEVER GO
OUT OF STYLE!

I LIKE
YOUR
STYLE!

✻FRIENDS

I Like Your Style [set of 7]
100144 **$19.95**

Stampin' Around **Swirl Style**
104081 **$5.95** *(Wheel only. Handle and ink cartridges sold separately. See pages 200-201, 225.)*

Just chicken in.

Peep!

Best of Cluck! Best of Cluck!

Now that's eggciting!

Thanks a bunch!

Best of Cluck [set of 7]
105254 **$22.95**

Best of Cluck! Best of Cluck!

WE'VE MOVED!

You make me feel Right at home!

Happy is the home that shelters a friend.

Welcome to the neighborhood!

WE'VE MOVED!

Thanks for your hospitality!

Right at Home [set of 7]
103765 **$19.95**

sentiments

95

ooh-la-la!

friends

happy together

hats off!

loves me

Princess

relax

ruff day?

showers of love

sweet

yeah, baby

purseonally

A Little Love [set of 12]
103739 **$16.95**

loves me

EVER NOTICE HOW MUCH BETTER RICE CAKES TASTE SMOTHERED IN HOT FUDGE?!?

EVER NOTICE HOW MUCH BETTER RICE CAKES TASTE SMOTHERED IN HOT FUDGE?!?

THANK YOU~ I'M SPEECHLESS.

THAT'S A FIRST!

I MISS HEARING FROM YOU...

IF LIFE'S BORING, MAKE SOMETHING UP!

NEXT YEAR I'LL FORGET MINE!

I MISS HEARING FROM YOU

IF LIFE'S BORING, MAKE SOMETHING UP!

JUST TO SHOW YOU HOW SORRY I AM FOR FORGETTING YOUR BIRTHDAY...

Stamp a background stamp or other image on the inside of the card, then fold the card front up to reveal the image.

try this

Wanda's Wit & Wisdom [set of 7]
104115 **$22.95**

I THOUGHT A CRUISE WOULD BE A GREAT WAY TO CELEBRATE YOUR BIRTHDAY!

THIS BIRTHDAY CARD IS A LOT LIKE A LOTTERY TICKET...

WILL YOU PICK UP MY MAIL WHILE I'M GONE?

THE CHANCES OF GETTING ANY MONEY OUT OF IT ARE ABOUT A MILLION TO ONE!

 MANY TANKS!

HAPPY BIRTHDAY!

Words by Wilson [set of 8]
104907 **$22.95**

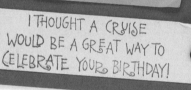

I THOUGHT A CRUISE WOULD BE A GREAT WAY TO CELEBRATE YOUR BIRTHDAY!

Your friendship Warms my heart.

Happy Birthday to a Regular Joe!

Just wanted to Espresso my thanks!

Friends are the coffee break in the business of life!

Espress Yourself [set of 9]
101755 **$24.95**

Your friendship Warms my heart.

sentiments

97

I never met a chocolate I didn't like.

Making the world sweeter, one chocolate at a time.

The best things in life are chocolate!

The best things in life are chocolate!

sweet

Oh So Sweet [set of 8]
103744 **$19.95**

sentiments

Just a Note

Just a Note

Jazzed Up [set of 6]
104137 **$17.95**

Stampin' Around **Chocolate Chips**
103794 **$5.95** *(Wheel only. Handle and ink cartridges sold separately. See pages 200–201, 225.)*

Stampin' Around **Jazz**
104158 **$5.95** *(Wheel only. Handle and ink cartridges sold separately. See pages 200–201, 225.)*

What's for Dinner [set of 9]
103909 **$26.95**

sentiments

99

Sorry to hear
you're under the
weather...
hope tomorrow
you're feeling
much better.

Repeatedly stamp a greeting on card
stock to create a fun background.

try this

Under the Weather [set of 6]
105507 **$14.95**

Oh, Hoppy Day!!!

enjoy being you

Oh, Hoppy Day!!!

How are things at your pad?

How are things at your pad?

i miss you

Frolicking Frogs [set of 5]
105175 **$22.95**

Thanks

All the Best

All the Best [set of 7]
103895 **$19.95**

Too cute for words

DANA in the backyard

SEPT 2004

Sweet Baby

Get Well

Happy Birthday

Best Wishes to You

Friends

To You From Me

Hello...

You're an Angel

Say Something Mice [set of 8]
105268 **$28.95**

Hello...

forever

Friends

Thank You

Thank You

Thank You

101

All Natural [set of 6]
104473 **$16.95**

I'm just glad...  wrinkles don't hurt.

Keep smiling... It makes people wonder what you've been up to.

I'm actually quite pleasant ...until I'm awake.

I try to lose weight ...but it keeps finding Me!

A balanced diet is... a chocolate in each hand.

Everyone is gifted. Some just open the package sooner.

Out of my Mind. Back in 5 minutes.

Wisecracks [set of 7]
105278 **$26.95**

ooh ~la~ la!

merci!

Paris in the Spring [set of 7]
103933 **$19.95**

ooh ~la~ la!

friend

sentiments

102

Stampin' Around **Springtime**
104044 **$5.95** *(Wheel only. Handle and ink cartridges sold separately. See pages 200-201, 225.)*

A real friend is
one who drops in
when the rest of the
world drops out.

Love is found where
you least expect it.

Friends are
flowers
that never
fade.

Friends
like you keep
me afloat.

Favorite Friends [set of 7]
103827 **$19.95**

Everything's better when shared
with a friend.

You made a
whole bunch of
happiness
bloom in my
heart!

Friends are
the umbrellas
in the storms
of life.

Still around the corner,
there may wait,
a new road or secret gate.
—J.R.R. Tolkien

And Everything Nice [set of 6]
105345 **$28.95**

Stampin' Around Jumbo **Hollyhock**
105520 **$7.95** *(Wheel only. Handle and ink cartridges sold separately. See pages 200-201, 225.)*

sentiments

103

sofa – so good!

it's a shore thing

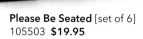
rock on!

ROCKON

chairished

chair up!

rock on!

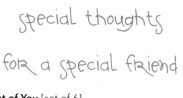

chairful welcome!

Please Be Seated [set of 6]
105503 **$19.95**

chair up!

for a special friend

104

that was so sweet of you!

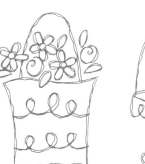

special thoughts

for a special friend

i miss you

Sweet of You [set of 6]
105456 **$19.95**

Are ewe doing okay?

Udderly Exhausted?

You Cured Yet?

Hope you're Buzzin' around soon

You Cured Yet?

Farm Fever [set of 4]
105339 **$17.95**

Love Birds

Happy BIRD-DAY

Flying by Just to Say Hi

Love Birds

sentiments

105

Sweet Songbirds [set of 6]
105154 **$21.95**

Return with Honor

Kindness Begins With Me

I Am a Child of God

Choose The Right

Jesus is the Reason for the Season

Love is Spoken Here

Make a joyful noise unto the Lord

Count Your Blessings

Kindness Begins With Me

Love is Spoken Here

All God's Children [set of 8]
100283 **$19.95**

My heart shall rejoice in thy salvation. —Psalms 13:5

My heart shall rejoice in thy salvation. —Psalms 13:5

Hope

Hope

Symbols of Salvation [set of 4]
105471 **$17.95**

sentiments

Bottles and booties,
bibs and more,
a new little
someone
to love and adore!

A New Little Someone [set of 7]
103635 **$19.95**

Stampin' Around Jumbo **Wash Day**
103749 **$7.95** *(Wheel only. Handle and ink cartridges sold separately. See pages 200-201, 225.)*

a b c d e f g h
i j k l m n o p
q r s t u v w
x y z a b c d
e f g h i j k l
m n o p q r s
t u v w x y z

i'm here

© 2004 STAMPIN' UP!

Gracie
at 6 months

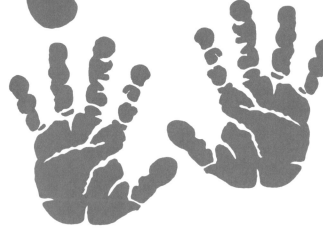

i'm here

I'm Here [set of 6]
104215 **$24.95**

don't miss it! This set coordinates with a Simply Scrappin' Kit on page 208.

The letters in this alphabet can be punched out with the 1/4-inch punches on page 218.

try this

i'm here

Nov 5

Jace

Stampin' Around **Hand Prints**
104103 **$5.95** *(Wheel only. Handle and ink cartridges sold separately. See pages 200-201, 225.)*

Stampin' Around **Sweet Feet**
100593 **$5.95** *(Wheel only. Handle and ink cartridges sold separately. See pages 200-201, 225.)*

growing up

108

Date:
Time:
Place:

Babies are bits of stardust blown from the hand of God.
—Larry Barretto

Buggies & Booties [set of 7]
105509 **$22.95**

try this

Achieve this look by brushing an ink pad directly against the card stock.

Baby Firsts [set of 8]
102341 **$19.95**

baby

Stampin' Around **Baby Time**
101420 **$5.95** *(Wheel only. Handle and ink cartridges sold separately. See pages 200-201, 225.)*

growing up

109

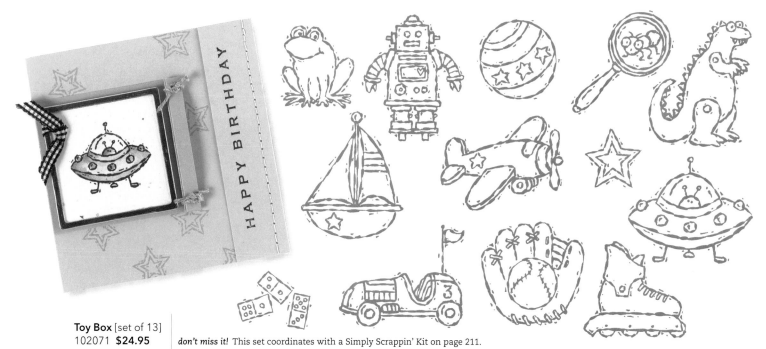

Toy Box [set of 13]
102071 **$24.95**

don't miss it! This set coordinates with a Simply Scrappin' Kit on page 211.

Caitlin and Ella have become fast friends in just a couple of months. I love to watch them interact together. We can't help dressing them alike sometimes. Having girls so close in age has been so fun!

September 2004

Buttons, Bows & Twinkletoes [set of 13]
103626 **$24.95**

don't miss it! This set coordinates with a Simply Scrappin' Kit on page 211.

Teacher's Aid [set of 6]
105059 **$19.95**

growing up

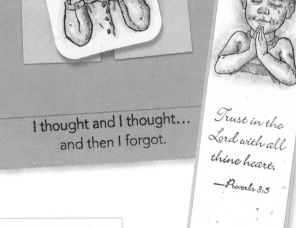

Charming Children [set of 4]
104235 **$14.95**

Punch out several squares with one of our square punches (shown on page 218) to create a nice background or frame.

try this

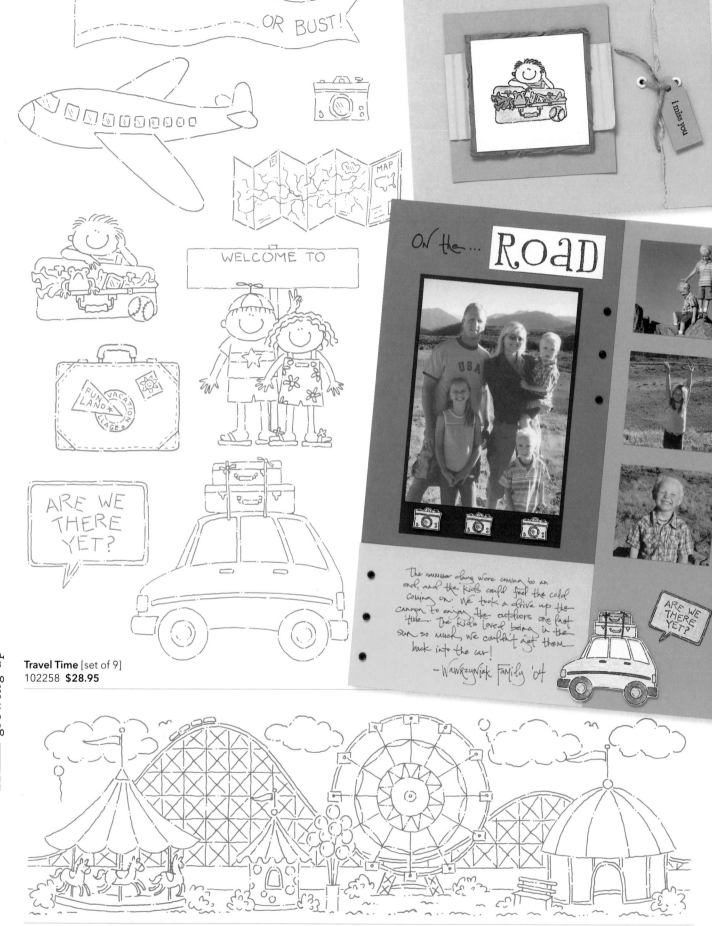

... OR BUST!

MAP

WELCOME TO

FUN VACATION LAND

ARE WE THERE YET?

Travel Time [set of 9]
102258 **$28.95**

i miss you

On the... ROAD

USA

the summer days were coming to an
end, and the kids could feel the cold
coming on. We took a drive up the
canyon to enjoy the outdoors one last
time. The kids loved being in the
sun so much, we couldn't get them
back into the car!
— Wawrzyniak Family '04

ARE WE THERE YET?

Stampin' Around Jumbo **Carnival Fun**
103748 **$7.95** *(Wheel only. Handle and ink cartridges sold separately. See pages 200-201, 225.)*

Time for Fun [set of 7]
103618 **$19.95**

At the Races [set of 7]
105252 **$19.95**

Stampin' Around **Making Tracks**
104100 **$5.95** *(Wheel only. Handle and ink cartridges sold separately. See pages 200–201, 225.)*

IT'S
Y✿UR
DAY!

Girlfriends

whatever!

together

Ashley and Kristie
.·2004··

Girlfriends

Girlfriends [set of 8]
101573 **$21.95**

DIARY

Girl
talk

DIARY

In
your
dreams!

© 2002 STAMPIN' UP! © 2002 STAMPIN' UP!

Girlfriend Accessories [set of 8]
103226 **$16.95**

you're invited

Lively Little Ones [set of 12]
105427 **$29.95**

Dance is a poem
of which each
movement is a word.

En Pointe [set of 4]
105408 **$17.95**

Add texture to a project by crumpling
the card stock or paper.

try this

All Wrapped Up [set of 7]
104036 **$19.95**

All Wrapped Up Accessories [set of 6]
104038 **$9.95**

*I'd rather
be shopping!*

*I hope your birthday
is, like, totally cool!*

Totally Cool [set of 7]
104073 **$19.95**

friends
are like
pockets...
you can
never have
too many!

a little
something
just
for you

Pocket Fun [set of 7]
100162 **$19.95**

munch love!

I chews you!

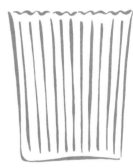

whole latte
love!

LOVE

Treat yourself to
a wonderful day!

growing up

Treat Yourself [set of 13]
105321 **$29.95**

ATHLETE
In training...

moments

Braxton has been playing sports since he was six. Basketball is one of his biggest passions. It has been fun watching him get better and better each year. We are so proud of our little athlete.

04

GO TEAM

party

GO TEAM SCORE

Sporting Goods [set of 14]
104120 **$28.95**

Stampin' Around Jumbo **Sports Fans**
104159 **$7.95** *(Wheel only. Handle and ink cartridges sold separately. See pages 200-201, 225.)*

LACROSSE

Matt's very favorite pastime is playing lacrosse. This past year his team went all the way to the championships to take first place. We drove all the way to Las Vegas just to support him and his team in their games. He was so excited and delighted with their much anticipated victory. His dedication to lacrosse and his teammates never ceases to amaze me. The minute one game ends, he is already focused on the next, strategizing and planning. I have never seen one boy quite so disciplined.

Las Vegas Classic
October 2004

Good Sport [set of 8]
103831 **$21.95**

Power Up [set of 6]
105479 **$17.95**

HAPPY BIRTHDAY

Stampin' Around **Builder Bits**
105518 **$5.95** *(Wheel only. Handle and ink cartridges sold separately. See pages 200-201, 225.)*

It's a Cheer Thing [set of 7]
105497 **$19.95**

Definitely Decorative **Crayon Kids** [set of 10]
101135 **$32.95**

Stampin' Around **Crayon ABCs**
100269 **$5.95** *(Wheel only. Handle and ink cartridges sold separately. See pages 200-201, 225.)*

LOVE IS A CIRCLE WITHOUT END.

Love

THANK YOU

f r i e n D

Love without End [set of 9]
100152 **$24.95**

don't miss it! This set has a coordinating Classy Brass embossing template sold on page 227.

LOVE IS A CIRCLE WITHOUT END.

Love

THANK YOU

Smile

Smile

Smile

Petal Pushers [set of 9]
104836 **$24.95**

flowers

121

Definitely Decorative **Gladsome Garden** [set of 6]
104113 **$22.95**

To re-create the look of this box,
attach a strip of Designer Series paper (sold on pages
206-207) to the flower edges of the unassembled box.
Next, trim the excess paper following the flower edges
of the box and assemble. Box is sold on page 212.

try this

Stampin' Around Jumbo **Posies & Polka Dots**
104067 **$7.95** *(Wheel only. Handle and ink cartridges sold separately. See pages 200-201, 225.)*

THANK you thanks

hawaii

Our trip to Hawaii was Abby's first time on an airplane. We loved watching her splash in the waves and playing in the sand. What a great trip!

July 2004

Buds & Blossoms [set of 7]
103633 **$19.95**

flowers

123

Stampin' Around Jumbo **Bold Blooms**
103752 **$7.95** *(Wheel only. Handle and ink cartridges sold separately. See pages 200-201, 225.)*

Stampin' Around **Delicate Design**
104101 **$5.95** *(Wheel only. Handle and ink cartridges sold separately. See pages 200-201, 225.)*

TIMELESS

TB

BEAUTY

2004

Best Wishes

124

Definitely Decorative **Bloomin' Wonderful** [set of 9]
104165 **$28.95**

don't miss it! This set has a coordinating Classy Brass embossing template sold on page 227.

Stampin' Around **Whirly-Twirly**
104098 **$5.95** *(Wheel only. Handle and ink cartridges sold separately. See pages 200-201, 225.)*

*All I have seen
teaches me to trust
the Creator
for all I have
not seen.*

—Ralph Waldo Emerson

All I Have Seen [set of 4]
105463 **$14.95**

Heartfelt Thanks [set of 9]
105429 **$28.95**

don't miss it! This set is sold as part of a kit on page 26.

flowers

125

Stampin' Around **Watercolor Joy**
105516 **$5.95** (*Wheel only. Handle and ink cartridges sold separately. See pages 200-201, 225.*)

SMILE smile

One weekend in September, when we made a quick trip to Denver, Brittian and I had some one-on-one time at the park. She was patient long enough for me to snap these pictures, then she insisted I push her "higher, higher" on the swings! She is fearless!

September • 2004

celebrate

Definitely Decorative **Daisy** [set of 13]
101486 **$29.95**

hope

Watercolor Minis [set of 12]
104468 **$17.95**

Petal Prints [set of 7]
104284 $26.95

Stampin' Around Jumbo **Lilies**
104155 **$7.95** *(Wheel only. Handle and ink cartridges sold separately. See pages 200-201, 225.)*

Stampin' Around **Leaf Prints**
104279 **$5.95** *(Wheel only. Handle and ink cartridges sold separately. See pages 200-201, 225.)*

Stipple Rose [set of 1]
101960 **$12.95**

Burst into Bloom [set of 4]
105457 **$11.95**

Perfect Petals [set of 4]
100327 **$14.95**

flowers

128

*Memory
is
the power
to gather
roses
in winter.*

*The fragrance lingers
in the hand that gives the rose.*

Definitely Decorative **Roses in Winter** [set of 9]
100386 **$28.95**

flowers

129

Flower Garden [set of 7]
105458 **$19.95**

Simple Florals [set of 4]
100325 **$19.95**

In Full Bloom [set of 9]
103829 **$24.95**

don't miss it! This set has a coordinating Simply Scrappin' Kit on page 209.

Stampin' Around **Bloomin'**
104070 **$5.95** *(Wheel only. Handle and ink cartridges sold separately. See pages 200-201, 225.)*

flowers

Create an elegant pocket by attaching a strip of vellum.

try this

Delicate Dandelions [set of 4]
105337 **$17.95**

flowers

131

Terrific Tulips [set of 9]
102783 **$24.95**

Delightful Doodles [set of 4]
100703 **$11.95**

flowers

Fresh Flowers [set of 9]
102751 **$24.95**

Stampin' Around **Blossoms & Bugs**
103112 **$5.95** *(Wheel only. Handle and ink cartridges sold separately. See pages 200-201, 225.)*

Friends are like flowers, each with its own beauty.

Friends

Friends Are Like Flowers [set of 5]
105178 **$22.95**

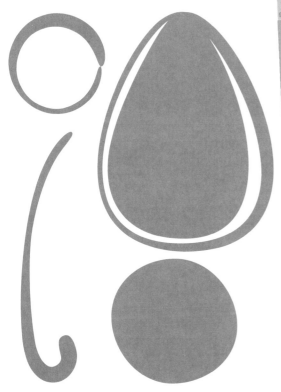

Definitely Decorative **Build a Blossom** [set of 4]
103538 **$16.95**

sweet • • • fun • • • all girl • • • happy • • • special • • • good sister • • • sweet • • • fun • • • all girl • • •

march 2004

megan

PrEciOus JeWeL

*My sweet Megan. You are such a gem.
I love your beautiful smile and shining
personality. You are so precious to us.
Love, Mom*

Live well,
laugh often,
love much.

Thank you very much

Live well,
laugh often,
love much.

Spring Garden [set of 9]
101857 **$24.95**

flowers

134

Thanks for

touching my life

with your special

friendship!

Watercolor Garden [set of 13]
101352 **$26.95**

Definitely Decorative **Gorgeous Grapevine** [set of 9]
105491 **$28.95**

Autumn Leaf Prints [set of 6]
105481 **$19.95**

nature

135

Natural Beauty [set of 6]
104765 **$19.95**

How beautiful a day can be when friendship touches it.

It is Christmas in the heart that puts Christmas in the air.
W.T. Ellis

The greatest achievements were at first, and for some time, dreams.
-James Allen

Ageless Adornment [set of 7]
105459 **$26.95**

nature

136

FLOWER girl

2005

Too cute for words

HAPPY BIRTHDAY

Stampin' Up! will donate $2 from the sale of each Sweet & Sassy set to Ronald McDonald House Charities® (RMHC). For more information, see page 9.

RONALD McDONALD HOUSE CHARITIES®

Sweet & Sassy [set of 8]
105052 **$16.95**

Thinking OF YOU

Close to Nature [set of 4]
104475 **$11.95**

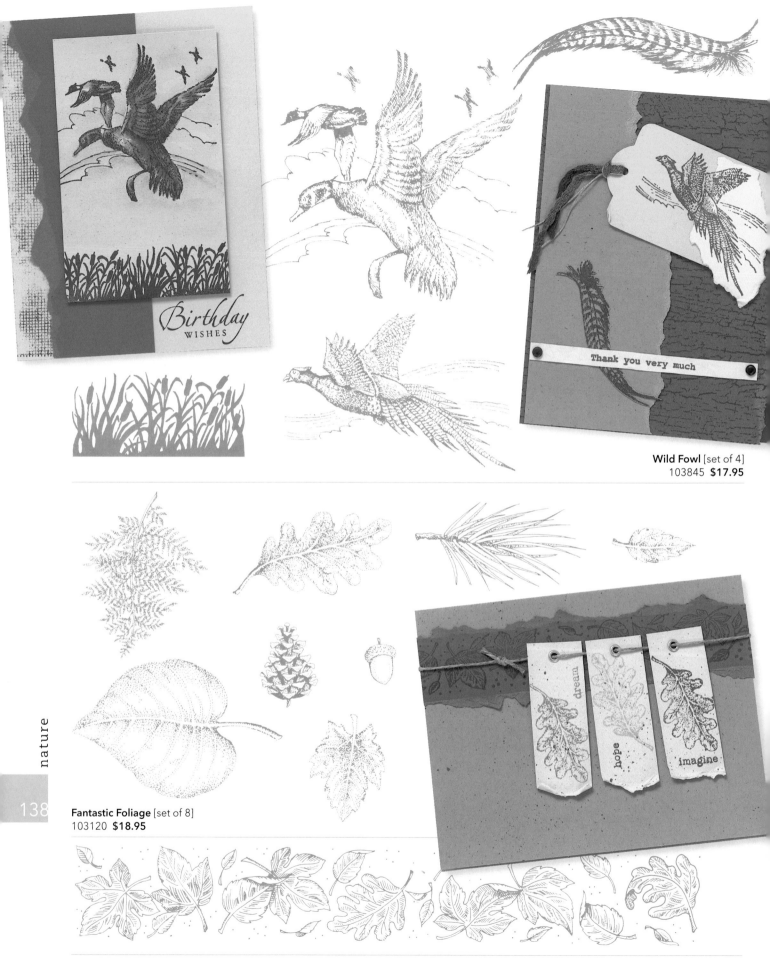

Birthday WISHES

Wild Fowl [set of 4]
103845 **$17.95**

Thank you very much

dream

hope

imagine

Fantastic Foliage [set of 8]
103120 **$18.95**

Stampin' Around **Swirling Leaves**
101909 **$5.95** *(Wheel only. Handle and ink cartridges sold separately. See pages 200-201, 225.)*

nature

138

Drawing on Nature [set of 4]
104812 **$14.95**

Definitely Decorative **Fresh Fruits** [set of 7]
105034 **$26.95**

nature

139

nature

140

ALASKA

vacation

Definitely Decorative **Pines** [set of 6]
100863 **$24.95**

Stampin' Around **Great Outdoors**
101525 **$5.95** *(Wheel only. Handle and ink cartridges sold separately. See pages 200-201, 225.)*

Lovely As a Tree [set of 6]
101223 **$24.95**

In the Wild [set of 6]
100321 **$19.95**

don't miss it! This set coordinates with the On Safari background stamp on page 175.

Stampin' Around **Heart of Africa**
104062 **$5.95** *(Wheel only. Handle and ink cartridges sold separately. See pages 200-201, 225.)*

nature

141

nature

142

Definitely Decorative **Bold Butterfly** [set of 6]
103804 **$28.95**

Stampin' Around Jumbo **Flitting By**
104156 **$7.95** *(Wheel only. Handle and ink cartridges sold separately. See pages 200-201, 225.)*

Life is a picnic, eat hearty!

Ladybug Picnic [set of 5]
103777 **$22.95**

A little note of thanks.

Happiness is knowing you.

Winged Things [set of 8]
104373 **$21.95**

For you

A little note of thanks.

nature

Stampin' Around **Wings & Things**
105033 **$5.95** *(Wheel only. Handle and ink cartridges sold separately. See pages 200-201, 225.)*

try this

Make a tiny tag with any word from the Expressive Flexible Phrases set on page 191.

Fintastic [set of 4]
103812 **$18.95**

Aquaria [set of 7]
103823 **$19.95**

nature

144

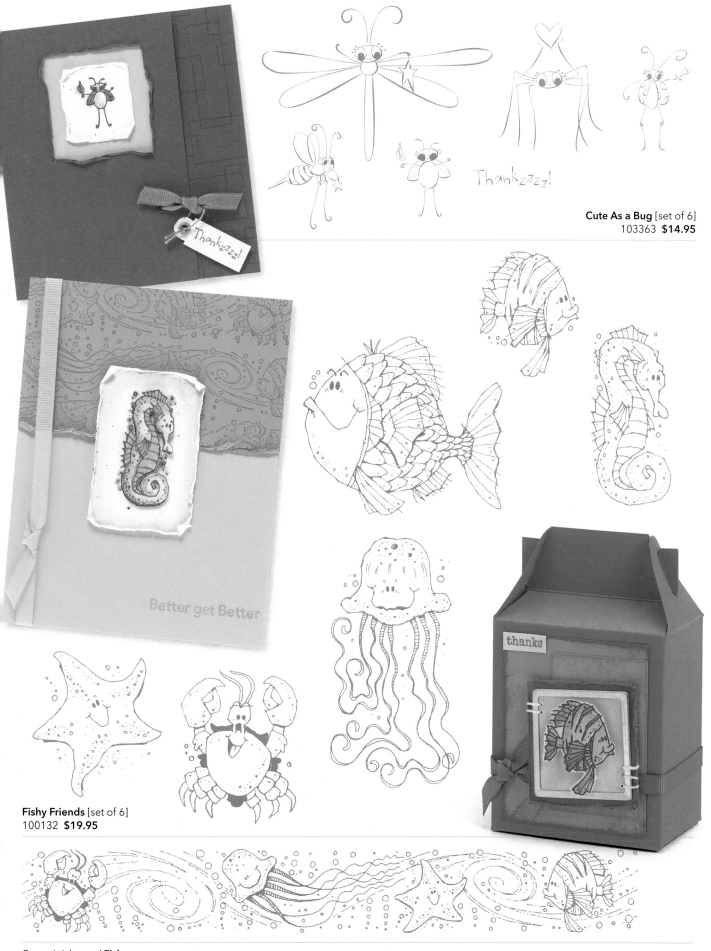

Cute As a Bug [set of 6]
103363 **$14.95**

Thankzzzz!

Better get Better

thanks

Fishy Friends [set of 6]
100132 **$19.95**

nature

145

Stampin' Around **Fishy**
104065 **$5.95** (*Wheel only. Handle and ink cartridges sold separately. See pages 200-201, 225.*)

father

Noble Deer [set of 4]
103825 **$17.95**

try this

Folding back the band adds to the masculine look of this card.

HAPPY BIRTHDAY

nature

146

Angler [set of 4]
103963 **$17.95**

© 2004 STAMPIN' UP!

The Wind of heaven
is that which
blows between a
horse's ears.

Bareback [set of 4]
103907 **$18.95**

Stampin' Around Jumbo **Farmyard**
104066 **$7.95** *(Wheel only. Handle and ink cartridges sold separately. See pages 200-201, 225.)*

nature

147

The Cat's Meow [set of 5]
105042 **$22.95**

Ruff Day [set of 6]
105351 **$17.95**

148

Stampin' Around **Pounce**
105361 **$5.95** *(Wheel only. Handle and ink cartridges sold separately. See pages 200-201, 225.)*

Stampin' Around **Ruff Play**
105362 **$5.95** *(Wheel only. Handle and ink cartridges sold separately. See pages 200-201, 225.)*

YOU MAKE ME HAPPY!

Hiking day at
on F   unique

andrew

Definitely Decorative **Going Buggy** [set of 8]
105465 **$22.95**

Stampin' Around **Tropical Turf**
105517 **$5.95** *(Wheel only. Handle and ink cartridges sold separately. See pages 200-201, 225.)*

Travel Post [set of 9]
104288 **$28.95**

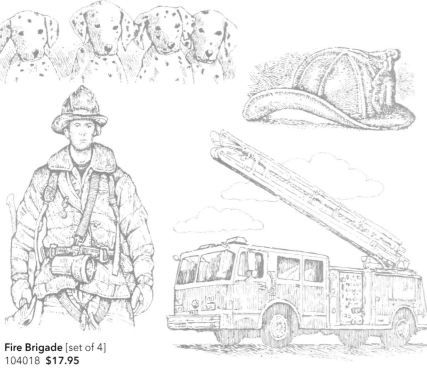

Fire Brigade [set of 4]
104018 **$17.95**

Office Ephemera [set of 9]
104885 **$24.95**

Nature gives to every time and season some beauties of its own.
--Charles Dickens

On Gossamer Wings [set of 9]
105501 **$28.95**

Set Sail [set of 4]
103837 **$17.95**

try this

Create interesting corner accents by folding small pieces of crumpled card stock over the front of the card.

After the showers, the smell of flowers.

Henry Van Dyke

vintage

152

Netherlands [set of 4]
103897 **$16.95**

© 2004 STAMPIN' UP!

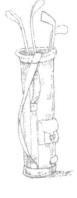

Stamp a border image in a light color to go under a greeting.

try this

The Back Nine [set of 4]
104122 **$17.95**

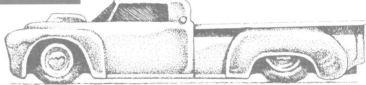

you're a
CLASSIC

Classic Pickups [set of 5]
105190 **$22.95**

best brother

Really, I like you

for
you
dad

you're a
CLASSIC

What each of us becomes
is fashioned from
the Stardust of
our dreams

Stardust [set of 4]
103818 **$18.95**

Balmy Breezes [set of 7]
104962 **$19.95**

It is love of country that lights
and keeps glowing
the fire of patriotism.
~ G. Horace McFarland ~

God bless
America!

Where liberty
dwells
there is my
country.

Land That I Love [set of 7]
105264 **$22.95**

Star-Spangled Banner [set of 4]
103839 **$14.95**

vintage

155

It is only with the heart that one can see rightly what is invisible to the eye.

An act of kindness is long remembered

See with the Heart [set of 5]
104889 **$22.95**

THINKING OF YOU
ON
Father's Day

AIR MAIL

Thinking of Father [set of 4]
103931 **$17.95**

vintage

156

It takes a
long time to
grow an
old friend.

Good friends are like rare books,
hard to find, precious and few.
I'm glad I have a friend like you.

Knobbly Gnomes [set of 7]
105061 **$22.95**

vintage

157

What sweet delights
a quiet life affords.
William Drummond

A Quiet Life [set of 4]
104818 **$18.95**

Definitely Decorative **Toile Blossoms** [set of 7]
100418 **$32.95**

try this

The Horizontal Slot punch on page 218 creates the perfect-sized hole for our grosgrain ribbon to thread through.

vintage

Mostly Flowers [set of 4]
104480 **$11.95**

Gentler Times [set of 7]
103746 **$22.95**

Appreciation

is the

memory

of the heart.

Memory of the Heart [set of 6]
104479 **$16.95**

vintage

159

don't miss it! The Forever Family page uses Weathered background paper from the Timeworn Collection (page 205).

Artifacts [set of 7]
105419 **$22.95**

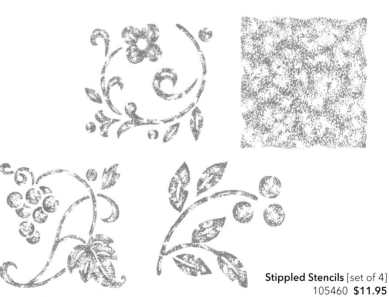

vintage

160

Stippled Stencils [set of 4]
105460 **$11.95**

Elegant Ornaments [set of 4]
100277 **$14.95**

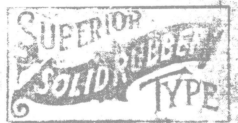

Aged to Perfection [set of 7]
105410 **$22.95**

don't miss it! Each of the papers in the Timeworn Collection (page 205), such as the Heirloom paper used on the mini book here, coordinate beautifully with the Artifacts and Aged to Perfection stamp sets.

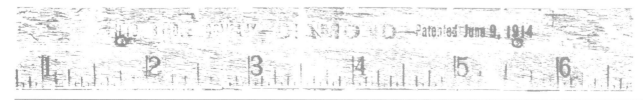

Stampin' Around **Size It Up**
105448 **$5.95** *(Wheel only. Handle and ink cartridges sold separately. See pages 200–201, 225.)*

Kanji [set of 4]
102081 **$11.95**

和 *harmony*　愛 *love*

安 *tranquility*　智 *wisdom*

和 *harmony*

Oriental Brushstrokes [set of 4]
104089 **$17.95**

神 *spirit*

Ancient Asia [set of 6]
105485 **$19.95**

Add speckles to a project by using a watercolor brush with a combination of ink and water. Lightly tap the brush handle against your fingers.

Frame & Flourishes [set of 7]
101931 **$28.95**

try this

friend

He Loves Me

The greatest joy in my life is to have you as a friend.
June 2004

Travis and Jen

© 2004 STAMPIN' UP!

© 2004 STAMPIN' UP!

special mother

YoU aRe SpeciaL

164

Flora & Fauna [set of 7]
104142 **$28.95**

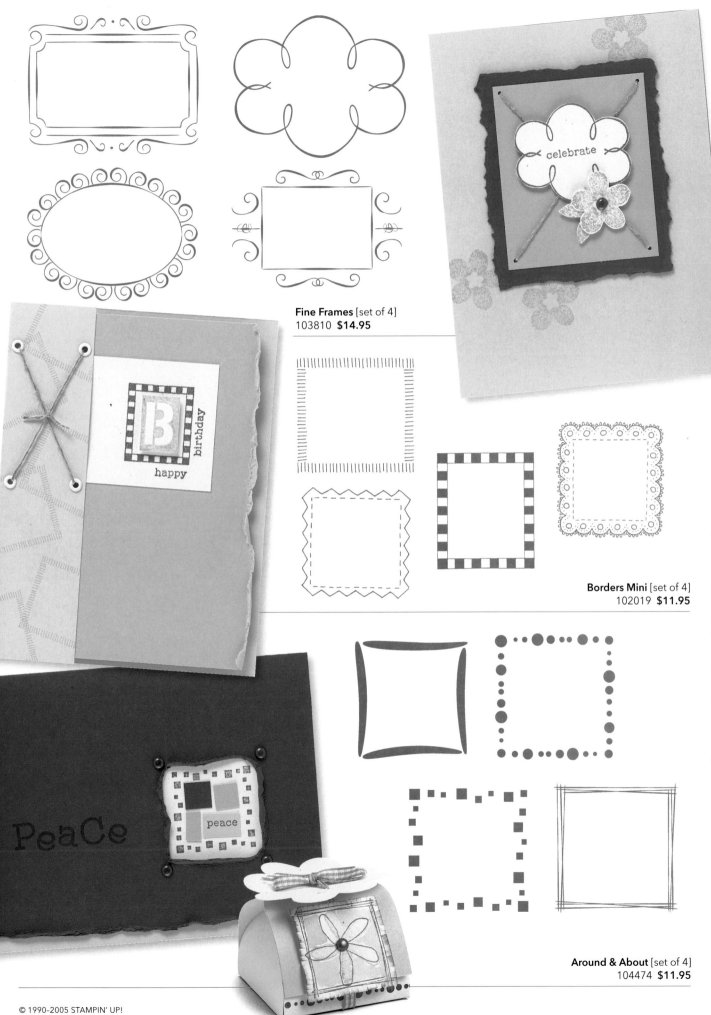

Fine Frames [set of 4]
103810 **$14.95**

Borders Mini [set of 4]
102019 **$11.95**

Around & About [set of 4]
104474 **$11.95**

frames, borders & backgrounds

165

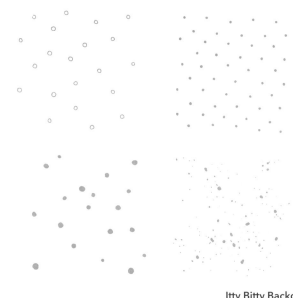

Itty Bitty Backgrounds [set of 4]
101893 **$11.95**

Stars & Swirls [set of 4]
100851 **$11.95**

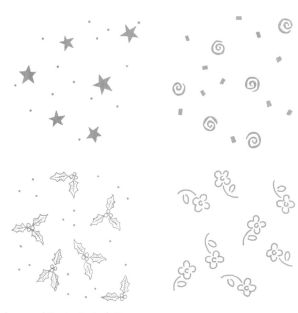

Background Basics [set of 4]
100970 **$11.95**

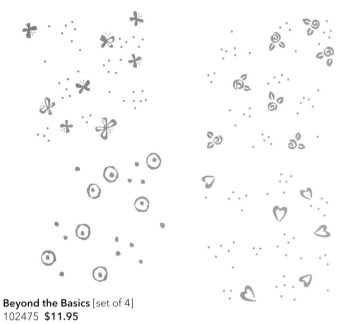

Beyond the Basics [set of 4]
102475 **$11.95**

Petite Patterns [set of 4]
101717 **$11.95**

Fresh Fillers [set of 4]
104476 **$11.95**

frames, borders & backgrounds

167

Border Builders [set of 9]
102573 **$21.95**

Smorgasborders [set of 9]
103798 **$16.95**

friends

all my love

So Nice!

LOVE

Arianne
July 2004

smile

happiness

frames, borders & backgrounds

168

Itty Bitty Borders [set of 4]
100554 **$11.95**

sweet friend

Colter loves playing at the park. Last week it was a struggle for him to stand still just long enough for this photograph. As soon as the shutter clicked, he ran off to find more adventures. It's so wonderful to hear him laugh and giggle as he runs on the grass.

August 2004

Great Shapes [set of 4]
103971 **$27.95**

Stampin' Around Jumbo **Square Pegs**
104160 **$7.95** *(Wheel only. Handle and ink cartridges sold separately. See pages 200-201, 225.)*

cel·e·brate \se-lə-brāt\ vb
(ca 1669) 1 a: to honor (as a
holiday) by ceremonies b: to
mark an anniversary or event

celebrate

often in a social gathering
with acquaintances, friends and
loved ones b: a horn-blowing
confetti-throwing good time

cher·ish \cher-ish\ vt (14c) 1 a:
to hold dear: feel or show
affection for b: to keep or cul-
tivate with care and affection:
NU **cherish** or
ha rly
resolutely (still ~es that memory) b: regard with deep appreciation c: to treasure, value
~holding in the highest regard

Travis and Jennifer
Summer 2004

friend \frend\ n (bef. 12c) 1 a:
one attached to another by
affection, esteem, or love b:
ACQUAINTANCE 2 a: a favored
com **friend** res
a f or
association 3: a pal, chum,
soul mate, or companion
who is available to share
life's little ups and downs

Lexicon of Love [set of 4]
105464 **$14.95**

thanks \than(k)s \ n pl (bef. 12
c) 1: kind and grateful thought
GRATITUDE 2 a: an expression of
gratitude or appreciation
oft **thanks** on-
tai as
a polite and informal expression of gratitude for benefit
received or kindness rendered
b. acknowledging good things

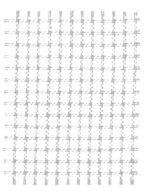

Wonderful Weaves [set of 4]
105359 **$14.95**

From

To

Too **cute** for words

Label Classics [set of 6]
105262 **$19.95**

cherish

love

frames, borders & backgrounds

171

EASTER

mallorie
2004

The stamps in the Little Pieces set are
nicely sized for use with our 1/2-inch
Circle Punch (page 218).

Little Pieces [set of 12]
105063 **$16.95**

try this

Simple Shapes [set of 10]
103606 **$22.95**

Celebrate in Style!

By Design [set of 4]
100349 **$14.95**

happy birthday today— happy times all year!

bloom

Shape-Ups [set of 4]
103973 **$11.95**

How cute is that

Laura 10·07

you make me smile

hello

hello

HELLO!

HELLO!

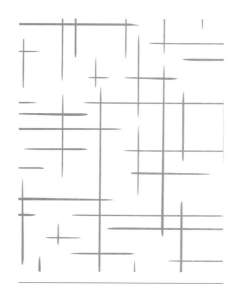

Word by Word [set of 1]
105280 **$16.95**

Approximate dimensions for all background stamps on pages 174–176 are 4-1/2 x 5-3/4 (large enough to cover a standard-sized card). With the exception of the full stamp shown at left, all background stamps show a portion of the pattern at actual size.

love ('ləv)' n. 1. A de
feeling of affection and
uch as that arising fro
attractive qualities, c
oneness. / harmony ('hä
feeling; accord: live
combination of elements
3. The combination of sin
a chord. / peace (pēs) n
or quiet. 2. The absence o
reedom from quarrels a
(frend) n. 1. One who

By Definition [set of 1]
100307 **$16.95**

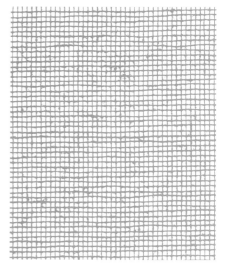

Crosshatch [set of 1]
105258 **$16.95**

Canvas [set of 1]
104421 **$16.95**

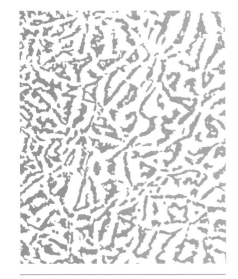

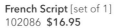

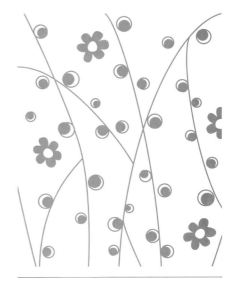

French Script [set of 1]
102086 **$16.95**

Bitty Blossoms [set of 1]
103536 **$16.95**

Ephemera [set of 1]
105493 **$16.95**

Fine Lace [set of 1]
105050 **$16.95**

Houndstooth [set of 1]
105423 **$16.95**

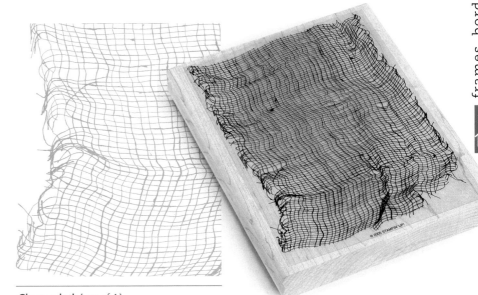

On Safari [set of 1]
104209 **$16.95**

Cheesecloth [set of 1]
105353 **$16.95**

frames, borders & backgrounds

175

Simple Stripes [set of 1]
103534 **$16.95**

Soft Swirls [set of 1]
100413 **$16.95**

Bamboo II [set of 1]
100275 **$16.95**

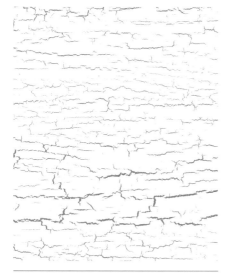

Weathered [set of 1]
105276 **$16.95**

Linograph [set of 1]
104990 **$16.95**

Print Pattern [set of 1]
105167 **$16.95**

Floral [set of 1]
104769 **$16.95**

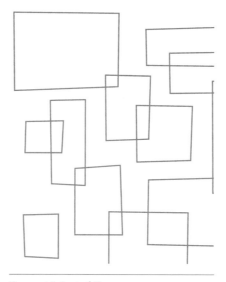

Geometric [set of 1]
104012 **$16.95**

Just Jeans [set of 1]
100259 **$16.95**

frames, borders & backgrounds

176

Personalized stamps

A. TEXT-ONLY STAMPS

> Up to 32 characters per line (spaces count as a character)
> Capitals count as 2 spaces
> Choose from 1–4 lines of text

1. Classic

104541	Classic One-Line	$ 9.95
104540	Classic Two-Line	$ 12.95
104539	Classic Three-Line	$ 14.95
104538	Classic Four-Line	$ 16.95

2. Contemporary

104545	Contemporary One-Line	$9.95
104544	Contemporary Two-Line	$12.95
104543	Contemporary Three-Line	$14.95
104542	Contemporary Four-Line	$16.95

3. Script

104549	Script One-Line	$9.95
104548	Script Two-Line	$12.95
104547	Script Three-Line	$14.95
104546	Script Four-Line	$16.95

B. TEXT-AND-IMAGE STAMPS

> Up to 32 characters per line (spaces count as a character)
> Capitals count as 2 spaces
> Choose from 1–4 lines of text
> Font styles and images cannot be interchanged

1. Best Bee

104533	Best Bee Three-Line	$17.95
104532	Best Bee Four-Line	$19.95

2. Elegant Flower

104529	Elegant Flower Three-Line	$17.95
104528	Elegant Flower Four-Line	$19.95

3. Playful Confetti

104531	Playful Confetti Three-Line	$17.95
104530	Playful Confetti Four-Line	$19.95

C. "HAND STAMPED BY" STAMPS

> One line of personalized text (for name)
> Your name is in all caps
> Up to 16 capital letters for name (spaces count as a character)

1. Tag It

103516	Tag It	$17.95

2. On a Whim

104534	On a Whim	$17.95

3. Decorative Design

104535	Decorative Design	$17.95

D. LARGE TEXT-ONLY STAMPS

> Up to 16 characters per line (spaces count as a character)
> Capitals count as 2 spaces
> Choose either 1 or 2 lines of text

1. Simple Serif

104536	Simple Serif One-Line*	$12.95
104537	Simple Serif Two-Line*	$14.95

*Set uses Shag Mystery Font from House Industries. Font by Ken Barber.

Stamp your personal belongings and correspondence with Stampin' Up!'s personalized stamps. You can create personal stationery, desktop memo sheets, address labels, and more! Personalized stamps must be ordered on special forms. Please ask your demonstrator for assistance. *(Please note: No returns can be accepted on personalized stamps.)*

A text-only stamps

1 First & Last Name
1234 Your Street
City, State 12345
(123) 456-7890

2 First & Last Name
1234 Your Street
City, State 12345
(123) 456-7890

3 *First & Last Name
1234 Your Street
City, State 12345
(123) 456-7890*

B text-and-image stamps

 1 First & Last Name
1234 Your Street
City, State 12345
(123) 456-7890

 2 First & Last Name
1234 Your Street
City, State 12345
(123) 456-7890

 3 First & Last Name
1234 Your Street
City, State 12345
(123) 456-7890

C "hand stamped by" stamps

1 YOUR NAME HERE
COPYRIGHT STAMPIN' UP!

2 Hand Stamped by
YOUR NAME HERE
© Stampin' Up!

3 HAND STAMPED BY
YOUR NAME HERE
© STAMPIN' UP!

D large text-only stamps

 1 Name Here
(123) 456-7890

angel policy

The "Hand Stamped By" Personalized Name Stamps shown above fulfill the requirements of Stampin' Up!'s angel policy, which governs the sale of hand-stamped items. Your demonstrator can give you full details. For more information, contact your demonstrator or go to www.stampinup.com.

say it with stamps

HOLIDAY
Greetings

BEST
wishes

THANKS
so much

Good LUCK

Thinking OF YOU

Get well SOON

YOU'RE
Invited

Birthday WISHES

Sincere Salutations [set of 8]
105156 **$19.95**

much
appreciated

Thank you

thanks

Thank you very much

Much Appreciated [set of 4]
105169 **$12.95**

Thank you very much

FRIEND

A B C D E
F G H I J K
L M N O P
Q R S T U
V W X Y Z

a b c d e
f g h i j k
l m n o p
q r s t u
v w x y z

A B C D E
F G H I J K
L M N O P
Q R S T U
V W X Y Z

A B C D E
F G H I J K
L M N O P
Q R S T U
V W X Y Z

Use our 1/4-inch punches (page 218) to
punch out individual letters from this set
and add a special touch to your projects.

try this

Alphabits [set of 4]
104968 **$14.95**

say it with stamps

178

miss

BLESS

THANK   HAPPY FOR

GOOD FOR   just be

are the best

CELEBRATE   U

LOVE

All about U [set of 12]
105530 **$25.95**

Add a unique frame with the paper-piercing tool from our Crafters' Tool Kit (shown on page 228).

try this

	1998	2004
NAME	1999	2005
	2000	2006
	2001	2007
DATE	2002	2008
	2003	2009

JAN	JUL
FEB	AUG
MAR	SEPT
APR	OCT
MAY	NOV
JUN	DEC

WINTER

SPRING

SUMMER

AUTUMN

1 2 3 4 5 6 7
8 9 10 11 12 13 14
15 16 17 18 19 20 21
22 23 24 25 26 27 28
29 30 31

It's a Date [set of 6]
105046 **$14.95**

say it with stamps

179

Congratulations   hugs and
kisses

many
thanks   P E A C E

From the Heart   merry & bright   J O Y

warmest wishes   *Happy Easter*   L O V E

a happy hello   for you

it's your day!   *thinking*
O F   Y O U

many
thanks

All-Year Cheer I [set of 12]
102189 **$29.95**

thank you
very much

Happy Holidays

HAPPY
FATHER'S
DAY   to:

from: H A P P Y
Mother's Day

Celebrate!

You're a great baby
friend!

for:

i miss you   Happy   on:

you're
invited   Happy
Birthday   at:

by:

All-Year Cheer II [set of 12]
102176 **$29.95**

However you may celebrate, whatever you may do— hope your day is filled with love and wishes that come true!

Best Wishes

Sharing in the happiness of your wonderful news!

When everything is said and done,

being sick is never fun!

Get Well Soon!

Thank You

Just a little note, Just a word or two— Thanking you for who you are And everything you do!

Happy Birthday

HAPPY
Valentine's
Day

Thank You

Just a little note,

Happy St. Patrick's Day

Congrats, Graduate

to my mom

say it with stamps

181

H A P P Y
Valentine's
Day

Happy
Wedding
Day

Happy
Anniversary

just a note

Merry Christmas

Happy
New
Year!

good luck

H A P P Y
Thanksgiving

Happy
Halloween

thank you

Celebrate

friendship

love

thank you

Wonderful Words [set of 4]
103875 **$19.95**

don't miss it! This set has a coordinating Classy Brass embossing template sold on page 227.

HAPPY BIRTHDAY to you

Just because

thanks for your kindness

you make me smile

Simple Sayings II [set of 4]
100174 **$19.95**

say it with stamps

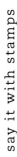

forever

hope

peace

smile

Wonderful Words II [set of 4]
104964 **$19.95**

smile

Better get **Better**

Really, I like you

I'm **happy** for you

Too **cute** for words

Quick Thinking [set of 4]
105160 **$12.95**

Lucky you!

happy holidays

give thanks

you're invited

Thanks a Melon

To: From:

happy new baby

you make me smile!

you're a star!

Love you

Let it snow!

For you

Tiny Talk [set of 12]
103877 **$16.95**

Really, I like you

you're invited

Thank you so much!

Have A Great Day!

Happy Birthday

I miss you

Thank you so much!

Vogue Verses [set of 4]
101954 **$19.95**

i love you more!
★ YOU'RE MY HERO! ★
YOU MAKE ME HAPPY!
You're my favorite!

Sassy Sayings I [set of 4]
103903 **$19.95**

Just because I care!
Just what I wanted!
You take the cake!
H A P P Y · B I R T H D A Y
I want to be you when I grow up!

Sassy Sayings II [set of 4]
103901 **$19.95**

To every thing there is a season, and a time to every purpose under the heaven.

— *Ecclesiastes 3:1*

My presence will go with thee, and I will give thee rest.

— *Exodus 33:14*

Trust in the Lord with all thine heart.

— *Proverbs 3:5*

Be still, and know that I am God.

— *Psalms 46:10*

Each one of us is God's special work of art.

— *Joni Eareckson Tada*

God understands our prayers even when we can't find the words to say them.

— *Author Unknown*

Words of Wisdom [set of 6]
103957 **$19.95**

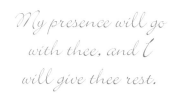

say it with stamps

184

WITH *Sympathy*

Whatever happens,
God is there
to keep you safe
within his care.

After the
showers,
the smell of
flowers.

Henry Van Dyke

May the beautiful
memories that fill
your heart help to
bring you comfort.

Tomorrow's forecast:
Brighter than today!

The best thing
about the future is
that it comes only
one day at a time.

Abraham Lincoln

Brighter Tomorrow [set of 6]
104229 **$19.95**

Sending sincere thanks for your thoughtfulness.

Thank You

Best Wishes

May happiness be yours today and always.

Thinking of you on this special day in a very warm and loving way.

Happy Birthday

Thinking of You

Just a little note to tell you how special you are.

Elegant Greetings [set of 8]
101163 **$26.95**

say it with stamps

185

Just wanted you
to know
how special you are!

May the simple
joys of life
fill this special day
and be yours throughout
the coming year.

Sending warmest wishes
for a future that will bring
all life's simple pleasures
and the best of everything!

Your thoughtfulness
warms my heart
and brightens my day!

Hoping that each day
finds you feeling
more and more
like your wonderful self!

Wishing you all
the love and happiness
two people can share.

Wishing you
merry days,
a heart that's light,
family and friends,
a season bright!

Best wishes
on this
wonderful occasion!

Versatile Verses [set of 8]
102226 **$26.95**

Just wanted you
to know
how special you are!

I'm here for you always...
please know that I care.

186

If wishes
could make you well...
you'd be better already!

Sending you a little
something
wrapped in a whole lot
of love!

One little baby...
many happy hearts!

Time passes...
friendship stays
right where it's put!

You're a wonderful reason
to celebrate!

Wishing you love
and laughter...
forever after!

I'm here for you always...
please know that I care.

Two simple words
that come with so much
gratitude...thank you.

Curvy Verses [set of 8]
104879 **$19.95**

Each and every year you grow you just become more fun to know!

Birthdays are the **BEST**

They say it's your birthday!

LIFE IS NOT A MATTER OF COUNTING YEARS, IT'S A MATTER OF MAKING YEARS COUNT.

It's Your Birthday [set of 9]
105173 **$28.95**

HAPPY BIRTHDAY

Happy *Birthday*

HAPPY BIRTHDAY

Someone like you should be celebrated every day.

I thought and I thought… and then I forgot.

Happy Belated Birthday

Now these three remain: faith, hope and love. But the greatest of these is love. *1 Corinthians 13:13*

Elegant Inspirations [set of 6]
105341 **$19.95**

Be joyful in hope, patient in affliction, faithful in prayer. *Romans 12:12*

I can do all things through Him who strengthens me. *Philippians 4:13*

Now these three remain: faith, hope and love. But the greatest of these is love. *1 Corinthians 13:13*

By day the Lord directs His love, at night His song is with me. *Psalms 42:8*

say it with stamps

187

hand-stamped with love
© STAMPIN' UP!

stamped from the heart
© STAMPIN' UP!

© STAMPIN' UP!

HAND MADE WITH LOVE
© STAMPIN' UP!

Handmade with Love [set of 4]
103016 **$11.95**

stamp art
© STAMPIN' UP!

original design by:
© STAMPIN' UP!

hand crafted
© STAMPIN' UP!

HAND STAMPED
© STAMPIN' UP!

Handmade with Love II [set of 4]
102840 **$11.95**

For a great Hostess!

GREAT ★NEW★ ADDITIONS!

A gift for you!

☆Special☆ ⊙Offer!☆

Bring a friend!

I love what I do... You can too!

THANK YOU ♡ FOR YOUR BUSINESS!

Thank You for your patience!

Business Memos [set of 8]
102403 **$21.95**

Word Play [set of 6]
104167 **$19.95**

Para:
De:

Te
extraño

Para Ti,
Padre

Para Ti,
Madre

Felices
Fiestas!

MUCHAS
GRACIAS!

bebé

Para:
De:

Una
invitación...

Gracias
por tu
amistad!

Feliz
Cumpleaños!

vamos a
CeLebRaR!

Para Ti [set of 12]
105469 **$29.95**

Add to your joy by counting your blessings.

Thinking of you.

Sunshine in the heart not only warms thine own, but all that comes in contact with it.

—James T. Fields

How beautiful a day can be when kindness touches it.

—George Elliston

Thank You!

God writes the gospel not in the Bible alone, but on trees, and flowers, and clouds, and stars.

—Martin Luther

Count your life by smiles, not tears. Count your age by friends, not years.

Happy Birthday!

Hope is the thing with feathers—
That perches in the soul—
And sings the tune without the words—
And never stops—at all.

—Emily Dickinson

Friend to Friend [set of 6]
103965 **$24.95**

How beautiful a day can be when kindness touches it.

—George Elliston

Thank You!

say it with stamps

190

May your Holidays and New Year be filled with Happiness!

May Christmas bring carolers, holly and snow, bright twinkling lights upon your tree... popcorn for stringing and mistletoe, the warmth of friends and family.

Wishing you all the wonder, joy, and peace the season brings.

May love and laughter fill your season!

Merry Christmas

Season's Greetings

Happy Holidays

Thinking of you at this time of year, and though we are miles apart, may the special love that's sent your way keep us close at heart.

May your Holidays and New Year be filled with Happiness!

Season's Greetings [set of 8]
100529 **$29.95**

! your all * best birthday family together
" and boy ... friend for winter father &
thanks just baby valentine { fun day wish party
daughter spring laugh girl my happy grand
fall celebrate mother peace
Christmas little Halloween
favorite good love brother imagine dream son
stamp sweet special hope time
summer vacation sister
joy

Everyday Flexible Phrases [set of 56, 28 blocks]
104383 **$39.95**

january february march april

may june @ july august

september october november december

: date time place for rsvp

who what when where #

Day-to-Day Flexible Phrases [set of 24, 12 blocks]
105188 **$21.95**

authentic beautiful hello cherish is
memories wishes journey + you
laughter moments home live me
wonder play ? because enjoy
unique sassy are believe us of
precious discover being story dad
courage explore simple wife the it's
remember be (always spirit to
definition art honor = with
mom happiness our husband forever create journal inspire

Expressive Flexible Phrases [set of 56, 28 blocks]
105184 **$39.95**

a perfect day
Hangin' out with
How cute is that
me & my

Phrase Starters II [set of 4]
104481 **$19.95**

don't miss it! See a sample using this set on page 173.

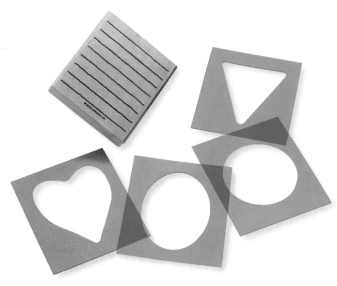

Just Journaling I [set of 1 stamp and 4 templates]
100869 **$16.95**

Our Family

Memories of

Thankful for

Remember when

Just Journaling II [set of 1 stamp and 4 templates]
101995 **$16.95**

don't miss it! See a sample using this set on page 163.

Elegant Beginnings [set of 4]
101798 **$19.95**

i adore u

Jack and Mom
October 9, 2004

"This was Benjamin's
first trip to the beach,
and he was thrilled!
He played in the sand
and paddled around in
the ocean for hours.
He couldn't stop
smiling the whole time
we were there.
Now he always asks
when we are going to
go back again!"

Bear Lake
Summer 2004

smile

sTayIng
cool

Journaling Fun [set of 4]
102943 **$26.95**

headline alphabet

ABC!?

Headline Alphabet [set of 28 stamps, 14 blocks]
105767 **$39.95**

012&#

Headline Numbers [set of 12 stamps, 6 blocks]
105761 **$21.95**

letterpress alphabet

ABC!?

Letterpress Alphabet [set of 28 stamps, 14 blocks]
105763 **$39.95**

012&#

Letterpress Numbers [set of 12 stamps, 6 blocks]
105759 **$21.95**

The oversized letters and numbers from Headline Alphabet and Letterpress Alphabet were designed to mount two per block—one on each side.

classic alphabet

AaBbCcDd&'!?

Classic Alphabet [set of 56 letters, 28 blocks]
104433 **$38.95**   double

0123(#$

Classic Numbers [set of 12]
104434 **$16.95**

Classic Caps [set of 28]
104435 **$26.95**

simple type alphabet

AaBbCc"*!?**

Simple Type Alphabet* [set of 56 letters, 28 blocks]
104207 **$38.95**   double

0123$#&

Simple Type Numbers* [set of 12]
104205 **$16.95**

newsprint alphabet

AaBbCc&'"?!

Newsprint Alphabet [set of 56 letters, 28 blocks]
103961 **$38.95**   double

0123@(#

Newsprint Numbers [set of 12]
104140 **$16.95**

say it with stamps

194

With double alphabet sets, both uppercase and lowercase letters are included. Mount them both on the same block for double the fun! Look for sets marked with this logo.

double

all-around alphabet

AaBbCc)?!;

double

All-Around Alphabet [set of 56 letters, 28 blocks]
104451 **$38.95**

0123$#

All-Around Numbers [set of 12]
104452 **$16.95**

brushstroke alphabet

AaBbCc!?"¿

double

Brushstroke Alphabet [set of 56 letters, 28 blocks]
104438 **$38.95**

0123$#

Brushstroke Numbers [set of 12]
104439 **$16.95**

bold alphabet

AaBbCc?!")

double

Bold Alphabet [set of 56 letters, 28 blocks]
104436 **$38.95**

0123$#

Bold Numbers [set of 12]
104437 **$16.95**

alphadots

Alphadots [set of 28]
104042 **$26.95**

Alphadot Numbers [set of 12]
103849 **$16.95**

stencil alphabet

ABC!?

Stencil Alphabet [set of 28]
105044 **$26.95**

012&*

Stencil Numbers [set of 12]
105048 **$16.95**

tidy alphabet

abcd?!

don't miss it! This set has a coordinating Classy Brass embossing template on page 227.

Tidy Alphabet [set of 28]
104998 **$26.95**

Tidy Numbers [set of 12]
104988 **$16.95**

on the edge alphabet

ABCD&*

On the Edge Alphabet Upper [set of 28]
105272 **$26.95**

abcd!?

On the Edge Alphabet Lower [set of 28]
105270 **$26.95**

0123#+

On the Edge Numbers [set of 12]
105274 **$16.95**

say it with stamps

195

collage alphabet

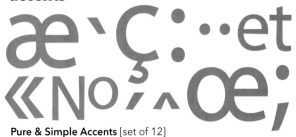

Collage Alphabet [set of 28]
104881 **$26.95**

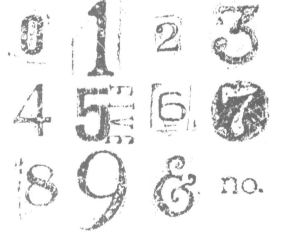

Collage Numbers [set of 12]
104883 **$16.95**

crazy alphabet

Crazy Alphabet [set of 28]
104453 **$26.95**

Crazy Numbers [set of 12]
104454 **$16.95**

accents

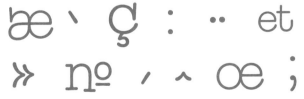

Pure & Simple Accents [set of 12]
105691 **$16.95**

Simple Type Accents [set of 12]
105689 **$16.95**

say it with stamps

196

pure & simple alphabet

ABCD?!

Pure & Simple Alphabet Upper [set of 28]
104455 **$26.95**

abcdƐ)

Pure & Simple Alphabet Lower [set of 28]
104456 **$26.95**

0123#$

Pure & Simple Numbers [set of 12]
104457 **$16.95**

whimsical alphabet

ABCD?

Whimsical Alphabet Upper [set of 28]
104994 **$26.95**

abc!and

Whimsical Alphabet Lower [set of 28]
104996 **$26.95**

0123❀#

Whimsical Numbers [set of 12]
104992 **$16.95**

Write Me a Memory Journaling Fonts CDs: Volume I & Volume II

Contains exclusive fonts offering the ease and flexibility of computer journaling while providing the handwritten look that makes each page feel unique and personal.

System Requirements: PC—Windows 95 or higher, Pentium/equivalent or higher; Macintosh–Macintosh Power PC Processor, System 8.5 or higher

[VOLUME I]

DECO SERIF
FARMER J
Favero Wide
Heritage
Kelly
LiesLy
Pittipat
Carefree
casual
CSS Hand

***Write Me a Memory* Journaling Fonts CD: Volume I** [10 fonts]
105812 **$14.95**

[VOLUME II]

JODYOLa
KP Quick
Little Lamb
marker j low
CONTEMPO CAPS
Passing Notes
Girly Girl
Steele Script
Harry Paul
Woodward Script

***Write Me a Memory* Journaling Fonts CD: Volume II** [10 fonts]
105813 **$14.95**

say it with stamps

197

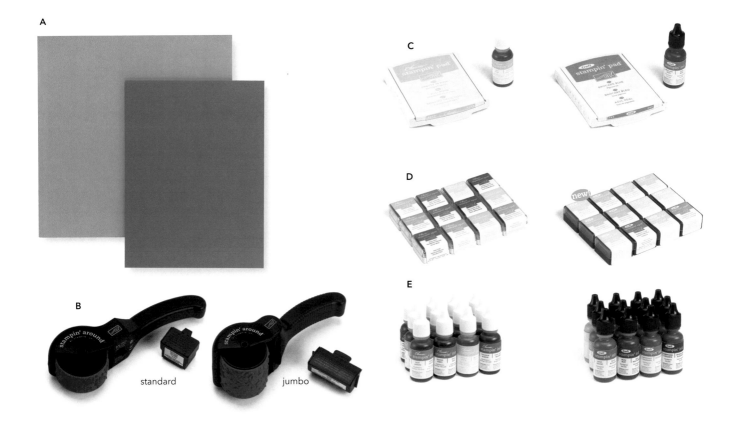

A

B
standard   jumbo

C

D

E

BOLD BRIGHTS

EARTH ELEMENTS

color families

accessories

A. CARD STOCK [sm]

Stampin' Up!'s 80 lb., high-quality card stock is dyed with pure color all the way through. Ideal for scrapbooking, this acid- and lignin-free card stock offers all sorts of stamping and scrapbooking options, from a simple background paper to the core elements of stunning cards and other stamping projects. It comes in both 12 x 12 and 8-1/2 x 11. See pages 200–201.

B. STAMPIN' AROUND CARTRIDGES

Fast and fun, Stampin' Around wheels are perfect for borders and backgrounds, and now you can choose from 2 sizes! Our jumbo wheels and cartridges add a new element to Stampin' Around. The larger images provide additional creative options for your quick-and-easy projects. Our Stampin' Around line also offers beautiful, fun, and easy color coordination. Stampin' Around standard and jumbo ink cartridges come in Stampin' Up!'s exclusive colors to coordinate with card stock, ink pads, and markers. Color made easy meets stamping made easy!

Refill with Classic ink refills. Acid free. 1/2 oz. Handles are sold separately and are available on page 225. Uninked cartridges and embossing cartridges are also available on page 225.

COLORS, ITEM NUMBERS & PRICES ARE LISTED ON PAGES 200–201

Note: While most of Stampin' Up!'s products are safe [sm] for your scrapbooks, our Stampin' Memories symbol identifies those that were specifically created for and are the best choice for scrapbooking.

C. STAMP PADS

Stampin' Up!'s revolutionary pads feature a patented, flip-top design that stores the inking surface upside-down, so the pad surface stays juicy between re-inkings. See pages 200–201.

Our **Craft Stampin' Pads** contain rich pigment inks that are ideal for scrapbooking, embossing, and other craft projects–they're your best choice for long-lasting color. Be sure to order a matching refill to keep your Craft pad moist. Nontoxic and acid free. [sm]

Our award-winning **Classic Stampin' Pads** feature our popular, fast-drying, dye-based inks. Nontoxic and acid free.

D. STAMPIN' SPOTS

Now in both Classic and Craft ink, these 1-inch-square ink pads are an affordable way to sample all of our colors. These pads use the same ink as the full-size Stampin' Pads, so they coordinate with our exclusive card stock, pastels, markers, and other fun accessories. See pages 200–201.

new 105549	Classic Spots* New Colors Set[1] (set of 12 new colors introduced in this Idea Book & Catalog)	$21.50

E. INK REFILLS

You'll want a refill for each of your ink pads, and you can order your Classic and Craft ink refills packaged in our own Stampin' Up! color families. (You can still order both Craft and Classic ink refills individually.) And when you order an entire set, you receive a discount of more than $2 on the Classic refills and $3 on the Craft refills! You can also use the Classic ink refills to fill your Stampin' Around cartridges and re-ink your Spectrum Pads. Acid free. 1/2 oz. See pages 200–201.

F

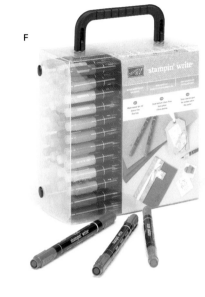

I

H

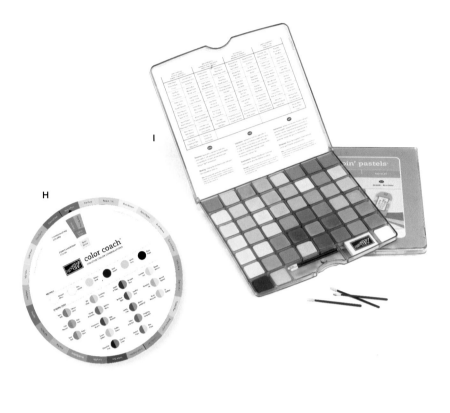

G

RICH REGALS

SOFT SUBTLES

F. STAMPIN' WRITE MARKERS

With a cap design exclusive to Stampin' Up!, these markers feature a fine tip for details and writing and a brush tip for wider color applications. Each marker is like getting 2 long-lasting markers in 1! Acid-free, water-based, dye ink. See pages 200-201 to purchase markers individually.

Many Marvelous Markers Set of 48 Stampin' Write dual-tip markers. Horizontal storage case keeps both tips inked evenly.

| 105541 | Many Marvelous Markers | **$119.95** |

G. STAMPIN' WRITE JOURNALERS ℠

Fade-resistant, waterproof, pigment markers ideal for journaling and scrapbooking. Now in 13 of our exclusive colors. Tip sizes: .6mm and 2.3 mm bullet. See pages 200–201.

H. COLOR COACH

Completely redesigned, our new double-sided Color Coach features complementary and coordinating color suggestions for our exclusive colors, plus a convenient chart of neutral and monochromatic color choices.

| new! 105796 | Color Coach | **$9.95** |

[1] Always Artichoke, Apricot Appeal, Bashful Blue, Bravo Burgundy, Certainly Celery, Elegant Eggplant, Handsome Hunter, Pixie Pink, Pumpkin Pie, Regal Rose, So Saffron, and Sahara Sand.

[2] Basic Black, Going Gray, Whisper White

[3] Always Artichoke, Apricot Appeal, Bashful Blue, Bravo Burgundy, Certainly Celery, Elegant Eggplant, Handsome Hunter, Pixie Pink, Pumpkin Pie, Regal Rose, So Saffron.

I. STAMPIN' PASTELS

Protected in a sturdy case complete with 6 applicators and an eraser. Each color family refill assortment includes 12 colors of chalk unless otherwise noted. Acid free.

105542	Stampin' Pastels*	**$24.95**
103174	Applicator Refill (15)	**$3.50**
100852	Pastel Erasers (2)	**$2.50**
new! 105543	Bold Brights Refills	**$10.95**
new! 105544	Earth Elements Refills	**$10.95**
new! 105545	Rich Regals Refills	**$10.95**
new! 105546	Soft Subtles Refills	**$10.95**
new! 105547	Neutrals[2] (set of 3)	**$2.95**
new! 105661	New Colors Refills[3] (set of 11)	**$9.95**

accessories

199

DON'T MISS these other products that come in a selection of our exclusive colors

Boxes, Cards, & Tags (p. 212-213)

Book Kits (p. 214)

Tag Sheets (p. 214)

Spectrum Pads (p. 222)

Watercolor Wonder Crayons (p. 223)

Eyelets (p. 229)

Buttons (p. 230)

bold brights	classic stampin' pad	classic ink refill	stampin' write marker	stampin' write journaler	craft stampin' pad	craft ink refill	8-1/2 x 11 card stock (24 sheets)	12 x 12 card stock (20 sheets)	stampin' around cartridge	stampin' around jumbo cartridge
	$4.95	**$2.50**	**$2.95**	**$2.95**	**$6.95**	**$3.95**	**$4.50**	**$6.50**	**$4.95**	**$6.95**
glorious green	103040	101453	100047	–	101436	100434	101697	102613	102212	103676
green galore	102122	101735	100048	–	101325	102772	101768	100544	100802	–
gable green	101673	101483	100049	–	101671	101232	102795	101405	102117	–
yoyo yellow	102717	101986	100050	–	101608	103325	102824	101786	102361	–
only orange	102696	102931	100051	–	101951	102111	102837	102009	101366	–
real red	103133	103287	100052	104173	101190	102104	102482	101554	102996	103675
pink passion	101212	102308	100053	–	102916	103036	102762	102615	102667	–
new! pixie pink	105212	105224	105112	105029	105236	105150	105121	105132	105203	–
orchid opulence	101859	101324	100055	–	101900	100464	100969	101941	100809	–
lovely lilac	102874	103077	100056	104177	102965	101695	100427	101601	101256	103677
brilliant blue	100691	100763	100057	–	101843	103006	100721	102164	100871	103674
tempting turquoise	100814	101041	100058	–	100741	100957	102067	103208	101199	–

earth elements	classic stampin' pad	classic ink refill	stampin' write marker	stampin' write journaler	craft stampin' pad	craft ink refill	8-1/2 x 11 card stock (24 sheets)	12 x 12 card stock (20 sheets)	stampin' around cartridge	stampin' around jumbo cartridge
	$4.95	**$2.50**	**$2.95**	**$2.95**	**$6.95**	**$3.95**	**$4.50**	**$6.50**	**$4.95**	**$6.95**
chocolate chip	100908	101065	100071	–	101816	102847	102128	100623	102496	–
close to cocoa	103139	102444	100072	new! 105028	100549	100925	101341	101316	100714	–
creamy caramel	103220	101478	100078	–	103034	102004	102514	103302	100654	103671
more mustard	103162	101962	100076	104176	103092	101990	100946	101566	100566	103672
new! pumpkin pie	105216	105229	105115	–	105240	105164	105117	105141	105200	–
really rust	102549	100685	100073	–	102437	103014	100661	100470	102927	–
ruby red	102259	100532	100075	–	101009	102448	102030	103030	102047	103673
cameo coral	103035	102238	100074	–	101933	101033	100475	100508	102785	–
summer sun	100537	101231	100077	–	101690	102765	103124	102480	100660	–
old olive	102277	100531	100079	104175	103063	101425	100702	101556	102021	103670
garden green	102272	102059	100080	–	101841	100519	102584	102651	103252	–
not quite navy	103008	102949	100059	–	103227	102310	101722	102443	103084	–

assorted	classic stampin' pads[1] (set of 12)	classic ink refills (set of 12)	stampin' write markers (set of 12)		craft stampin' pads[1] (set of 12)	new! craft ink refills (set of 12)	8-1/2 x 11 card stock (36 sheets, 3 ea. of 12 colors)	12 x 12 card stock (24 sheets, 2 ea. of 12 colors)	classic stampin' spots[1] (set of 12)	new! craft stampin' spots[1] (set of 12)
	$54.95	**$27.95**	**$29.95**		**$76.95**	**$43.95**	**$6.95**	**$7.95**	**$21.50**	**$24.95**
bold brights	105562	105554	105538	–	105558	105443	105548	105569	105550	105439
earth elements	105563	105555	105539	–	105559	105442	105566	105570	105551	105438
rich regals	105564	105556	105540	–	105560	105440	105567	105571	105552	105437
soft subtles	105565	105557	105537	–	105561	105441	105568	105572	105553	105370

[1] Comes with sturdy cardboard storage case.
[2] Ultrasmooth
[3] The Basic Brown and Basic Black Classic ink is waterproof when used on our Whisper White and Very Vanilla card stock.

rich regals

	classic stampin' pad	classic ink refill	stampin' write marker	stampin' write journaler	craft stampin' pad	craft ink refill	8-1/2 x 11 card stock (24 sheets)	12 x 12 card stock (20 sheets)	stampin' around cartridge	stampin' around jumbo cartridge
	$4.95	$2.50	$2.95	$2.95	$6.95	$3.95	$4.50	$6.50	$4.95	$6.95
bordering blue	102265	100940	100070	-	101374	102530	102630	101733	101186	-
brocade blue	101102	100408	100064	-	101593	100788	101166	101742	103198	-
ballet blue	100907	101713	100066	104179	102855	101732	100613	102899	102305	103662
night of navy	102977	103033	100069	105030	103181	103131	100867	100653	103027	103664
taken with teal	103257	100550	100068	-	100617	102049	101584	101176	100460	-
handsome hunter	105215	105227	105116	-	105239	105163	105122	105134	105198	105205
always artichoke	105219	105232	105113	105031	105243	105177	105119	105140	105199	
so saffron	105213	105225	105114	-	105237	105151	105118	105139	105201	
regal rose	105211	105223	105108	-	105235	105149	105130	105131	105196	
rose red	101778	102109	100063	-	101545	102915	102544	102327	100520	-
bravo burgundy	105214	105226	105109	105334	105238	105162	105123	105135	105197	105207
elegant eggplant	105210	105222	105110	-	105234	105148	105126	105138	105195	-

soft subtles

	classic stampin' pad	classic ink refill	stampin' write marker	stampin' write journaler	craft stampin' pad	craft ink refill	8-1/2 x 11 card stock (24 sheets)	12 x 12 card stock (20 sheets)	stampin' around cartridge	stampin' around jumbo cartridge
	$4.95	$2.50	$2.95	$2.95	$6.95	$3.95	$4.50	$6.50	$4.95	$6.95
perfect plum	101437	102107	100035	-	102869	100697	101889	101281	101139	103666
pale plum	102732	101268	100036	104174	103271	102202	101658	101615	101519	-
pretty in pink	101301	102295	100045	-	100857	101127	100459	101448	100562	103668
blush blossom	102609	100614	100037	-	102080	100935	103318	102814	101678	-
apricot appeal	105218	105231	105107	-	105242	105166	105124	105136	105202	-
barely banana	101170	100639	100039	-	101609	101676	102701	101929	101516	-
certainly celery	105217	105230	105106	-	105241	105165	105125	105137	105194	-
mellow moss	102774	101771	100038	-	101054	101967	102898	100638	102871	103667
sage shadow	102532	100720	100040	104180	103251	100711	101563	101815	101475	-
bashful blue	105209	105221	105111	-	105233	105146	105120	105133	105204	105206
almost amethyst	101723	102580	100043	-	101211	102282	102158	100704	100659	-
lavender lace	101305	100862	100041	-	103144	101590	101614	100905	101812	-

neutrals

	classic stampin' pad	classic ink refill	stampin' write marker	stampin' write journaler	craft stampin' pad	craft ink refill	8-1/2 x 11 card stock (40 sheets)	12 x 12 card stock (20 sheets)	stampin' around cartridge	stampin' around jumbo cartridge
	$4.95	$2.50	$2.95	$2.95	$6.95	$3.95	$6.50	$5.95	$4.95	$6.95
whisper white	-	-	-	-	101731	101780	100730[2]	101874[2]	sold on p. 225	-
very vanilla	-	-	-	-	104308	104328	101650[2]	100467[2]	-	-
sahara sand	105208	105220	105105	-	-	-	105328	105327	-	-
basic brown	104315[3]	104314[3]	-	-	-	-	-	-	-	-
going gray	103274	102521	100081	-	102669	103136	103154	100939	101821	-
basic black	101179[3]	102512[3]	100082	105394	102192	102995	102851	100856	104581[3]	104582[3]

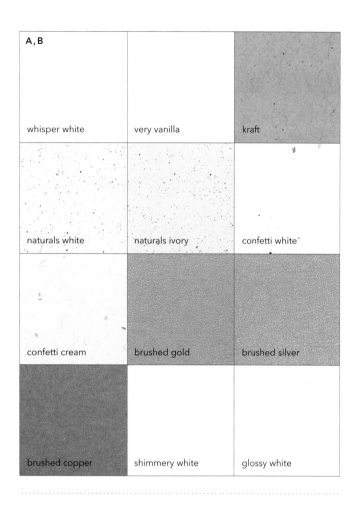

A, B

whisper white | very vanilla | kraft
naturals white | naturals ivory | confetti white
confetti cream | brushed gold | brushed silver
brushed copper | shimmery white | glossy white

C

white vellum

D

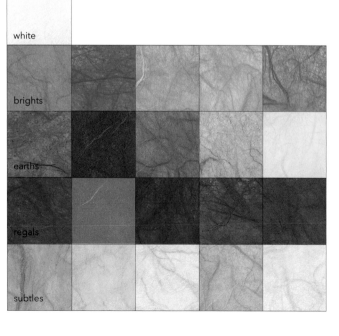

white
brights
earths
regals
subtles

A. CARD STOCK 8-1/2 X 11

100730	Whisper White* (40) a, l, b	*sm*	$6.50
101650	Very Vanilla* (40) a, l, b	*sm*	$6.50
102125	Kraft (40) a, l, b	*sm*	$6.50
102316	Naturals White (40) a, l, b	*sm*	$6.50
101849	Naturals Ivory (40) a, l, b	*sm*	$6.50
102028	Confetti White (40) a, l, b	*sm*	$7.95
102835	Confetti Cream (40) a, l, b	*sm*	$7.95
102935	Brushed Gold (10) a		$6.95
100712	Brushed Silver (10) a		$6.95
103975	Brushed Copper (10) a		$6.95
101910	Shimmery White (10)		$6.95
102599	Glossy White (25)		$4.95

B. CARD STOCK 12 X 12

101874	Whisper White* (20) a, l, b	*sm*	$5.95
100467	Very Vanilla* (20) a, l, b	*sm*	$5.95
101119	Kraft (20) a, l, b	*sm*	$5.95
105680	Naturals White & Ivory (20, 10 of ea. color) a, l, b	*sm*	$5.95
105681	Confetti White & Cream (20, 10 of ea. color) a, l, b	*sm*	$7.50

C. WHITE VELLUM

101856	8-1/2 x 11 Card Stock (20) a, l	*sm*	$6.50
101839	8-1/2 x 11 Paper (20) a, l	*sm*	$4.95
103598	12 x 12 Paper (12) a, l	*sm*	$6.95

D. MULBERRY PAPER

Available in colors that work beautifully with Stampin' Up!'s exclusive color-coordinated papers, markers, and ink pads. 8-1/2 x 11. Assortments include 10 sheets, 2 ea. of 5 colors.

102678	White (5 sheets)	$3.95
102370	Brights	$6.95
100860	Earths	$6.95
101693	Regals	$6.95
102253	Subtles	$6.95

E. WATERCOLOR PAPER

100% cotton, cold-pressed 140 lb. watercolor paper. Sized perfectly to layer on your card front. 3-3/4 x 5. 20 sheets per pkg.

new! 105019	Watercolor Paper	$6.95

*ultrasmooth   a = acid free   l = lignin free   b = buffered

E

try this Use permanent StazOn™ ink for best results on watercolor paper. Let ink dry completely before watercoloring.

accessories

202

envelope size key

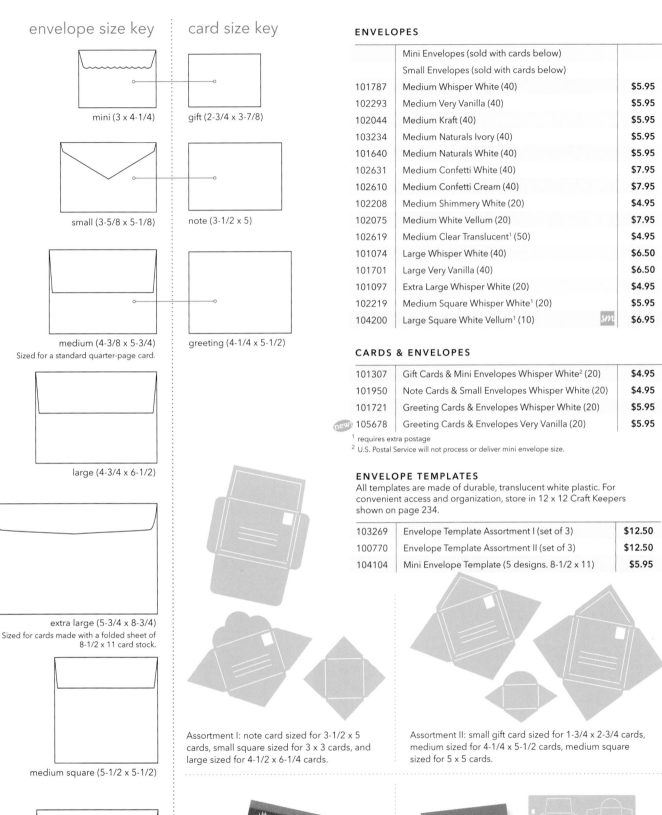

mini (3 x 4-1/4)

small (3-5/8 x 5-1/8)

medium (4-3/8 x 5-3/4)
Sized for a standard quarter-page card.

large (4-3/4 x 6-1/2)

extra large (5-3/4 x 8-3/4)
Sized for cards made with a folded sheet of
8-1/2 x 11 card stock.

medium square (5-1/2 x 5-1/2)

large square (6-1/2 x 6-1/2)
Sized for a brag book page.

card size key

gift (2-3/4 x 3-7/8)

note (3-1/2 x 5)

greeting (4-1/4 x 5-1/2)

ENVELOPES

	Mini Envelopes (sold with cards below)		
	Small Envelopes (sold with cards below)		
101787	Medium Whisper White (40)		**$5.95**
102293	Medium Very Vanilla (40)		**$5.95**
102044	Medium Kraft (40)		**$5.95**
103234	Medium Naturals Ivory (40)		**$5.95**
101640	Medium Naturals White (40)		**$5.95**
102631	Medium Confetti White (40)		**$7.95**
102610	Medium Confetti Cream (40)		**$7.95**
102208	Medium Shimmery White (20)		**$4.95**
102075	Medium White Vellum (20)		**$7.95**
102619	Medium Clear Translucent[1] (50)		**$4.95**
101074	Large Whisper White (40)		**$6.50**
101701	Large Very Vanilla (40)		**$6.50**
101097	Extra Large Whisper White (20)		**$4.95**
102219	Medium Square Whisper White[1] (20)		**$5.95**
104200	Large Square White Vellum[1] (10)	*sm*	**$6.95**

CARDS & ENVELOPES

101307	Gift Cards & Mini Envelopes Whisper White[2] (20)	**$4.95**
101950	Note Cards & Small Envelopes Whisper White (20)	**$4.95**
101721	Greeting Cards & Envelopes Whisper White (20)	**$5.95**
new! 105678	Greeting Cards & Envelopes Very Vanilla (20)	**$5.95**

[1] requires extra postage
[2] U.S. Postal Service will not process or deliver mini envelope size.

ENVELOPE TEMPLATES

All templates are made of durable, translucent white plastic. For convenient access and organization, store in 12 x 12 Craft Keepers shown on page 234.

103269	Envelope Template Assortment I (set of 3)	**$12.50**
100770	Envelope Template Assortment II (set of 3)	**$12.50**
104104	Mini Envelope Template (5 designs. 8-1/2 x 11)	**$5.95**

Assortment I: note card sized for 3-1/2 x 5 cards, small square sized for 3 x 3 cards, and large sized for 4-1/2 x 6-1/4 cards.

Assortment II: small gift card sized for 1-3/4 x 2-3/4 cards, medium sized for 4-1/4 x 5-1/2 cards, medium square sized for 5 x 5 cards.

Mini Envelope Template: sized for a 2 x 3 card, 2 x 2 card, and a 1-1/2 x 1-1/2 card.

accessories

203

post albums

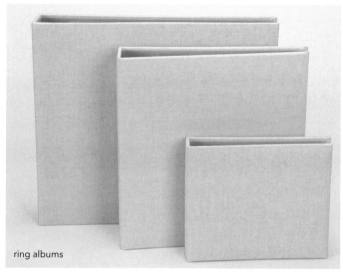
ring albums

real red linen

mellow moss linen

navy linen

natural linen

black leather

LINEN POST ALBUMS *sm*

These linen albums come in 3 sizes and are designed for long-lasting durability. Includes 10 page protectors.

new! 105381	Real Red 6 x 6 Brag Book	$19.95
new! 105382	Real Red 8-1/2 x 11	$24.95
new! 105383	Real Red 12 x 12	$29.95
new! 105384	Mellow Moss 6 x 6 Brag Book	$19.95
new! 105385	Mellow Moss 8-1/2 x 11	$24.95
new! 105386	Mellow Moss 12 x 12	$29.95
104516	Navy 6 x 6 Brag Book	$19.95
104517	Navy 8-1/2 x 11	$24.95
104518	Navy 12 x 12	$29.95
104515	Natural 6 x 6 Brag Book	$19.95
104520	Natural 8-1/2 x 11	$24.95
104519	Natural 12 x 12	$29.95

LEATHER POST ALBUMS *sm*

High-quality bonded leather. Includes 10 page protectors.

104188	Black 6 x 6 Brag Book	$24.95
100700	Black 8-1/2 x 11	$34.95
102782	Black 12 x 12	$39.95

LINEN RING ALBUMS *sm*

Another option in our linen finish. The 12 x 12 and 8-1/2 x 11 albums feature three 1-1/2 inch straight D rings. The 6 x 6 brag book features two 1-inch straight D rings. Includes 10 page protectors.

new! 105387	Real Red 6 x 6 Brag Book	$16.95
new! 105388	Real Red 8-1/2 x 11	$21.95
new! 105389	Real Red 12 x 12	$26.95
new! 105391	Mellow Moss 6 x 6 Brag Book	$16.95
new! 105392	Mellow Moss 8-1/2 x 11	$21.95
new! 105393	Mellow Moss 12 x 12	$26.95
104512	Navy 6 x 6 Brag Book	$16.95
104513	Navy 8-1/2 x 11	$21.95
104514	Navy 12 x 12	$26.95
104509	Natural 6 x 6 Brag Book	$16.95
104510	Natural 8-1/2 x 11	$21.95
104511	Natural 12 x 12	$26.95

The full sheet of a selection of our Timeworn papers is shown here.

POST PAGE PROTECTORS *sm*
These styles are specifically designed to lie flat in our post-bound albums. Post extenders and 3 cardboard spacers included. Polypropylene. 20 per pkg.

103687	6 x 6	$5.95
103145	8-1/2 x 11	$6.95
100670	12 x 12	$9.95
104184	Post Extenders (12 per pkg. Not shown.)	$5.95

RING PAGE PROTECTORS *sm*
Select this option for protecting your scrapbook pages when using our ring albums. Available without the side gusset provided for post-bound albums, these polypropylene page protectors offer the same roominess and high quality you depend on from all Stampin' Up! page protectors. 20 per pkg.

104521	6 x 6	$5.95
104523	8-1/2 x 11	$6.95
104522	12 x 12	$9.95

MEMORABILIA POCKETS *sm*
Polypropylene, adhesive-backed assortment includes two 2 x 2, two 2 x 4-1/8, two 4 x 4-1/8, and one 5 x 4-15/16 pockets. Acid free.

103685	Memorabilia Pockets	$4.95

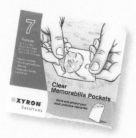

TIMEWORN COLLECTION PAPER *sm*
Designed and photographed exclusively by Stampin' Up!, these papers coordinate with our color palette and several vintage stamp sets for an endless array of creative possibilities. 12 sheets per pkg., 2 ea. of 6 designs. 12 x 12.

new! 105369	Heirloom	$5.95
new! 105368	Rustic	$5.95
new! 105367	Weathered	$5.95

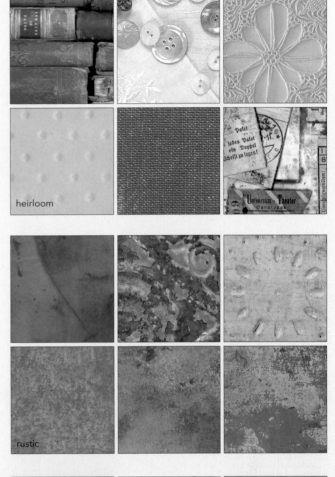

heirloom

rustic

weathered

All pattern swatches are shown at 50%.

DESIGNER SERIES PAPER *sm*

Sized for 12 x 12 scrapbooks, you can easily cut the sheets down for 8-1/2 x 11 scrapbooks, smaller brag book pages, or cards. 12 sheets, 2 of ea. design. Acid free, lignin free, and buffered.

102204	Candy	$5.95
102076	Splash	$5.95
new! 105366	Cambridge	$5.95
new! 105365	Oxford	$5.95
103655	Tickles	$5.95
103656	Pickles	$5.95
103658	Sweet	$5.95
103657	Sassy	$5.95
104136	Pool Party	$5.95
104135	Slumber Party	$5.95
104133	Copper Kiss	$5.95
104134	Silver Bliss	$5.95

DESIGNER SERIES VELLUM *sm*

Terrific designs based on Stampin' Up!'s exclusive Designer Series paper. 12 x 12. 12 sheets, 2 of ea. design. Acid and lignin free.

102037	Candy	$9.95
102034	Splash	$9.95
new! 105364	Cambridge	$9.95
new! 105363	Oxford	$9.95
103651	Tickles	$9.95
103652	Pickles	$9.95
103654	Sweet	$9.95
103653	Sassy	$9.95
104132	Pool Party	$9.95
104131	Slumber Party	$9.95
104129	Copper Kiss	$9.95
104130	Silver Bliss	$9.95

accessories

206

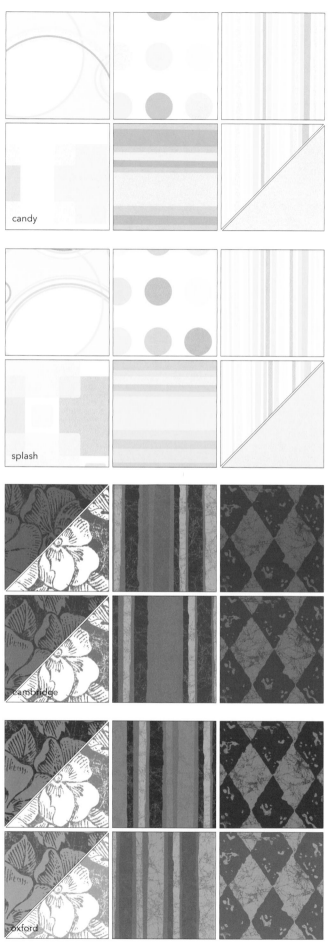

candy

splash

cambridge

oxford

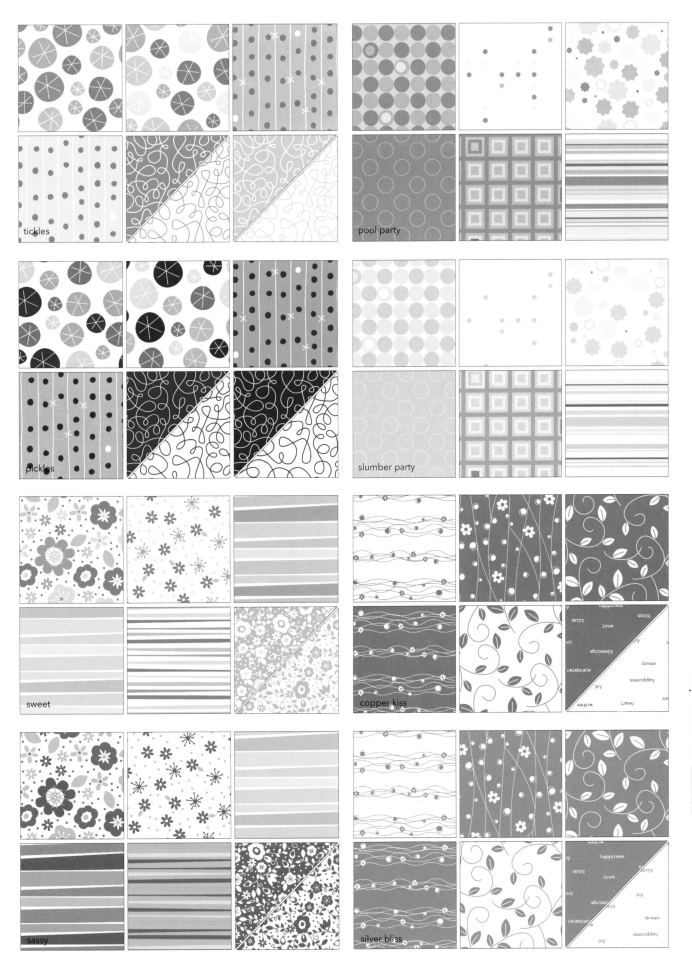

tickles

pool party

pickles

slumber party

sweet

copper kiss

sassy

silver bliss

All pattern swatches are shown at 50%. Swatches that are split are different in the paper and vellum packages. The top swatch represents paper and the bottom swatch represents the vellum.

quick strips *sm*

These full-color images make quick and easy borders, journaling boxes, or page accents. Combine with Stampin' Up!'s alphabet stamp sets to make page titles. Contains 6 sheets of self-adhesive Quick Strips (6 x 12). Quick Strips I is designed to coordinate with our Designer Series paper and vellum; Quick Strips II features versatile patterns that highlight several new Stampin' Up! exclusive colors.

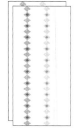 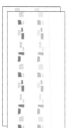 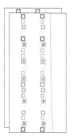

new! Simply Scrappin' **Quick Strips I**
105798 **$6.95**

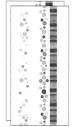 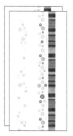 

new! Simply Scrappin' **Quick Strips II**
105799 **$6.95**

simply scrappin' kits *sm*

Our Simply Scrappin' Kits contain 18 sheets of coordinating materials designed to help you create distinctive and quick scrapbook pages: 8 sheets of 12 x 12 solid-color card stock; 4 sheets of 12 x 12 patterned card stock; 6 sheets of 6 x 12 self-adhesive die cuts featuring exclusive images and Quick Strips. All sheets can be easily trimmed to create 8-1/2 x 11 and 6 x 6 pages. Use your scraps to make quick cards. Acid & lignin free.

accessories

208

3 sheets
Bashful Blue–Boy
Pretty in Pink–Girl

3 sheets
Certainly Celery

3 sheets
Whisper White

 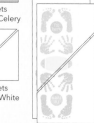 

new! Simply Scrappin' **I'm Here–Boy**
105800 **$12.95**

new! Simply Scrappin' **I'm Here–Girl**
105801 **$12.95**

All paper pattern swatches are shown at 50% on all Simply Scrappin' Kits.

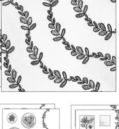

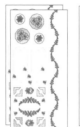

3 sheets
Sage Shadow

3 sheets
Barely Banana

2 sheets
Whisper White

Simply Scrappin' **In Full Bloom**
104362 **$12.95**

3 sheets
Perfect Plum

3 sheets
Mellow Moss

2 sheets
Whisper White

Simply Scrappin' **Summer Sketches**
104365 **$12.95**

3 sheets
Bordering Blue

3 sheets
Mellow Moss

2 sheets
Very Vanilla

Simply Scrappin' **Vintage Keepsakes**
104363 **$12.95**

3 sheets
Always Artichoke

3 sheets
Not Quite Navy

Whisper White
2 sheets

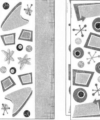

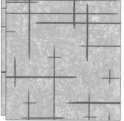
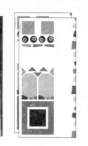

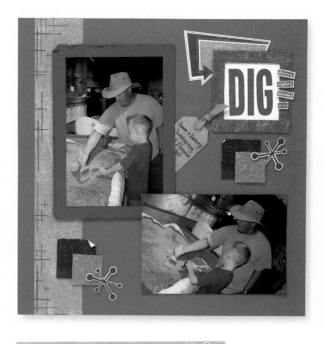

Simply Scrappin' **He's Too Cool**
105804 **$12.95**

3 sheets
Regal Rose

3 sheets
Certainly Celery

Whisper White
2 sheets

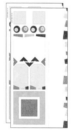

Simply Scrappin' **She's Too Cool**
105803 **$12.95**

accessories

210

3 sheets
Not Quite Navy

3 sheets
Real Red

Whisper White
2 sheets

Simply Scrappin' **Sparkling Holiday**
104367 **$12.95**

All paper pattern swatches are shown at 50% on all Simply Scrappin' Kits.

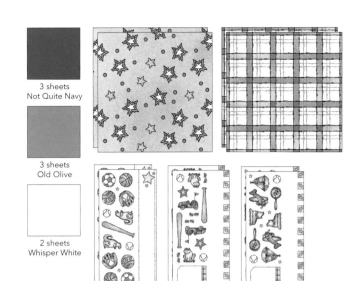

Simply Scrappin' **Toy Box**
104359 **$12.95**

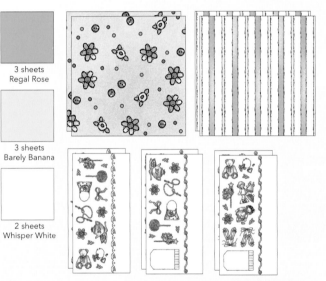

Simply Scrappin' **Buttons, Bows & Twinkletoes**
105805 **$12.95**

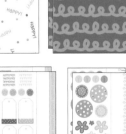

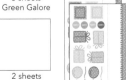

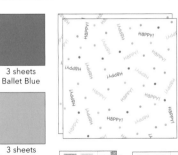

Simply Scrappin' **Polka Dot Party**
104366 **$12.95**

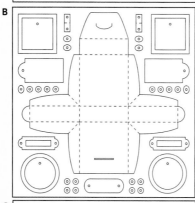

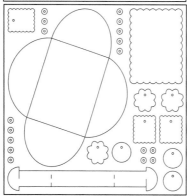
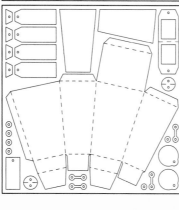

A

B

C

D

A. PARTY FAVOR BOXES & TAGS

6 sheets per pkg. Color packages include 1 of ea. color listed at bottom of page plus Confetti White and Kraft. 12 x 12.
(Approx. box size: 2 x 2 x 1-1/2)

100226	Bold Brights	$6.95
100229	Earth Elements	$6.95
105665	Rich Regals	$6.95
105664	Soft Subtles	$6.95
100230	Confetti White & Kraft (3 ea. of 2 colors)	$6.95
104202	Whisper White (6 sheets)	$6.95
104201	Very Vanilla (6 sheets)	$6.95

B. BLOOMIN' BOXES & TAGS

6 sheets per pkg. Color packages include 1 of ea. color listed at bottom of page plus Confetti White and Kraft. 12 x 12.
(Approx. box size: 3-1/4 x 1 x 3-1/4)

105075	Bold Brights	$6.95
105076	Earth Elements	$6.95
105077	Rich Regals	$6.95
105078	Soft Subtles	$6.95
105079	Confetti White & Kraft (3 ea. of 2 colors)	$6.95
105080	Whisper White & Very Vanilla (3 ea. of 2 colors)	$6.95

C. PETAL CARDS & TAGS

6 sheets per pkg. Color packages include 1 of ea. color listed at bottom of page plus Confetti White and Kraft. 12 x 12.
(Approx. card size: 4 x 5-1/4)

105069	Bold Brights	$6.95
105070	Earth Elements	$6.95
105071	Rich Regals	$6.95
105072	Soft Subtles	$6.95
105073	Confetti White & Kraft (3 ea. of 2 colors)	$6.95
105074	Whisper White & Very Vanilla (3 ea. of 2 colors)	$6.95

D. PILLAR BOXES & TAGS

6 sheets per pkg. Color packages include 1 of ea. color listed at bottom of page plus Confetti White and Kraft. 12 x 12.
(Approx box size: 3-1/4 x 2-1/2 x 6)

104316	Bold Brights	$6.95
104317	Earth Elements	$6.95
105663	Rich Regals	$6.95
105662	Soft Subtles	$6.95
104320	Confetti White & Kraft (3 ea. of 2 colors)	$6.95
104321	Whisper White & Very Vanila (3 ea. of 2 colors)	$6.95

Our exclusive boxes, cards & tags remove the hassle of creating patterns for a variety of projects. Simply punch out, stamp, assemble, and embellish to create a unique gift package for any occasion. Use our Sticky Strip on page 220 to secure sides of the box. It's also easy to create your own custom box by cutting away part of the existing box.

bold brights: Brilliant Blue, Glorious Green, Lovely Lilac, Real Red

rich regals: Bravo Burgundy, Ballet Blue, Night of Navy, Handsome Hunter

earth elements: More Mustard, Old Olive, Creamy Caramel, Ruby Red

soft subtles: Barely Banana, Bashful Blue, Mellow Moss, Pretty in Pink

E. MINI GABLE BOXES & TAGS

6 sheets per pkg. Color packages include 1 of ea. color listed at bottom of previous page plus Confetti White and Kraft. 12 x 12. (Approx. box size: 2-1/2 x 1-1/2 x 4-1/4)

104322	Bold Brights	$6.95
104323	Earth Elements	$6.95
105667	Rich Regals	$6.95
105666	Soft Subtles	$6.95
104326	Confetti White & Kraft (3 ea. of 2 colors)	$6.95
104327	Whisper White & Very Vanilla (3 ea. of 2 colors)	$6.95

F. PURSE BOXES & TAGS

6 sheets per pkg. Color packages include 1 of ea. color listed at bottom of previous page plus Confetti White and Kraft. 12 x 12. (Approx. box size: 4-1/2 x 2 x 3-1/2)

105081	Bold Brights	$6.95
105082	Earth Elements	$6.95
105083	Rich Regals	$6.95
105084	Soft Subtles	$6.95
105085	Confetti White & Kraft (3 ea. of 2 colors)	$6.95
105086	Whisper White & Very Vanilla (3 ea. of 2 colors)	$6.95

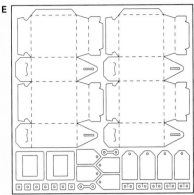
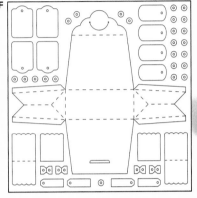

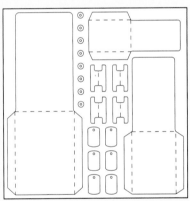
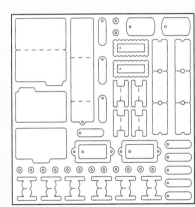

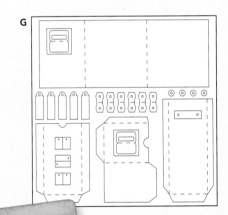

G. POCKETS & PIECES ℠

Inspired by an office supply theme, each page is filled with pockets, tags, file folders, dividers, tabs, reinforcers, and more. Available in 2 color assortments. 9 sheets per pkg. Each package contains 3 ea. of 3 colors, shown below. 12 x 12.

105067	Assortment 1	$8.95
105068	Assortment 2	$8.95

assortment 1: Chocolate Chip, Very Vanilla, Kraft

assortment 2: Basic Black, Confetti White, Sahara Sand

accessories

213

BOOK KITS Each package includes materials for 2 books, plus an instruction sheet for assembly. 6 sheets per pkg. Each package contains 3 each of 2 colors, shown below. 12 x 12. *sm*

A. ACCORDION BOOK KIT
(Approx. book size: 3-1/2 x 3-1/2)

105097	Assortment 1	$6.95
105096	Assortment 2	$6.95
105095	Assortment 3	$6.95
105094	Assortment 4	$6.95
105093	Assortment 5	$6.95
105092	Assortment 6	$6.95
105091	Assortment 7	$6.95

B. SADDLE STITCH BOOK KIT
(Approx. book size: 6 x 3-3/4)

105104	Assortment 1	$6.95
105103	Assortment 2	$6.95
105102	Assortment 3	$6.95
105101	Assortment 4	$6.95
105100	Assortment 5	$6.95
105099	Assortment 6	$6.95
105098	Assortment 7	$6.95

assortment 1: Bashful Blue, Ballet Blue

assortment 2: Pixie Pink, Pretty in Pink

assortment 3: So Saffron, Barely Banana

assortment 4: Always Artichoke, Mellow Moss

assortment 5: Kraft, Basic Black

assortment 6: Ruby Red, Creamy Caramel

assortment 7: Sahara Sand, Confetti White

accessories

214

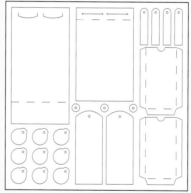
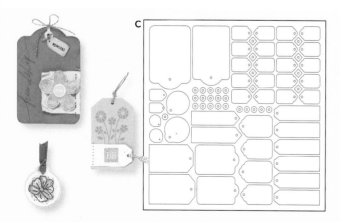
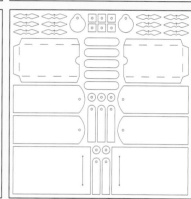
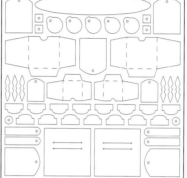

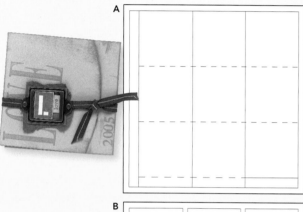

A

B

C

C. TAG SHEETS *sm*
6 assortments to choose from based on our most popular color choices. Each assortment includes six 12 x 12 sheets of die-cut tags, 264 individual tags in all. Layer them or use them alone to add the perfect touch to your project. 6 sheets per pkg. Color packages include 1 of ea. color listed below plus Confetti White and Kraft. 12 x 12.

100214	Bold Brights	$6.95
100217	Earth Elements	$6.95
105658	Rich Regals	$6.95
105653	Soft Subtles	$6.95
100218	Confetti White & Kraft (3 ea. of 2 colors)	$6.95
100219	Whisper White & Very Vanilla (3 ea. of 2 colors)	$6.95

bold brights: Brilliant Blue, Glorious Green, Lovely Lilac, Real Red

earth elements: More Mustard, Old Olive, Creamy Caramel, Ruby Red

rich regals: Bravo Burgundy, Ballet Blue, Night of Navy, Handsome Hunter

soft subtles: Barely Banana, Bashful Blue, Mellow Moss, Pretty in Pink

D

D. METAL EDGE TAGS

Available in your choice of 3 metals with white card stock or white vellum. Choose circle or square tags. Each package contains six 2-inch tags and six 1-1/2-inch tags.

103372	Aluminum White Squares	$3.95
103374	Aluminum White Circles	$3.95
103371	Aluminum Vellum Squares	$3.95
103373	Aluminum Vellum Circles	$3.95
103888	Brass White Squares	$4.95
103890	Brass White Circles	$4.95
103887	Brass Vellum Squares	$4.95
103889	Brass Vellum Circles	$4.95
103892	Copper White Squares	$4.95
103894	Copper White Circles	$4.95
103891	Copper Vellum Squares	$4.95
103893	Copper Vellum Circles	$4.95

E. METAL MAGIC™ TAGS

Metal Magic tags, available in 3 metals, include an impressive assortment of tags in a variety of shapes and sizes. The tags feature predrilled holes, which make it even easier to add eyelets, brads, or other embellishments. 12 tags, 6 square reinforcers, 8 circle reinforcers.

103659	Stainless Steel Assortment I	$7.95
103660	Stainless Steel Assortment II	$7.95
104085	Brass Assortment I	$8.95
104086	Brass Assortment II	$8.95
104083	Copper Assortment I	$8.95
104084	Copper Assortment II	$8.95

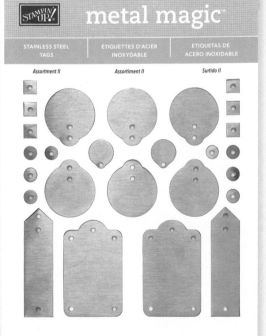

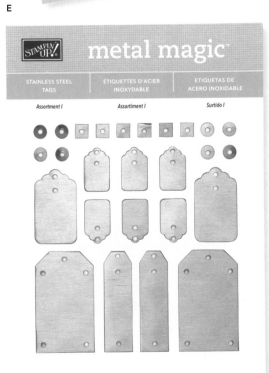

E

accessories

215

A

B

C

D

E

A. CHECKBOOK COVERS
Stamp and personalize for distinctive spending. Vinyl. 2 per pkg.

101958	Checkbook Covers	**$4.95**

B. PUZZLES & ENVELOPES
5-1/2 x 4. 10 per pkg.

101824	Puzzles & Envelopes	**$5.50**

C. MEMO CUBE
2-3/4 cube. Blank on 3 sides for stamping.

103062	Memo Cube	**$5.50**

D. WRAPPING PAPER
Create custom wrapping paper perfect for each special occasion. 50 ft. long, 18 inches wide.

105652	Wrapping Paper	**$9.95**

E. WINDOW SHEETS
8-1/2 x 11. 3 sheets per pkg.

101249	Window Sheets	**$2.95**

F. BIRTHDAY CALENDAR
Keep track of birthdays and other important occasions with these perpetual date trackers. Acid free, lignin free, and buffered. 5-1/2 x 14. Whisper White.

101398	Birthday Calendar	**$7.95**

G. DAYS-TO-REMEMBER CALENDARS _sm_
Scrapbook pages you create enliven each month. The perforated pages can be removed from the calendar and added to an album. Acid free, lignin free, and buffered. Whisper White.

104144	6 x 6 Desktop Calendar	**$7.95**
102174	8-1/2 x 11 Wall Calendar	**$7.95**
103604	12 x 12 Wall Calendar	**$10.95**

F

G

I. GABLE BOXES
8 x 4-3/4 x 5-1/4; 6 per pkg.

101752	White	$6.95
100493	Kraft	$6.95

J. GIFT SACKS
4-3/4 x 8 x 10-1/2. 3 per pkg.

100900	White	$2.95
103321	Oatmeal	$2.95

K. DOOR HANGERS & TAGS
8 x 3-1/2. 18 door hangers and 18 tags.

105056	Whisper White	$5.50
100942	Confetti White	$5.50

L. LARGE BOOKMARKS
2-1/8 x 5-5/8. 25 per pkg.

102133	Whisper White	$4.50

M. DOOR HANGER POUCHES
6-3/4 x 3-1/2. 12 per pkg.

102749	Whisper White	$3.95

N. CELLOPHANE BAGS
50 per pkg.

102210	Large Flat (6 x 8)	$4.95
102757	Medium Flat (4 x 6)	$4.50
103104	Small Flat (3 x 5)	$3.95
101028	Large Gusset (5 x 3 x 11-1/2)	$6.50
100664	Medium Gusset (4 x 2-1/2 x 9-1/2)	$5.25

O. ORGANDY BAGS
Stamp these versatile bags with your own design. Makes a great gift bag for any occasion. Sizes are approximate. 3 per pkg.

100993	Medium (5-1/2 x 9)	$3.95
101623	Small (4-3/4 x 5-1/2)	$2.95

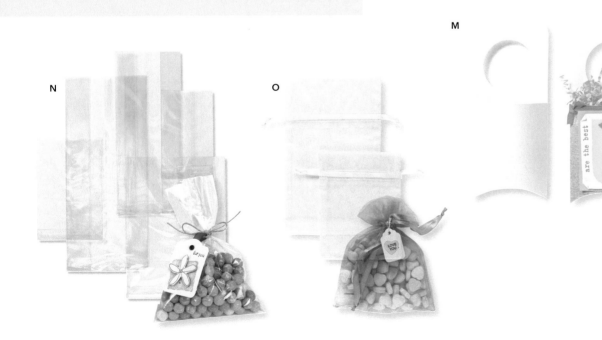

accessories

217

A tool punches

1

2

3

4

5

9

10

6

11

12

7

13

8

You'll love the ease of our thumb punch available on our entire line of tool, shape, and corner punches.

A. TOOL PUNCHES

104401	1.	1-3/8-inch Circle	**$13.95**
104403	2.	1-1/4-inch Circle	**$13.95**
103375	3.	1-3/8-inch Square	**$13.95**
104400	4.	1-1/4-inch Square	**$13.95**
104406	5.	Paper Piecing	**$13.95**
new! 105090	6.	Word Window	**$13.95**
104389	7.	Double Circle	**$4.95**
new! 105088	8.	Double Rectangle	**$4.95**
104388	9.	Slit	**$4.95**
104390	10.	1/2-inch Circle	**$4.95**
104942	11.	1/4-inch Circle	**$4.95**
104943	12.	1/4-inch Square	**$4.95**
new! 105089	13.	Horizontal Slot	**$4.95**

B. SHAPE PUNCHES

104397	1.	Snowman	**$9.95**
104398	2.	Snowflake	**$9.95**
104404	3.	Concave Square	**$9.95**
104405	4.	Convex Square	**$9.95**
104394	5.	Balloon	**$9.95**
104395	6.	Party Hat	**$9.95**
104392	7.	Daisy	**$9.95**
104396	8.	Diaper Pin	**$9.95**
104393	9.	Butterfly	**$9.95**
104399	10.	Leaf	**$9.95**
103377	11.	Folk Heart	**$9.95**
103376	12.	Folk Star	**$9.95**

C. CORNER PUNCHES

104407	1.	Notched	**$10.95**
103379	2.	Large Corner Rounder	**$10.95**
103378	3.	Small Corner Rounder	**$5.95**

D. CORNER POCKET PUNCHES

103381	1.	Square Steps	**$10.95**
104408	2.	Create-a-Corner	**$10.95**

E. CORNER SLOT PUNCHES

104391	1.	Simplicity	**$10.95**
103380	2.	Wrought Iron	**$10.95**

F. HAND-HELD PUNCHES

100392	1.	1/4-inch Circle	**$8.95**
100391	2.	1/8-inch Circle	**$8.95**
101227	3.	1/16-inch Circle	**$8.95**
102686	4.	Rectangle	**$8.95**

B shape punches

1   2   3   4

5   6   7   8

9   10   11   12

C corner punches

1   2   3

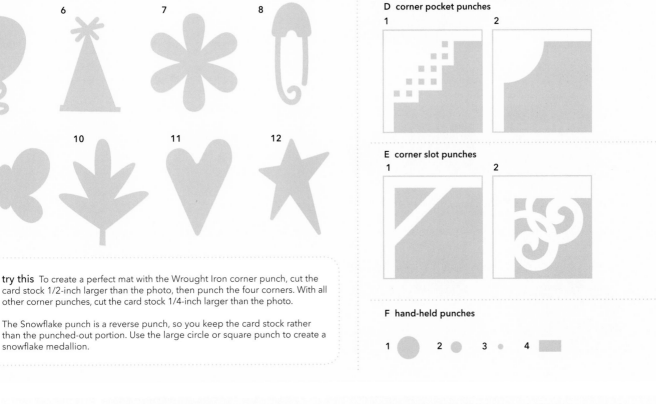

D corner pocket punches

1   2

E corner slot punches

1   2

F hand-held punches

1   2   3   4

try this To create a perfect mat with the Wrought Iron corner punch, cut the card stock 1/2-inch larger than the photo, then punch the four corners. With all other corner punches, cut the card stock 1/4-inch larger than the photo.

The Snowflake punch is a reverse punch, so you keep the card stock rather than the punched-out portion. Use the large circle or square punch to create a snowflake medallion.

cloud, moon & stars

plaidmakers

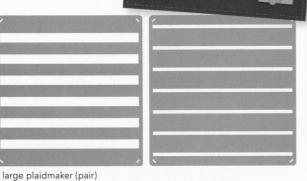

large plaidmaker (pair)

small plaidmaker (pair)

CLOUD, MOON, & STARS STENCIL

101808	Cloud, Moon & Stars (9-1/8 x 7-3/8)	$4.50

PLAIDMAKER™

Made with translucent durable plastic, these templates can be used with a foam brayer or sponge to create custom plaids in any color combination. 2 templates in each set. Notched to hold 12 x 12 card stock; works with 8-1/2 x 11 too!

102338	Large Plaidmaker	$11.95
102697	Small Plaidmaker	$11.95

accessories

219

A

B

A. 2-WAY GLUE PEN

This adhesive is temporary when allowed to dry before adhering or permanent when adhered promptly. Acid free. 10 grams.

| 100425 | 2-Way Glue Pen | **$3.50** |

B. LIQUID GLUE

Dual-tipped applicator lets you apply this clear, gel-like glue in thin lines or over wide areas. Acid free. 24 ml.

| 102620 | Liquid Glue | **$3.95** |

C

D

C. SNAIL ADHESIVE *sm*

Try this **S**imple, **N**eat, **A**ffordable, **I**n-**L**ine, double-stick adhesive; its convenient dispenser features a Stampin' Up! look. This permanent multipurpose adhesive is a cost-effective choice. Acid free. 472 inches.

| 104332 | SNAIL™ Adhesive | **$6.95** |
| 104331 | SNAIL Refill | **$4.50** |

D. DOTTO *sm*

Tiny repositionable adhesive dots in a convenient dispenser. 585 in. Acid free.

| 103305 | Dotto™ | **$11.95** |
| 100902 | Dotto Refill | **$6.50** |

E

F

E. HEAT & STICK POWDER

This product lets you apply glitter or Pearl Ex to your entire stamped image with precision. Acid free. 1/2 oz.

| 100625 | Heat & Stick Powder | **$4.50** |

F. ANYWHERE GLUE STICK

Rectangle shape allows you access to even the corners of your project. 2 per pkg. Acid free. 20 grams each.

| 104045 | Anywhere Glue Stick™ | **$3.95** |

G

H

G. STICKY STRIP

Use this double-sided, extra-tacky strip to adhere beads or make boxes stick tightly. Acid free. 1/4-inch wide. Approx. 10 yards.

| 104294 | Sticky Strip | **$6.95** |

H. STAMPIN' DIMENSIONALS

300 each of 1/16-inch thick double-sided, adhesive foam dots. Acid free.

| 104430 | Stampin' Dimensionals® | **$3.95** |

I

I. GLUE DOTS

Glue Dots are a super-sticky adhesive designed for use on three-dimensional accents used to embellish cards, scrapbook pages, and other projects. Glue Dots hold fast to paper, fabric, wood, foam, plastic, and more. This fast, clean adhesive is safe for kids too. No fumes, no mess, no drying time required. Acid free.

| 103683 | Mini Glue Dots® (3/16-in. diameter, 250 dots.) | **$4.95** |
| 104183 | Pop-Up Glue Dots (1/2-in. diameter, 1/8-in. thick. 75 dots.) | **$3.95** |

J

K

J. CRYSTAL EFFECTS

Add a dimensional, lacquered look to any stamped image. Acid free. 2 oz.

| 101055 | Crystal Effects™ | **$6.25** |

K. ADHESIVE REMOVER

This adhesive remover works like an eraser. Simply rub it on the sticky area, and that sticky problem will disappear. Note: It does not remove tape. 2 x 2.

| 103684 | Adhesive Remover | **$1.95** |

L. CUTTING MAT

This no-slip mat allows for safe cutting while protecting your work surface. Grid lines provide a guide for precise cutting with your hobby blade every time. 12 x 18.

101087	Cutting Mat	$14.95

M. ACRYLIC GRAPH & GRID

Large, easy-to-read numbers in 2 directions eliminate the need to turn the ruler. The computer-generated grid ensures accurate and consistent cuts with your hobby blade. 6 x 12.

103158	Acrylic Graph & Grid	$9.95

N. HOBBY BLADE

Extra sharp, with 5 refill blades. Comes in a convenient storage tube.

102449	Hobby Blade & Refills	$4.50

O. THE TEARING EDGE

Create natural-looking torn edges with precision. Approx. 13 x 1-1/2.

102930	The Tearing Edge™	$19.95

P. COLUZZLE CUTTING SYSTEM

Includes circle and oval template, cutting mat, and cutting knife in our 8-1/2 x 11 Craft Keeper.

102264	Coluzzle® Starter Set	$19.95
102721	Coluzzle Refill Blades (2)	$4.50

Q. PAPER CUTTER

Cuts paper up to 12 inches. Features easy-to-read grid lines and black base. Measures widths up to 15-1/2 inches. Rigid blade guide ensures straighter cut. Comes with 2 cutting blades. Refills include either a cutting and scoring blade or 2 cutting blades.

104152	Paper Cutter	$24.95
104154	Cutting & Scoring Blade Refills	$4.95
104153	Cutting Blade Refills	$4.95

R. PAPER SNIPS

These small, thin-blade scissors provide expert cutting in even the tiniest of areas, and the precision-ground tips allow you to cut to the end of the blade. 2-1/2-inch blade length.

103579	Paper Snips	$9.95

S. CRAFT & RUBBER SCISSORS

These sharp, short-bladed scissors are great for multipurpose use and are especially suited for trimming your rubber stamps before assembling them. 1-3/4-inch blade length.

103179	Craft & Rubber Scissors	$19.95

T. LAYER EASE

These discs allow you to cut perfect mats in any shape you desire. Achieve perfect 1/8-inch, 1/4-inch, 3/8-inch, or 1/2-inch mats with ease.

100683	Layer Ease	$13.50

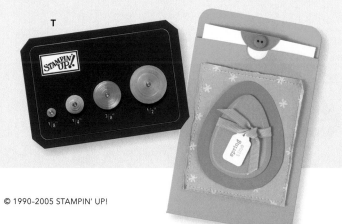

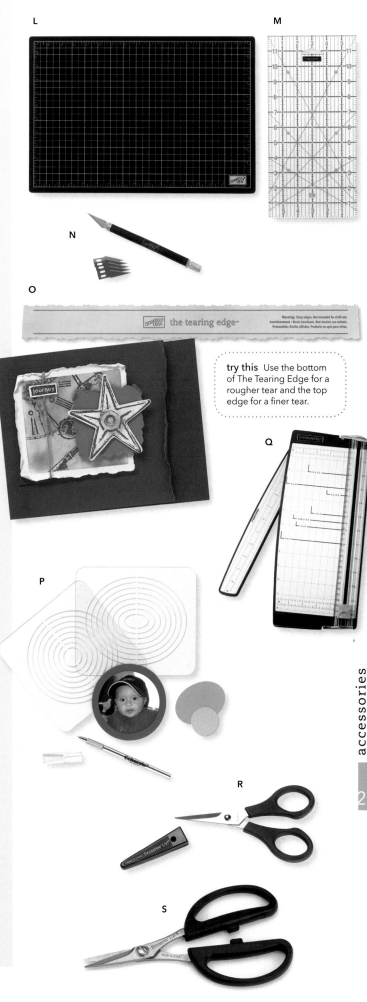

try this Use the bottom of The Tearing Edge for a rougher tear and the top edge for a finer tear.

accessories

221

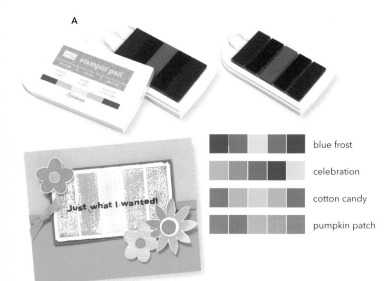

A. SPECTRUM PADS

These multicolor pads use the same acid-free dye inks as our Classic Stampin' Pads, so your Classic Stampin' Ink refills will re-ink both pads. (Specific colors used are listed on each Spectrum pad for easy refilling.) The innovative and easy-to-use pad design prevents the inks from bleeding during storage.

105580	Blue Frost	$11.95	105579	Cotton Candy	$11.95
101492	Celebration	$11.95	101336	Pumpkin Patch	$11.95

Create your own color combination with our Classic Ink refills!

100000	Uninked Spectrum Pad	$8.95

blue frost
celebration
cotton candy
pumpkin patch

B. VERSAMARK ℠

Create a tone-on-tone design or a watermark effect with this pad and marker. Acid free. Nontoxic. Refill: 1/2 oz.

102283	VersaMark® Pad	$7.50
102193	VersaMark Pad Refill (not shown)	$3.95
100901	VersaMarker™	$3.25

C. COLOR BOX® PETAL POINT® CHALK PADS ℠

For a soft, rich look, choose these hybrid (dye and pigment) inks, which coordinate with a selection of our exclusive colors. Fast drying and great for scrapbooking and direct-to-paper techniques. Refills are available in packs of 4. Each refill is 1/2 oz.

PADS			REFILLS		
105659	Brights/Subtles	$16.95	104273	Brights	$14.95
104278	Earths/Regals	$16.95	104272	Earths	$14.95
			104275	Regals	$14.95
			105660	Subtles	$14.95

brights/subtles
earths/regals

D. TOP BOSS TINTED EMBOSSING PAD

Acid free. Refill: 1/2 oz.

101248	Top Boss® Tinted Embossing Pad	$6.25
103137	Top Boss Tinted Embossing Ink Refill	$3.95

E. ENCORE!® PADS ℠

Add a rich, metallic look to your stamped projects with these acid-free, fade-resistant pigment ink pads. Metallic inks should be heat embossed when used in a scrapbook. These inks come in stackable, easy-to-hold pads. Refills: 1/2 oz.

PADS			REFILLS		
101017	Gold	$8.95	101242	Gold	$4.25
101039	Silver	$8.95	102124	Silver	$4.25
104280	Copper	$8.95	104281	Copper	$4.25

gold
silver
copper

F. STAZON™ INK PADS

This quick-drying, permanent ink works great on nonporous surfaces. Refills: 1/2 oz.

PADS			REFILLS		
103359	Azure	$7.95	103356	Azure	$4.95
103000	Blazing Red	$7.95	101234	Blazing Red	$4.95
103360	Forest Green	$7.95	103357	Forest Green	$4.95
101406	Jet Black	$7.95	102566	Jet Black	$4.95
101987	Mustard	$7.95	102850	Mustard	$4.95
102079	Olive Green	$7.95	101438	Olive Green	$4.95
103358	Pumpkin	$7.95	103355	Pumpkin	$4.95
103353	Royal Purple	$7.95	103354	Royal Purple	$4.95
103088	Timber Brown	$7.95	100945	Timber Brown	$4.95
103146	Ultramarine	$7.95	102378	Ultramarine	$4.95

azure
blazing red
forest green
jet black
mustard
olive green
pumpkin
royal purple
timber brown
ultramarine

accessories

222

G. ZIG® PAINTY
Double-tipped opaque pen.

| 102673 | Gold/Silver | **$6.50** |

H. uni-ball® SIGNO GEL PEN sm
The smooth-rolling ink of this gel pen allows you to add text or creative touches on dark card stock. Medium ballpoint tip.

| *new!* 105021 | White Gel Pen | **$3.95** |

I. AQUA PAINTER
Use this versatile tool for controlled watercoloring and tearing mulberry paper. It's less messy and more transportable than a cup and watercolor brush. To use, fill reservoir with water. (1 medium and 1 large per pkg.)

| 103954 | Aqua Painter™ | **$16.95** |

J. WATERCOLOR BRUSHES

100894	Flat	**$10.95**
101551	Medium	**$6.95**
101331	Small	**$5.95**

K. BLENDER PENS
2 brush tips on each. Use with Watercolor pencils and Stampin' Pastels to blend color. 3 per pkg. Acid free & xylene free.

| 102845 | Blender Pens | **$9.95** |

L. METALLIC ART PENCILS sm
Add a rich shimmery luster to your stamped images. Convenient storage tube included. Acid free. 12 assorted colors.

| 101120 | Metallic Art Pencils | **$19.95** |

M. PURE COLOR PENCILS sm
Color goes on smooth. Color runs throughout the no-wood pencil, but it can be sharpened just like a regular pencil. Thin black coating can be scraped away. Acid free. 12 assorted colors.

| 100271 | Pure Color Pencils | **$19.95** |

N. WATERCOLOR PENCILS sm
Made with deep pigments, our brilliantly colored pencils come in a sturdy tin container. Use alone to color stamped images or use with a blender pen, dampened watercolor brush, or Aqua Painter for lovely watercolor effects. Acid free. 24 assorted colors.

| 101879 | Watercolor Pencils | **$19.95** |

O. PENCIL SHARPENER
Sharp steel blade gives a fine point every time. 2 sizes accommodate a range of pencils. Removable receptacle for shavings keeps things neat.

| 100745 | Pencil Sharpener | **$4.95** |

P. WATERCOLOR WONDER CRAYONS sm
Use these deeply pigmented crayons in Stampin' Up!'s exclusive colors to create beautiful watercolor artwork. Water-soluble and easy-to-blend crayons allow an almost unlimited range of shades. Set of 48.

| *new!* 104835 | Watercolor Wonder Crayons | **$59.95** |

accessories

223

A. STAMPIN' SCRUB

Dual-sided tray contains replaceable black fiber scrubbing pads. Clean stamp on one side, blot dry on the other. Sized to fit even our largest stamps. Each pad is approx. 7 x 5-3/4. Refills available in pkgs. of 2.

102642	Stampin' Scrub*	$14.95
101230	Stampin' Scrub Refill Pads	$8.50

B. STAMPIN' MIST STAMP CLEANER

Light rose-scented spray cleans and conditions your rubber stamps. For best results, clean stamp immediately after use.

102394	Stampin' Mist* (2 oz.)	$3.95
101022	Stampin' Mist Refill (8 oz.)	$8.95

C. GRID PAPER

Oversized pad of paper protects your stamping work surfaces. Serves as scratch paper and makes cleanup a snap! Printed on one side with a grid and ruler for convenient measurements. 11 x 17. 100 sheets

102787	Grid Paper	$9.95

D. STAMPING SPONGES

101610	Stamping Sponges (3)	$3.50

E. SPONGE DAUBERS

102892	Sponge Daubers (12)	$9.95

F. BRAYER

Use for special-effects backgrounds and uniform inking on large stamps. Includes handle and soft rubber attachment. Acrylic and Foam snap-in attachments fit in the brayer handle shown and are sold separately.

102395	Handle with Rubber Attachment	$12.50
100430	Acrylic Attachment	$7.95
101052	Foam Attachment	$6.95

G. BONE FOLDER

Use to score paper and make crisp folds.

102300	Bone Folder	$6.50

H. CRIMPER

Crimps wire and paper up to 6-1/2 inches wide.

101618	Crimper	$19.95

I. STAMP-A-MA-JIG

Use this stamp positioner for fast and precise stamp alignment every time. Nonskid base. Includes reusable, wipe-clean imaging sheet for easy placement. (Stamp shown not included.)

101049	Stamp-a-ma-jig™	$11.95
103953	Imaging Sheets Refill (3)	$2.50

J. SANDING BLOCKS

Use to distress the surface of your paper or to sand a rough edge. 2 per pkg.

103301	Sanding Blocks	$3.50

accessories

224

K. STAMPIN' AROUND HANDLES

Does not include cartridge. Ink cartridges are sold on pages 200-201.

102971	Stampin' Around Standard Handle	$3.95
103661	Stampin' Around Jumbo Handle	$5.95

L. UNINKED CARTRIDGES

These cartridges come uninked, ready to create your own custom color combinations with any of our Classic ink refills.

103678	One-Cell Jumbo Cartridge (not shown)	$6.95
101529	One-Cell Cartridge	$4.95
102879	Two-Cell Cartridge	$4.95
102576	Three-Cell Cartridge	$4.95

EMBOSSING INK CARTRIDGE & INK REFILL

Not pictured. Standard size. Acid free.

104432	Clear Embossing Cartridge & Ink Refill	$9.95
102391	Clear Embossing Ink Refill (1/2 oz.)	$3.95

WHISPER WHITE CARTRIDGE & INK REFILL

Not pictured. Standard size. Acid free.

101460	Whisper White Cartridge & Ink Refill	$9.95
103017	Whisper White Ink Refill (1/2 oz.)	$5.50

M. STAMPIN' AROUND WHEEL GUIDE

Wheel perfect background papers, borders, or mitered corners without worrying about crooked lines or overlapping images with this handy tool. Rubber feet keep the guide from moving or slipping. The guide can be configured for both standard and jumbo wheels.

104834	Wheel Guide	$9.95

See page 235 for our standard and jumbo wheel storage options, which allow you to store your wheels quickly and neatly.

K

standard   jumbo

L

one-cell   two-cell   three-cell

M

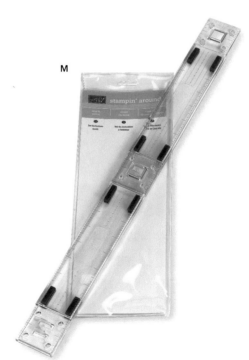

accessories

225

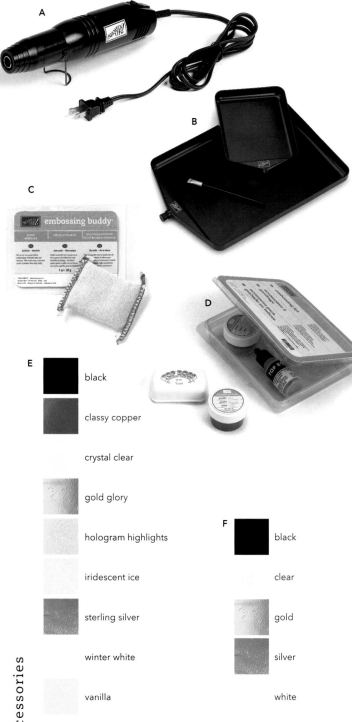

A. HEAT TOOL
Use this electric heat tool with embossing powders, Heat & Stick Powder, and to heat-set pigment ink.

100005	Heat Tool	**$26.95**

B. POWDER PALS
Keep your work area neat and save glitters and powders with this terrific tool. Comes with 2 trays and a brush for clean up.

102197	Powder Pals	**$19.95**

C. EMBOSSING BUDDY
Rub across paper to reduce static. Use before embossing or adding glitter.

103083	Embossing Buddy	**$4.50**

D. EMBOSSING KIT
Contents: 1/2 oz. Sterling Silver Stampin' Emboss® Powder, 1/2 oz. Gold Glory Stampin' Emboss Powder, Mini Top Boss Tinted Embossing Pad, 1/2 oz. Top Boss Tinted Embossing ink refill, and instructions for use.

103280	Embossing Kit	**$14.95**

E. STAMPIN' EMBOSS POWDER
Add dimension and impact to any image. Acid free.

102440	Black (1 oz.)	**$4.50**
100442	Classy Copper (1 oz.)	**$4.50**
101058	Crystal Clear (1 oz.)	**$4.50**
100837	Gold Glory (1 oz.)	**$4.50**
103151	Hologram Highlights (1/2 oz.)	**$4.50**
101930	Iridescent Ice (1/2 oz.)	**$4.50**
103273	Sterling Silver (1 oz.)	**$4.50**
100551	Winter White (1 oz.)	**$4.50**
new! 105323	Vanilla (1 oz.)	**$4.50**
100477	Glassy Glaze Enamel (1 oz.)	**$4.50**

F. DETAIL EMBOSSING POWDER
Preserves the fine detail of your stamped images. 1/2 oz.

101040	Black	**$4.50**
101428	Clear	**$4.50**
103342	Gold	**$4.50**
101781	Silver	**$4.50**
100963	White	**$4.50**

G. EMBOSSING STACKS
With stacks, it's easy to coordinate colors. 4 stacks available with 1/2 oz. of 4 colors listed at left.

100091	Brights	**$16.95**
100089	Earths	**$16.95**
100090	Regals	**$16.95**
100088	Subtles	**$16.95**

accessories

black

classy copper

crystal clear

gold glory

hologram highlights

iridescent ice

sterling silver

winter white

vanilla

glassy glaze enamel
ultrathick, clear powder for incredible stained-glass effects

black

clear

gold

silver

white

brights
red, green, orange, pink

earths
maize, olive, rust, dark brown

regals
burgundy, forest green, blue, navy

subtles
light blue, light pink, lavender, sage

226

H. LIGHT TABLE

Our light table features a stainless steel frame, thick plexiglass top, tilt-up device, and bright, even light. This gives you the perfect surface for use with our Classy Brass templates. 10 x 12 work area.

| 102888 | Light Table | $49.95 |

I. STYLUS

Use small tip for lightweight papers and large tip for card stock.

| 100663 | Stylus | $2.50 |

J. EMPRESSOR STYLUS

Dual-tipped, roller-ball embossing tool features comfort grips and works with any template. Smooth-rolling action reduces paper tearing. Small tip is perfect for small patterns and lightweight papers; large tip works great on card stock.

| 100716 | Empressor™ Stylus | $10.95 |

K. CLASSY BRASS TEMPLATES

All Classy Brass templates feature exclusive designs that coordinate with popular Stampin' Up! sets.

new!	105587	Fun Filled	$9.95
new!	105588	Little Layers	$9.95
new!	105589	Simply Circles	$9.95
new!	105590	Tidy Alphabet	$9.95
new!	105591	'Tis the Season	$9.95
	100402	Love without End	$14.95
	104292	Shapes	$14.95
	100400	Snowflakes	$14.95
	104293	Bloomin' Wonderful	$14.95
new!	105586	Wonderful Words	$14.95
	103603	Everyday Edges	$19.95
new!	105585	Shapes & Shadows	$19.95

fun filled   little layers

simply circles   tidy alphabet

'tis the season   love without end   shapes   snowflakes

bloomin' wonderful   wonderful words   everyday edges   shapes & shadows

accessories

227

A. PEARL EX POWDERS

Achieve fabulous effects from a smooth, pearly luster to a highly metallic sheen with these versatile iridescent powders! Mix with Lumiere® liquid medium to apply as a paint, or apply dry with a watercolor or stipple brush or sponge. Mix with embossing powder for shimmery embossing. 3 grams per bottle.

104299	Assortment I	$11.95
104300	Assortment II	$11.95
104301	Assortment III	$11.95
101319	Lumiere (2.25 fl. oz.)	$5.95

B. STAMPIN' GLITTER*

Apply with Heat & Stick powder, Liquid Glue, or a 2-Way Glue Pen, sold separately. 1/2 oz.

102023	Dazzling Diamonds	$4.50
103352	Romantic Red	$4.50
103349	Silver Shine	$4.50

C. STIPPLE BRUSHES

No. 2 and No. 4. 2 per pkg.

101399	Stipple Brushes	$6.95

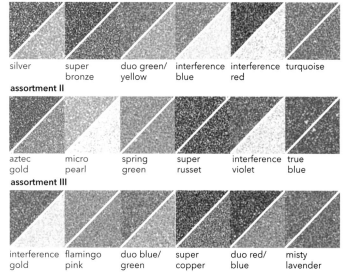

A **assortment I**

| silver | super bronze | duo green/ yellow | interference blue | interference red | turquoise |

assortment II

| aztec gold | micro pearl | spring green | super russet | interference violet | true blue |

assortment III

| interference gold | flamingo pink | duo blue/ green | super copper | duo red/ blue | misty lavender |

The top swatch represents each color applied to black paper, and the bottom swatch is applied to white paper.

lumiere

B

| dazzling diamonds | romantic red | silver shine |

C

accessories

228

D. EYELET TOOL KIT
Includes 1/8-inch anywhere punch and universal eyelet setter.

101016	Eyelet Tool Kit	$7.95

E. CRAFTERS' TOOL KIT
Includes 3/16- and 1/8-inch anywhere punches, universal eyelet setter, two needles, paper-piercing tool, bottle-nosed pliers with wire cutter, cross-lock tweezers, and hammer. Also includes paper-piercing pad, paper-piercing template, and setting mat, each 4 x 4. Instructions included. All packaged in a durable nylon zip case with outside pocket.

104310	Crafters' Tool Kit	$39.95

F. MAT PACK
Paper-piercing pad, paper-piercing template, and setting mat, each 4 x 4.

new! 105826	Mat Pack	$9.95

D

E

F

EYELETS

Colors coordinate with many of our exclusive colors. Eyelet tools sold separately. Single-color eyelets include approx. 200 ea. Assortments include approx. 50 ea. of 4 colors.

105379	Silver					$5.95
105320	Basic				Basic Black, Whisper White, Real Red, Sahara Sand	$5.95
105319	Metallic				Gold, Silver, Copper, Antique Brass	$5.95
100375	Bold Brights I				Brilliant Blue, Glorious Green, Real Red, Yoyo Yellow	$5.95
105317	Bold Brights II				Green Galore, Lovely Lilac, Only Orange, Pixie Pink	$5.95
100381	Earth Elements				Creamy Caramel, More Mustard, Old Olive, Really Rust	$5.95
105316	Rich Regals				Bravo Burgundy, Bordering Blue, Handsome Hunter, Night of Navy	$5.95
100378	Soft Subtles I				Barely Banana, Mellow Moss, Perfect Plum, Pretty in Pink	$5.95
105315	Soft Subtles II				Bashful Blue, Blush Blossom, Lavender Lace, Sage Shadow	$5.95
100369	Small Flowers				Barely Banana, Lavender Lace, Pretty in Pink, Whisper White	$9.95
100364	Squares				Brocade Blue, Close to Cocoa, More Mustard, Ruby Red	$9.95
100362	Stars				Brilliant Blue, Real Red, Silver, Summer Sun	$9.95
100363	Triangles				Green Galore, Only Orange, Silver, Tempting Turquoise	$9.95

("new!" badges appear on 105320 Basic and 105319 Metallic)

BRADS

Can be embossed to create a variety of colors! Use a 1/16-inch Circle punch to make holes for these tiny fasteners. Approx. 200 per container. Assortment includes approx. 50 each of 4 colors.

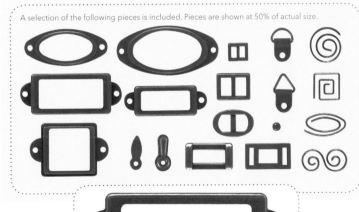

104337	Gold		$6.95
104336	Silver		$6.95
104583	Vintage	Black, Silver, Copper, Antique Gold	$7.95

new! HODGEPODGE HARDWARE

Each kit contains an assortment of shaped clips, label holders, ribbon charms, buckles, fasteners, and photo anchors you can use on cards, scrapbook pages, and handmade books. With approximately 138 pieces of hardware, plus 100 matching brads, this kit is a great value!

105532	Aged Copper	$26.95
105531	Antique Brass	$26.95
105515	Pewter	$26.95

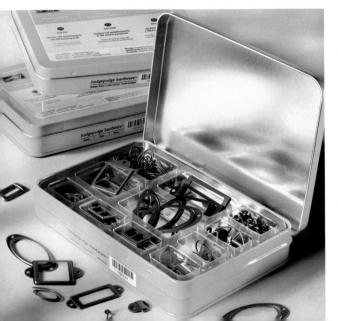

A selection of the following pieces is included. Pieces are shown at 50% of actual size.

This piece is shown at actual size in our Antique Brass finish.

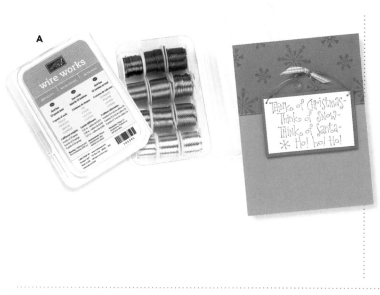

A

B

C

D

A. WIRE WORKS
Contains 3 ea. of the following colors, 1 of ea. size (20-, 22-, and 26-gauge): Pewter, Brass, Silver, and Copper. 12 spools per package. 4 yards per spool of 20 gauge, 6 yards per spool of 22 gauge, and 8 yards per spool of 26 gauge.

new! 105395	Metallic Wire Works	$19.95

B. BEADS
Micro beads are clear without holes. Approx. .8 mm. Colored beads are a mix of glass-seed and glass-bugle beads. Approximately 30 grams per container.

104270	Brights	$4.95
104269	Earths	$4.95
104268	Regals	$4.95
104267	Subtles	$4.95
104271	Neutrals	$4.95
104266	Micro	$4.95

C. COLORED BUTTONS
Hand-dyed to coordinate with a selection of our exclusive colors; available colors listed below. Approx. 80 square and circle buttons in 2 sizes.

103981	Earth Elements & Neutrals Basic Black, Close to Cocoa, Creamy Caramel, Very Vanilla	$6.95
103977	Bold Brights Brilliant Blue, Green Galore, Lovely Lilac, Real Red	$6.95
103978	Earth Elements More Mustard, Old Olive, Really Rust, Ruby Red	$6.95
105446	Rich Regals Ballet Blue, Bravo Burgundy, Handsome Hunter, Night of Navy	$6.95
105445	Soft Subtles Bashful Blue, Mellow Moss, Pale Plum, Pretty in Pink	$6.95

D. CLEAR BUTTONS
Dress up these buttons by stamping and attaching a cut-out shape to the button. 8 ea. in three sizes: 3/4-inch circle, 1-inch circle, and 1-inch square.

new! 105447	Clear Buttons	$4.95

E

F

G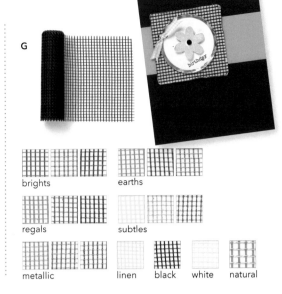

brights		earths
regals		subtles
metallic		linen	black	white	natural

H

   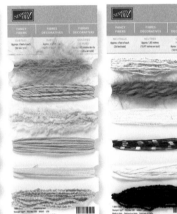 

brights   earths   regals   subtles   neutrals

I

E. HEMP TWINE
Approx. 12 yards. Listed in the order shown.

101259	Black	$2.50	100982	Natural	$2.50
101080	Green	$2.50	102875	Red	$2.50
102859	Purple	$2.50	101509	Blue	$2.50
101949	Gold	$2.50			

F. LINEN THREAD
Diameter is fine enough for use with buttons or with needles from our Crafters' Tool Kit. 15 yds.

104199	Linen Thread	$4.50

G. MAGIC MESH™
Approx. 2-1/2-inch wide. 1 yard ea. color. Mesh colors may vary depending on dye lots.

104197	Brights	$12.95	104198	Linen	$4.50
104196	Earths	$12.95	103682	Black	$4.50
104194	Regals	$12.95	103680	White	$4.50
104193	Subtles	$12.95	103681	Natural	$4.50
104195	Metallic	$12.95			

H. FANCY FIBERS
Coordinates with our exclusive colors. Available in 5 different coordinating packages; assortment may vary. 6 colors on a card. Approx. 2 yards of ea. color, approx. 12 yards total. Please purchase sufficient fibers to complete your projects.

100395	Brights	$6.95
100396	Earths	$6.95
100393	Regals	$6.95
100394	Subtles	$6.95
100397	Neutrals	$6.95

I. TWILL TAPE
Use alone or stamp for a custom look. 100% cotton twill tape can be dyed with our Classic Stampin' Ink refills. Approx. 9 yards: 3 yards ea. of 3/8-inch, 3/4-inch, and 1-1/2-inch tape.

new! 105245	Twill Tape	$5.95

accessories

231

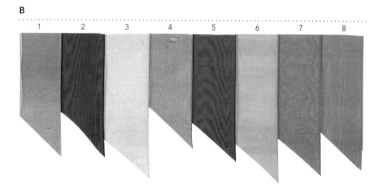

A

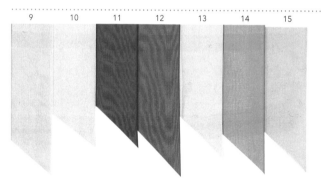

B

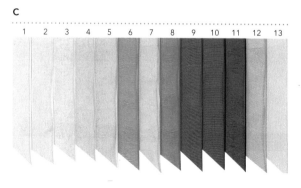

C

accessories

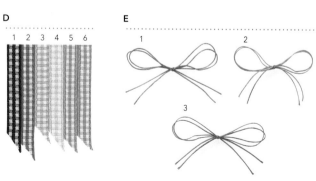

D

E

A. GROSGRAIN RIBBON
1/4-inch wide; approx. 25 yards.

102712	1. Black	$5.95	103114	13. Spring Moss		$5.95
102819	2. White	$5.95	105373	14. Celery	new!	$5.95
100455	3. Cream	$5.95	105376	15. Hunter	new!	$5.95
101156	4. Taupe	$5.95	105378	16. Navy	new!	$5.95
105374	5. Chocolate new!	$5.95	100538	17. Bluebird		$5.95
105372	6. Burgundy new!	$5.95	102950	18. French Blue		$5.95
102682	7. Red	$5.95	102119	19. Turquoise		$5.95
103064	8. Tangerine	$5.95	105375	20. Eggplant new!		$5.95
105371	9. Apricot new!	$5.95	103113	21. Delphinium		$5.95
105377	10. Mustard new!	$5.95	101666	22. Light Orchid		$5.95
101298	11. Maize	$5.95	101569	23. Rose		$5.95
101637	12. Apple Green	$5.95	101926	24. Light Pink		$5.95

B. WIDE ORGANDY RIBBON
7/8-inch wide; approx. 25 yards.

101441	1. Rainbow	$8.95	102735	9. Light Pink	$6.25
103315	2. Black	$6.25	102978	10. White	$6.25
102153	3. Celery	$6.25	103283	11. Navy	$6.25
102388	4. Olive Green	$6.25	100437	12. Burgundy	$6.25
101854	5. Hunter Green	$6.25	100525	13. Ivory	$6.25
101597	6. Lavender	$6.25	103107	14. Gold	$6.25
101224	7. Red	$6.25	103270	15. Silver	$6.25
103046	8. Bright Pink	$6.25			

C. NARROW ORGANDY RIBBON
3/8-inch wide; approx. 25 yards.

101613	1. White	$4.95	104258	8. Olive	$4.95
100589	2. Ivory	$4.95	104260	9. Wine	$4.95
103019	3. Light Pink	$4.95	104256	10. Navy	$4.95
101644	4. Orchid	$4.95	104254	11. Black	$4.95
102217	5. Blue	$4.95	104257	12. Gold	$4.95
104255	6. Green	$4.95	104253	13. Silver	$4.95
104259	7. Celery	$4.95			

D. GINGHAM RIBBON
3/16-inch wide; approx. 15 yards.

104832	1. Black	$6.95	104828	4. Light Pink	$6.95
104827	2. Red	$6.95	104831	5. Moss new!	$6.95
104829	3. Light Blue	$6.95	104830	6. Caramel new!	$6.95

E. CORD
Approx. 75 yds.

104303	1. Gold	$5.95
104304	2. Silver	$5.95
104302	3. Copper	$5.95

A. STAMPIN' KIDS® PADS

The ink in these recessed pads is new and improved. Cleanup is easier than ever! Pad surface is 1-7/8 x 2-3/4.

105677	Bear Brown	**$2.95**
105676	Beetle Black	**$2.95**
105675	Boxcar Blue	**$2.95**
105674	Gumball Green	**$2.95**
105673	Poppin' Purple	**$2.95**
105672	Princess Pink	**$2.95**
105671	Robin Red	**$2.95**
105670	Yahoo Yellow	**$2.95**

B. STAMPIN' KIDS MARKERS

Fun and economical way to introduce kids to the fun of paper arts. As with any child's art project, cover child's clothing for protection. 20 assorted colors.

102328	Stampin' Kids Markers	**$4.95**

C. TATTOO KITS

FD&C-approved inks are nontoxic. Stamp images below are shown actual size.

Tattoo Kit I Contents: Navy pad, 6 markers (Black, Blue, Green, Henna, Red, Yellow), and 6 stamps in a vinyl pouch.

new! 105668	Tattoo Kit I	**$13.95**
101562	Navy Tattoo Ink Refill (1/2 oz.)	**$3.95**

Tattoo Kit II Contents: Black pad, 6 markers (Blue, Green, Orange, Pink, Purple, Red), and 6 stamps in a vinyl pouch.

new! 105669	Tattoo Kit II	**$13.95**
101982	Black Tattoo Ink Refill (1/2 oz.)	**$3.95**

D. TATTOO MARKERS

Dries quickly and washes off easily. FD&C-approved. 6 per pkg. (Black, Blue, Green, Orange, Pink, Purple)

100390	Tattoo Markers	**$6.95**

A

- bear brown
- beetle black
- boxcar blue
- gumball green
- poppin' purple
- princess pink
- robin red
- yahoo yellow

B
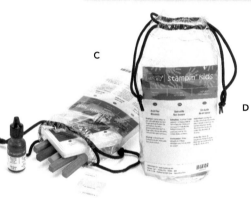

C

D

tattoo kit I

tattoo kit II

233

A. COLOR CADDY
Holds 48 Classic or Craft pads and 48 refills. Rotates for easy access. Some assembly required. Pads & refills not included.

104335	Color Caddy™	$59.95

B. STAMPIN' STACK & STORE
Keep your craft supplies organized and at your fingertips with this complete storage system—or pick and choose the pieces that work best for you. Complete system includes 1 Stampin' Stack, 4 Stampin' Store containers and 4 Mini Stampin' Store containers. You can also customize your own Stampin' Stack. It is designed to hold 6 eyelet or button containers or regular Stampin' Store containers (2-1/2 x 7/8) or 12 bead or Mini Stampin' Store containers (2-1/2 x 7/16). Beads and eyelets not included.

103646	Stampin' Stack & Store (complete)	$8.95
103648	Stampin' Stack	$5.95
103649	Stampin' Store Containers (6)	$3.95
103647	Mini Stampin' Store Containers (6)	$3.95

C. CRAFT KEEPERS
Safe storage for photos, papers, card stock, templates, and more. Velcro® closure. Expands to 1-inch thick. 3 per pkg.

104181	12 x 12 (actual size: 13 x 13)	$7.95
104182	8-1/2 x 11 (actual size: 9 x 11-1/2)	$6.95

D. STAMPIN' CARRY
This strong but lightweight black bag, which also features the Stampin' Up! logo, makes packing what you need a cinch. You can fit a light table inside! Shoulder strap included. 13 x 13-1/2 x 3-1/2.

103578	Stampin' Carry™	$16.95

E. STAMP & SUPPLY BOXES
These storage boxes will hold stamps, accessories, and embellishments. The divided box is perfect for many of your alphabet stamps. Sold in sets of 4.

105744	1. Extra Small (2-1/6 x 3-7/16 x 1-1/8)	$4.95
105745	2. Small (3 x 4-3/16 x 1-1/8)	$5.95
105746	3. Medium (4-3/16 x 5-3/16 x 1-1/8)	$6.95
105734	4. Large (4-1/2 x 6-5/16 x 1-1/8)	$7.95
105747	5. Extra Large (5-3/16 x 7-15/16 x 1-1/8)	$8.95
105749	6. Jumbo (5-1/16 x 10-1/4 x 1-1/8)	$9.95
105748	7. Extra Large with Dividers (5-3/16 x 7-15/16 x 1-1/8)	$8.95

F. FORGET-ME-NOT KEEPER
Use for photo storage or card organization. Includes 12 dividers that allow you to sort photos by theme or cards by month or occasion. 8-5/8 x 6-5/8 x 5.

105525	Forget-Me-Not Keeper™	$11.95

G. STAMPIN' AROUND WHEEL STORAGE
Sold in sets of 2.

105743	Standard (Stores 10 wheels)	$6.95
105741	Jumbo (Stores 6 jumbo wheels)	$6.95

accessories

234

B

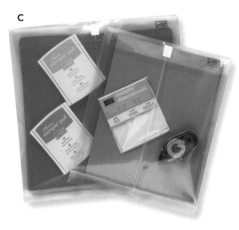

Stampin' Stack & Store (complete)

Stampin' Stack

Stampin' Store containers (6)

Mini Stampin' Store containers (6)

C

D

Products shown in all storage items above not included.

E

6
5
4
3
2
1

7

F

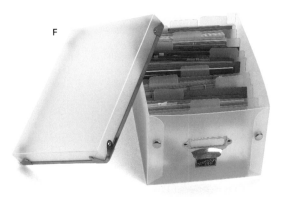

G

standard

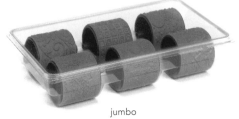

jumbo

235

stamp index

237

Standard size

100360 **Acorns** **$5.95** (p. 62)

104069 **All Heart** **$5.95** (p. 32)

101420 **Baby Time** **$5.95** (p. 109)

103112 **Blossoms & Bugs** **$5.95** (p. 132)

104070 **Bloomin'** **$5.95** (p. 130)

105518 **Builder Bits** **$5.95** (p. 119)

103296 **Candy Cane Christmas** **$5.95** (p. 53)

100398 **Candy Cane Craze** **$5.95** (p. 41)

103794 **Chocolate Chips** **$5.95** (p. 98)

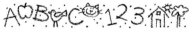

100269 **Crayon ABCs** **$5.95** (p. 120)

104101 **Delicate Design** **$5.95** (p. 123)

101100 **Double-Line Stitched Plaid** **$5.95** (p. 71)

104065 **Fishy** **$5.95** (p. 145)

104102 **Funky Firs** **$5.95** (p. 41)

103195 **Gifts Galore** **$5.95** (p. 44)

101829 **Gingerbread Man** **$5.95** (p. 40)

101525 **Great Outdoors** **$5.95** (p. 140)

104103 **Hand Prints** **$5.95** (p. 108)

100267 **Happy Jacks** **$5.95** (p. 36)

103150 **Heart Angels** **$5.95** (p. 39)

104062 **Heart of Africa** **$5.95** (p. 141)

104157 **Holiday Sweets** **$5.95** (p. 52)

104312 **Hot to Dot** **$5.95** (p. 78)

105449 **Island** **$5.95** (p. 91)

104158 **Jazz** **$5.95** (p. 98)

104279 **Leaf Prints** **$5.95** (p. 127)

101965 **Lovely Ladybugs** **$5.95** (p. 66)

102254 **Love Swirls** **$5.95** (p. 31)

104100 **Making Tracks** **$5.95** (p. 113)

100417 **Many Mittens** **$5.95** (p. 42)

103543 **Only Ornaments** **$5.95** (p. 46)

102671 **Party** **$5.95** (p. 82)

100358 **Party Fun** **$5.95** (p. 77)

101090 **Paw Tracks** **$5.95** (p. 70)

102604 **Pindot** **$5.95** (p. 62)

101088 **Pine Bough** **$5.95** (p. 45)

104099 **Polka Dot Blocks** **$5.95** (p. 69)

105361 **Pounce** **$5.95** (p. 148)

105362 **Ruff Play** **$5.95** (p. 148)

105448 **Size It Up** **$5.95** (p. 161)

101233 **Snowflake** **$5.95** (p. 38)

101927 **Snowman Fun** **$5.95** (p. 55)

104063 **Splat** **$5.95** (p. 83)

100351 **Spooky Spiders** **$5.95** (p. 36)

104044 **Springtime** **$5.95** (p. 102)

101638 **Star** **$5.95** (p. 42)

104061 **Star Studded** **$5.95** (p. 54)

100593 **Sweet Feet** **$5.95** (p. 108)

100622 **Swirl Fun** **$5.95** (p. 60)

104081 **Swirl Style** **$5.95** (p. 94)

101909 **Swirling Leaves** **$5.95** (p. 138)

Jumbo size

105519 **Tailgating** **$5.95** (p. 29)

104524 **Time for a Tree** **$5.95** (p. 29)

105517 **Tropical Turf** **$5.95** (p. 149)

104893 **Twinkle** **$5.95** (p. 56)

105516 **Watercolor Joy** **$5.95** (p. 125)

100268 **Whimsical Blossoms** **$5.95** (p. 84)

104098 **Whirly-Twirly** **$5.95** (p. 124)

105033 **Wings & Things** **$5.95** (p. 143)

105523 **Adoring Hearts** **$7.95** (p. 81)

105522 **Baby Rattle** **$7.95** (p. 81)

103752 **Bold Blooms** **$7.95** (p. 123)

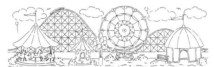

103748 **Carnival Fun** **$7.95** (p. 112)

105032 **Cool** **$7.95** (p. 90)

104066 **Farmyard** **$7.95** (p. 147)

104156 **Flitting By** **$7.95** (p. 142)

105520 **Hollyhock** **$7.95** (p. 103)

105524 **Leaves & Swirls** **$7.95** (p. 81)

104155 **Lilies** **$7.95** (p. 127)

104895 **Millinery** **$7.95** (p. 93)

104424 **Poinsettia** **$7.95** (p. 49)

104067 **Posies & Polka Dots** **$7.95** (p. 122)

105521 **Spooky Skyline** **$7.95** (p. 37)

104159 **Sports Fans** **$7.95** (p. 118)

104160 **Square Pegs** **$7.95** (p. 169)

104425 **Swirling Stars** **$7.95** (p. 49)

103749 **Wash Day** **$7.95** (p. 107)

104423 **Woodcut Holly** **$7.95** (p. 49)

All wheels are shown at 30% actual size.

accessories index

240

[Cover A] Label Classics, Little Pieces, and It's Your Birthday sets; Certainly Celery, Tempting Turquoise, and Whisper White card stock; Certainly Celery and Tempting Turquoise Classic Stampin' Pads; linen thread; White Circle Aluminum Metal Edge tags; Soft Subtles II eyelets; Celery grosgrain ribbon; Stampin' Dimensionals; Crafters' Tool Kit; Daisy, 1/8" Circle, and 1-1/4" Circle punches; watercolor brush; staples; bleach

[Cover B] Frolicking Frogs, Headline Alphabet, and Classic Numbers sets; Canvas background stamp; Apricot Appeal, Certainly Celery, Chocolate Chip, Tempting Turquoise, and Very Vanilla card stock; Apricot Appeal, Basic Black, Certainly Celery, Chocolate Chip, Taken with Teal, and Tempting Turquoise Craft Stampin' Pads; Basic Black Stampin' Write journaler; Earth Elements eyelets; Aged Copper Hodgepodge Hardware; Natural hemp twine; Stampin' Dimensionals; Crafters' Tool Kit

[Cover C] Heartfelt Thanks set; Print Pattern and Canvas background stamps; Bashful Blue, Certainly Celery, and Naturals Ivory card stock; Bashful Blue, Certainly Celery, and Taken with Teal Craft Stampin' Pads; Bashful Blue and Certainly Celery Classic Stampin' Pads; Aged Copper Hodgepodge Hardware Kit; twill tape; Crafters' Tool Kit

[3 A] Flower Filled, Expressive Flexible Phrases, Everyday Flexible Phrases, Classic Alphabet, Simple Type Alphabet, and Letterpress Alphabet sets; Certainly Celery, Taken with Teal, and Whisper White card stock; Basic Black, Old Olive, Taken with Teal, Tempting Turquoise, and Whisper White Craft Stampin' Pads; Basic Black Stampin' Write journaler; Pewter Hodgepodge Hardware; Rich Regals bead; linen thread; Daisy and 1/4" Circle punches

[3 B] Flower Filled, Expressive Flexible Phrases, and Whimsical Alphabet sets; Print Pattern background stamp; Whisper White card stock; White Circle Aluminum Metal Edge tags; Whisper White & Very Vanilla Bloomin' boxes & tags; Bashful Blue, Certainly Celery, and Close to Cocoa Classic Stampin' Pads; Soft Subtles II eyelets; Chocolate grosgrain ribbon; linen thread; Crafters' Tool Kit; 1/8" Circle punch

[3 C] Flower Filled, Newsprint Alphabet, and Classic Alphabet sets; Always Artichoke, Certainly Celery, Taken with Teal, Tempting Turquoise, and Very Vanilla card stock; Always Artichoke, Certainly Celery, Taken with Teal, and Tempting Turquoise Craft Stampin' Pads; Natural hemp twine; linen thread; twill tape; Aged Copper Hodgepodge Hardware; Crafters' Tool Kit; bleach; paint can

[3 D] Flower Filled, Label Classics, and Much Appreciated sets; Bashful Blue, Certainly Celery, Naturals Ivory, and Very Vanilla card stock; Bashful Blue, Certainly Celery, and Close to Cocoa Classic Stampin' Pads; Chocolate grosgrain ribbon; Neutrals bead; Stampin' Dimensionals; watercolor brush

[3 E] Flower Filled, Classic Alphabet, Newsprint Alphabet, and Letterpress Alphabet sets; Certainly Celery and Taken with Teal card stock; watercolor paper; Almost Amethyst, Apricot Appeal, Old Olive, and Taken with Teal Craft Stampin' Pads; Basic Black Stampin' Write marker; Stampin' Dimensionals; watercolor brush; wooden frame

[3 F] Flower Filled and Much Appreciated sets; Certainly Celery, Taken with Teal, and Tempting Turquoise card stock; Whisper White & Very Vanilla tag sheets; Bashful Blue, Old Olive, and Temping Turquoise Classic Stampin' Pads; Pewter Hodgepodge Hardware; Natural hemp twine; Stampin' Dimensionals; Paper Piecing punch; watercolor brush

[4 A] Heartfelt Thanks set; Watercolor Joy wheel; Always Artichoke and Sahara Sand card stock; Always Artichoke, Regal Rose, and Rose Red Classic Stampin' Pads; Whisper White & Very Vanilla tag sheets; twill tape; Pewter Hodgepodge Hardware; linen thread; Crafters' Tool Kit; Regals and Neutrals Fancy Fibers; watercolor brush; linen thread

[4 B] Headline Alphabet, Heartfelt Thanks, It's a Date, and Classic Alphabet Numbers sets; Watercolor Joy wheel; Always Artichoke, Barely Banana, Brocade Blue, Regal Rose, Sahara Sand, and Very Vanilla card stock; Pockets & Pieces, Assortment 1; Whisper White & Very Vanilla tag sheets; Barely Banana, Brocade Blue, Not Quite Navy, Regal Rose, Rose Red, and Sahara Sand Classic Stampin' Pads; Sahara Sand Classic Stampin' Around cartridge; twill tape; Stampin' Dimensionals; watercolor brush; linen thread

[4 C] Happy Occasions set; Word by Word background stamp; Adoring Hearts wheel; Regal Rose, Rose Red, and Very Vanilla card stock; Rose Red Classic Stampin' Pads; Rose Red Classic Stampin' Around cartridge; Light Pink 7/8" organdy ribbon; Rich Regals eyelets; Crafters' Tool Kit; linen thread; 1/16" Circle punch

[5 A] Artifacts, Expressive Flexible Phrases, Everyday Flexible Phrases, and Letterpress Alphabet sets; Size It Up wheel; Always Artichoke and Sahara Sand card stock; Rustic Timeworn Collection paper; Always Artichoke, Basic Black, and Sahara Sand Classic Stampin' Pads; Aged Copper Hodgepodge Hardware; Moss gingham ribbon; Stampin' Dimensionals; 1/16" and 1/8" Circle punches; watercolor brush; sanding blocks

[5 B] Artifacts, Letterpress Alphabet, Everyday Flexible Phrases, and Collage Alphabet sets; Cheesecloth background stamp; Always Artichoke, Bravo Burgundy, and Sahara Sand card stock; Heirloom Timeworn Collection paper; Chocolate Chip Stampin' Write journaler; Bravo Burgundy and Whisper White Craft Stampin' Pads; Brown Timber StazOn pad; Pewter Hodgepodge Hardware; linen thread; Olive Green 7/8" organdy ribbon; Stampin' Dimensionals; watercolor brush; bleach

[5 C] Aged to Perfection and Collage Alphabet sets; Size It Up wheel; Rose Red card stock; Confetti White & Kraft Bloomin' boxes & tags; Weathered Timeworn Collection paper; Basic Black Craft Stampin' Pad; Bravo Burgundy Classic Stampin' Pad; Basic Black Stampin' Around cartridge; Pewter Hodgepodge Hardware; Red hemp twine; Stampin' Dimensionals; 1/2" Circle punch

[5 D] Everyday Flexible Phrases, Office Ephemera, Aged to Perfection, Artifacts, Collage Alphabet, and Letterpress Alphabet sets; Size It Up wheel; Almost Artichoke, Bravo Burgundy, and Sahara Sand card stock; Basic Black and Bravo Burgundy Classic Stampin' Pads; Basic Black Stampin' Around cartridge; Aged Copper Hodgepodge Hardware; linen thread; Stampin' Dimensionals; 1/2" Circle punch; Crafters' Tool Kit

[6 A] Love without End, Little Pieces, and All-Year Cheer I sets; By Definition background stamp; Bashful Blue, Certainly Celery, and Confetti White card stock; Pockets & Pieces, Assortment 2; Certainly Celery and Close to Cocoa Classic Stampin' Pads; Soft Subtles II eyelets; Light Blue gingham ribbon; Soft Subtles button; linen thread; Stampin' Dimensionals; Crafters' Tool Kit; sanding blocks; staple

[8 A] Do the Hula set; Bashful Blue, Old Olive, Really Rust, and Whisper White card stock; Basic Black, Bashful Blue, Creamy Caramel, Old Olive, Really Rust, and Ruby Red Craft Stampin' Pads; Natural hemp twine; Stampin' Dimensionals; 1/8" Circle punch; watercolor brush

[8 B] Celebrate in Style set; Confetti White & Kraft tag sheets; Bold Brights Purse boxes & tags; Ballet Blue, Basic Black, Brilliant Blue, Creamy Caramel, Going Gray, Old Olive, Pixie Pink, Real Red, and Summer Sun Stampin' Pads; Wire Works; French Blue grosgrain ribbon; watercolor brush

[8 C] Buggies & Booties set; Bashful Blue, Really Rust, and Whisper White card stock; Rich Regals Petal card & tags; Bashful Blue Classic Stampin' Pad; White 3/8" organdy ribbon; Watercolor pencils; 1-1/4" Circle punch

[8 D] Celebrate in Style set; Crosshatch background stamp; Basic Black, Confetti White, and Old Olive card stock; Bold Brights Bloomin' boxes & tags; Basic Black, Brocade Blue, Lavender Lace, Old Olive, Only Orange, and Real Red Classic Stampin' Pads; Bold Brights I eyelets; Red gingham ribbon; Silver brads; Earth Elements buttons; Stampin' Dimensionals; Crafters' Tool Kit; 1/16" Circle punch; Slit punch; watercolor brush; crochet thread

[9 A] See 8 D

[10 A] Everyday Flexible Phrases and Classic Alphabet sets; Naturals Ivory card stock; Always Artichoke, Chocolate Chip, Pumpkin Pie, and Ruby Red Craft Stampin' Pads; Aged Copper Hodgepodge Hardware; Natural linen album

[10 B] Everday Flexible Phrases, Collage Alphabet, and Classic Alphabet sets; Always Artichoke, Naturals Ivory, Ruby Red, and So Saffron card stock; Weathered background stamp; Always Artichoke, Chocolate Chip, Mellow Moss, Pumpkin Pie, Ruby Red, and So Saffron Craft Stampin' Pads; Basic Black Stampin' Write journaler; Aged Copper Hodgepodge Hardware; Natural hemp twine; 1/16" Circle punch

[10 C] Balmy Breezes and It's a Date sets; Weathered background stamp; Chocolate Chip, Naturals Ivory, Pumpkin Pie, Ruby Red, and So Saffron card stock; Always Artichoke, Basic Black, Pumpkin Pie, Ruby Red, and Whisper White Craft Stampin' Pads; twill tape, Aged Copper Hodgepodge Hardware; 1/8" Circle punch

[11 A] See 10 B

[11 B] Power Up, Newsprint Alphabet, Headline Alphabet, and Headline Numbers sets; Builder Bits wheel; Always Artichoke, Kraft, Naturals Ivory, Pumpkin Pie, and Ruby Red card stock; Always Artichoke, Chocolate Chip, and Pumpkin Pie Stampin' Around cartridges; Always Artichoke, Chocolate Chip, Pumpkin Pie, and Ruby Red Craft Stampin' Pads; Always Artichoke and Chocolate Chip Stampin' Write markers; Natural hemp twine; Aged Copper Hodgepodge Hardware; window sheets; Stampin' Dimensionals; Write Me a Memory Journaling Fonts CD, Volume II; 1/8" Circle punch

[11 C] Going Buggy, Newsprint Alphabet, and Letterpress Alphabet sets; Always Artichoke, Certainly Celery, Naturals Ivory, Pumpkin Pie, Ruby Red, So Saffron, and Very Vanilla card stock; Always Artichoke, Certainly Celery, Chocolate Chip, Pumpkin Pie, Ruby Red, and So Saffron Craft Stampin' Pads; Pumpkin Pie Stampin' Write marker; Stampin' Dimensionals

[13 A] Fresh Fruits set; Canvas background stamp; Always Artichoke, Confetti White, Kraft, and More Mustard card stock; Always Artichoke, Chocolate Chip, Close to Cocoa, Creamy Carmel, and More Mustard Classic Stampin' Pads; Vintage brads; sewing machine and thread

[13 B] Petal Prints and Everyday Flexible Phrase sets; Chocolate Chip, Confetti White, and Really Rust card stock; watercolor paper; Earth Elements Mini Gable boxes & tags; Chocolate Chip, More Mustard, and Really Rust Classic Stampin' Pads; Chocolate Chip grosgrain ribbon; Natural hemp twine; Rectangle and 1/16" Circle punches; watercolor brush

[15 A] Pocket Full of Posies and Much Appreciated sets; Bashful Blue, Certainly Celery, and Confetti White card stock; Barely Banana, Bashful Blue, Brilliant Blue, and Certainly Celery Classic Stampin' Pads; Jet Black StazOn pad; Certainly Celery grosgrain ribbon; Soft Subtles buttons; watercolor brush; crochet thread

[15 B] Around the Block set; Canvas background stamp; Certainly Celery, Confetti White, and Regal Rose card stock; Certainly Celery and Regal Rose Craft Stampin' Pads; Basic Black Stampin' Write journaler; Clear buttons; 1-3/8" and 1-1/4" Square punches

[15 C] Timeworn Trim and Sincere Salutations sets; Chocolate Chip, Confetti White, and Regal Rose card stock; Earths mulberry paper; Chocolate Chip, Green Galore, Regal Rose, and Summer Sun Classic Stampin' Pads; Chocolate grosgrain ribbon; Stampin' Dimensionals; watercolor brush

[16 A] Small Script, All-Year Cheer I, and Heartfelt Thanks sets; Apricot Appeal, Certainly Celery, and Tempting Turquoise card stock; Subtles mulberry paper; Apricot Appeal, Certainly Celery, Regal Rose, and Tempting Turquoise Classic Stampin' Pads; Rose grosgrain ribbon; linen thread; Silver eyelets; Light Pink gingham ribbon; White Circle Aluminum Metal Edge tags; Stampin' Dimensionals; Crafters' Tool Kit; sewing machine and thread

[16 B] Flowers of Gratitude set; Floral background stamp; Apricot Appeal, Certainly Celery, Regal Rose, and Sahara Sand card stock; Confetti White & Kraft tag sheets; Apricot Appeal, Basic Black, Certainly Celery, Glorious Green, Regal Rose, Rose Red, and Sahara Sand Classic Stampin' Pads; Vintage brads; linen thread; Stampin' Dimensionals; watercolor brush

[16 C] Say It Simply set; Apricot Appeal, Certainly Celery, Regal Rose, and Whisper White card stock; Certainly Celery, Tempting Turquoise, and Regal Rose Craft Stampin' Pads; Mellow Moss Stampin' Write marker; Celery grosgrain ribbon; Stampin' Dimensionals; 1/8" Circle punch; sewing machine and thread

[16 D] Say It Simply and Expressive Flexible Phrases sets; Square Pegs wheel; Certainly Celery, Taken with Teal, Tempting Turquoise, and Whisper White card stock; Regal Rose and Taken with Teal Craft Stampin' Pads; Taken with Teal Stampin' Around cartridge; Basic Black Stampin' Write journaler; Turquoise grosgrain ribbon; linen thread; Silver brads; Stainless Steel Metal Magic tags, Assortment 1 or 2; Stampin' Dimensionals; Crafters' Tool Kit

[17 A] Made from Scratch, Everyday Flexible Phrases, Expressive Flexible Phrases, and Wonderful Words sets; Certainly Celery, Taken with Teal, and Whisper White card stock; Certainly Celery and Taken with Teal Classic Stampin' Pads; Silver eyelets; Celery grosgrain ribbon; Crafters' Tool Kit; Word Window punch

stampin' supplies

[17 B] Made from Scratch, Expressive Flexible Phrases, and Quick Thinking sets; Apricot Appeal, Certainly Celery, Regal Rose, and Whisper White card stock; Apricot Appeal, Certainly Celery, and Regal Rose Classic Stampin' Pads; Certainly Celery Stampin' Write marker; White Square Aluminum Metal Edge tags; Silver brads; Celery grosgrain ribbon; Stampin' Dimensionals; Crafters' Tool Kit

[17 C] Letterpress Alphabet set; Island Blossoms Simply Scrappin' Kit; Very Vanilla Craft Pad; Basic Black Stampin' Write journaler; Crystal Clear Stampin' Emboss powder; Subtles beads; Light Blue and Light Pink gingham ribbon; Cream and Rose grosgrain ribbon; Stampin' Dimensionals; Crafters' Tool Kit

[18 A] Provencal and Much Appreciated sets; Canvas background stamp; Elegant Eggplant, Sahara Sand, and Very Vanilla card stock; Whisper White & Very Vanilla tag sheets; Basic Black, Chocolate Chip, Elegant Eggplant, Going Gray, and Bravo Burgundy Classic Stampin' Pads; linen thread; Soft Subtles I eyelets; Vintage brads; Vellum Square Brass Metal Edge tags; Crafters' Tool Kit; watercolor brush

[18 B] Provencal, Sincere Salutations, and Expressive Flexible Phrases sets; Print Pattern background stamp; Always Artichoke and So Saffron card stock; watercolor paper; Always Artichoke, Chocolate Chip, and Creamy Caramel Classic Stampin' Pads; Whisper White Craft Stampin Pad; Black gingham ribbon; Antique Brass Hodgepodge Hardware; Soft Subtles eyelets; Crafters' Tool Kit; watercolor brush

[18 C] Provencal and Everyday Flexible Phrases sets; Elegant Eggplant, Kraft, Sahara Sand, and So Saffron card stock; Whisper White & Very Vanilla tag sheets; Basic Black, Creamy Caramel, Elegant Eggplant, and Ruby Red Classic Stampin' Pads; Black gingham ribbon; Eggplant grosgrain ribbon; linen thread; Pewter Hodgepodge Hardware; Stampin' Dimensionals; 1/2" and 1/8" Circle punches; watercolor brush

[18 D] Provencal and Sincere Salutations sets; Canvas background stamp; Bravo Burgundy, Sahara Sand, So Saffron, and Very Vanilla card stock; Earth Elements tag sheets; Always Artichoke, Basic Black, Bravo Burgundy, and Elegant Eggplant Classic Stampin' Pads; Black gingham ribbon; Antique Brass Hodgepodge Hardware; linen thread; Natural hemp twine; watercolor brush

[19 A] Haute Couture set; Print Pattern background stamp; Always Artichoke card stock; watercolor paper; Cambridge Designer Series paper; Always Artichoke, Basic Black, Bravo Burgundy, and Green Galore Classic Stampin' Pads; Antique Brass Hodgepodge Hardware; twill tape; Celery 3/8" organdy ribbon; linen thread; 1/16" Circle punch

[19 B] Haute Couture and Expressive Flexible Phrases sets; Confetti White and Sahara Sand card stock; Cambridge Designer Series paper; Basic Black, Bravo Burgundy, and Sahara Sand Classic Stampin' Pads; Antique Brass Hodgepodge Hardware; Vintage brads; linen thread; Stampin' Dimensionals

[19 C] Reverse Prints and Much Appreciated sets; Fine Lace background stamp; Bravo Burgundy, Sahara Sand, and Very Vanilla card stock; Bravo Burgundy and Sahara Sand Classic Stampin' Pads; Stampin' Pastels; Natural hemp twine; Stampin' Dimensionals; watercolor brush

[19 D] Reverse Prints set; Bravo Burgundy and Sahara Sand card stock; Bravo Burgundy Classic Stampin' Pad; Pewter Hodgepodge Hardware; Black gingham ribbon; Natural hemp twine

[20 A] Along the Same Lines and Wonderful Words sets; Print Pattern background stamp; Certainly Celery, Naturals Ivory, and So Saffron card stock; Old Olive and So Saffron Classic Stampin' Pads; Basic Black, Blush Blossom, Old Olive, and So Saffron Stampin' Write markers; Soft Subtles I eyelets; Celery grosgrain ribbon; linen thread; Crafters' Tool Kit; watercolor brush

[20 B] Along the Same Lines and It's Your Birthday sets; Print Pattern background stamp; Confetti Cream, Elegant Eggplant, and Mellow Moss card stock; Basic Black, Elegant Eggplant, and Mellow Moss Classic Stampin' Pads; Mellow Moss Stampin' Write marker; White Circle Aluminum Metal Edge tags; Soft Subtles I eyelets; linen thread; Eggplant grosgrain ribbon; Moss gingham ribbon; Crafters' Tool Kit; watercolor brush; paper clip

[20 C] Oh, My Word and Quick Thinking sets; Certainly Celery and Whisper White card stock; Saddle Stitch book kit, Assortment 3; Barely Banana, and Certainly Celery Classic Stampin' Pads; Vintage brads; Celery grosgrain ribbon; Moss gingham ribbon; Stampin' Dimensionals; 1/2" Circle punch

[20 D] Oh, My Word and Much Appreciated sets; Confetti Cream, Elegant Eggplant, and So Saffron card stock; Pockets & Pieces, Assortment 2; Certainly Celery, Elegant Eggplant, and So Saffron Classic Stampin' Pads; Linen Magic Mesh; Natural hemp twine; watercolor brush

[21 A] Fashion Statements, Day to Day Flexible Phrases, It's a Date, and Classic Alphabet sets; Certainly Celery, Elegant Eggplant, Kraft, So Saffon, and Very Vanilla card stock; Pockets & Pieces, Assortment 1; Certainly Celery, Elegant Eggplant, and So Saffron Classic Stampin' Pads; Elegant Eggplant Stampin' Write marker; Silver brads; Natural hemp twine; Delphinium grosgrain ribbon; Stampin' Dimensionals; 1/8" Circle and Rectangle punches; watercolor brush

[21 B] Fashion Statements set; Fine Lace background stamp; Elegant Eggplant, Naturals White, and Whisper White card stock; Whisper White Purse boxes & tags; Basic Black, Elegant Eggplant, Old Olive, and So Saffron Classic Stampin' Pads; Purple hemp twine; Pewter Hodgepodge Hardware; watercolor brush; staples

[21 C] Fashion Statements and Much Appreciated sets; Certainly Celery, Elegant Eggplant, and Naturals White card stock; Whisper White & Very Vanilla tag sheets; Certainly Celery and Elegant Eggplant Classic Stampin' Pads; Celery grosgrain ribbon; White Square Aluminum Metal Edge tags; Purple hemp twine; Stampin' Dimensionals; Crafters' Tool Kit; 1/4" Circle punch; watercolor brush; staples

[22 A] Nature's Secret, Much Appreciated, and Wonderful Words sets; Barely Banana and Confetti Cream card stock; Earth Elements Petal boxes & tags; Basic Black and So Saffron Classic Stampin' Pads; Cream grosgrain ribbon; Black gingham ribbon; linen thread; Ivory 7/8" organdy ribbon; watercolor brush

[22 B] Nature's Secret set; Confetti Cream, Old Olive, and Rose Red card stock; Old Olive and Rose Red Classic Stampin' Pads; Black gingham ribbon; Antique Brass Hodgepodge Hardware; watercolor brush

[22 C] Nature's Secret, Classic Alphabet, and Whimsical Alphabet Upper sets; Basic Black, Confetti Cream, Rose Red, and Taken with Teal card stock; Basic Black, Rose Red, and Taken with Teal Craft Stampin' Pads; Black hemp twine; Rich Regals eyelets; Vintage brads; Stampin Dimensionals; Crafters' Tool Kit

[23 A] Island Blossoms, Classic Alphabet, Simple Type Alphabet, and Letterpress Alphabet sets; Old Olive, Rose Red, So Saffron, Taken with Teal, and Very Vanilla card stock; Old Olive, Rose Red, So Saffron, and Taken with Teal Craft Stampin' Pads; Earth Elements and Rich Regals eyelets; Stampin' Dimensionals; Crafters' Tool Kit; staples

[25 A] Loads of Love set; Close to Cocoa, Creamy Caramel, Ruby Red, and Very Vanilla card stock; Basic Brown and Ruby Red Classic Stampin' Pads

[25 B] Loads of Love set; Chocolate Chip, Close to Cocoa, Ruby Red, and Very Vanilla card stock; Basic Brown and Ruby Red Classic Stampin' Pads; Stampin' Dimensionals

[25 C] Loads of Love, Loads of Love Accessories, and Newsprint Alphabet sets; Chocolate Chip, Creamy Caramel, Ruby Red, and Very Vanilla card stock; Chocolate Chip Craft Stampin' Pad; Basic Black Stampin' Write journaler; Stampin' Pastels; Natural hemp twine; Stampin' Dimensionals

[25 D] Loads of Love and Loads of Love Accessories sets; Close to Cocoa, Creamy Caramel, Ruby Red, and Very Vanilla card stock; Basic Brown and Ruby Red Classic Stampin' Pads; Stampin' Pastels; Natural hemp twine; Stampin' Dimensionals

[25 E] Fun Filled set; Always Artichoke, Brocade Blue, Elegant Eggplant, Rose Red, and Whisper White card stock; Always Artichoke, Brocade Blue, and Rose Red Classic Stampin' Pads; Stampin' Dimensionals; Crafters' Tool Kit

[25 F] Fun Filled set; Always Artichoke, Elegant Eggplant, Rose Red, and Whisper White card stock; Always Artichoke, Bashful Blue, and Rose Red Classic Stampin' Pads; Stampin' Dimensionals

[25 G] Fun Filled set; Always Artichoke, Rose Red, and Whisper White card stock; Always Artichoke and Rose Red Classic Stampin' Pads; Black gingham ribbon; Vintage brads; Stampin' Dimensionals; Slit punch

[25 H] Fun Filled and Tidy Alphabet sets; Always Artichoke, Brocade Blue, Elegant Eggplant, and Whisper White card stock; Always Artichoke and Brocade Blue Craft Stampin' Pads; Basic Black Stampin' Write journaler; Black gingham ribbon; Vintage brads; Stampin' Dimensionals

[26 A] Tag Time set; Gable Green, Real Red, Tempting Turquoise, and Whisper White card stock; Gable Green, Real Red, and Tempting Turquoise Classic Stampin' Pads; Stampin' Dimensionals

[26 B] Tag Time set; Gable Green, Real Red, Tempting Turquoise, and Whisper White card stock; Real Red Classic Stampin' Pad; Stampin' Dimensionals; Crafters' Tool Kit

[26 C] Tag Time and Headline Alphabet sets; Brilliant Blue, Gable Green, Tempting Turquoise, and Whisper White card stock; Gable Green and Tempting Turquoise Classic Stampin' Pads; Basic Black Stampin' Write journaler; Turquoise grosgrain ribbon; Clear buttons; Stampin' Dimensionals; crochet thread

[26 D] Tag Time set; Gable Green, Tempting Turquoise, and Whisper White card stock; Bold Brights Petal cards & tags; Gable Green, Real Red, and Tempting Turquoise Classic Stampin' Pads; Turquoise grosgrain ribbon; Clear buttons; crochet thread

[26 E] Heartfelt Thanks set; Certainly Celery, Perfect Plum, Pretty in Pink, and Whisper White card stock; Certainly Celery, Perfect Plum, and Pretty in Pink Classic Stampin' Pads; Stampin' Dimensionals

[26 F] Heartfelt Thanks set; Certainly Celery, Perfect Plum, Pretty in Pink, and Whisper White card stock; Certainly Celery, Perfect Plum, and Pretty in Pink Classic Stampin' Pads

[26 G] Heartfelt Thanks and Letterpress Alphabet sets; Certainly Celery, Perfect Plum, Pretty in Pink, and Whisper White card stock; Certainly Celery, Perfect Plum, and Pretty in Pink Craft Stampin' Pads; Basic Black Stampin' Write journaler; Silver brads; Celery grosgrain ribbon; Stampin' Dimensionals

[26 H] Heartfelt Thanks set; Certainly Celery, Perfect Plum, Pretty in Pink, and Whisper White card stock; Certainly Celery, Perfect Plum, and Pretty in Pink Classic Stampin' Pads; Silver brads; Celery grosgrain ribbon; Stampin' Dimensionals

[27 A] Collage Alphabet set; Always Artichoke, Bravo Burgundy, and Kraft card stock; Heirloom Timeworn Collection paper; Always Artichoke and Creamy Caramel Craft Stampin' Pads; Stampin' Dimensionals

[27 B] Collage Alphabet set; Always Artichoke, Bravo Burgundy, and Kraft card stock; Heirloom Timeworn Collection paper; Always Artichoke and Creamy Caramel Craft Stampin' Pads; Basic Black Stampin' Write journaler; Stampin' Dimensionals

[27 C] Collage Alphabet and Aged to Perfection stamp sets; Always Artichoke and Kraft card stock; Heirloom Timeworn Collection paper; Pockets & Pieces, Assortment 1; Always Artichoke and Creamy Caramel Craft Stampin' Pads; Antique Brass Hodgepodge Hardware; Chocolate grosgrain ribbon; Natural hemp twine; Stampin' Dimensionals

[27 D] Aged to Perfection and Collage Alphabet sets; Always Artichoke and Kraft card stock; Heirloom Timeworn Collection paper; Pockets & Pieces, Assortment 1; Always Artichoke and Creamy Caramel Craft Stampin' Pads; Antique Brass Hodgepodge Hardware; Chocolate grosgrain ribbon; Stampin' Dimensionals

[28 A] Tag Time and Everyday Flexible Phrases sets; By Definition background stamp; Always Artichoke and Mellow Moss card stock; Confetti White & Kraft tag sheets; Always Artichoke, Real Red, and Regal Rose Classic Stampin' Pads; Red, Moss, and Light Pink gingham ribbons; Silver brads; Wire Works; Stampin' Dimensionals; stamping sponges

[28 B] Tag Time, Expressive Flexible Phrases, and Fresh Fillers sets; Regal Rose card stock; Bold Brights Bloomin' boxes & tags; White Circle Aluminum Metal Edge tags; Basic Black, Real Red, and Regal Rose Classic Stampin' Pads; Light Pink grosgrain ribbon; Stainless Steel Metal Magic tags, Assortment 2; Silver eyelets; Stampin' Dimensionals; Crafters' Tool Kit; crochet thread

[28 C] Tag Time set; By Definition background stamp; Real Red card stock; Bold Brights tag sheets; Basic Black Classic Stampin' Pad; Black gingham ribbon; Bold Brights beads; Basic eyelets; Stampin' Dimensionals; Crafters' Tool Kit; crochet thread

[28 D] Festive Four set; Print Pattern background stamp; Real Red, Regal Rose, and Whisper White card stock; White mulberry paper; Basic Black, Going Gray, Real Red, and Regal Rose Classic Stampin' Pads; Basic eyelets; Light Pink gingham ribbon; Stampin' Dimensionals; Crafters' Tool Kit; watercolor brush

[28 E] Festive Four, Beyond the Basics, and Everyday Flexible Phrases sets; Always Artichoke, Confetti White, Mellow Moss, and Regal Rose card stock; Always Artichoke, Bashful Blue, Basic Black, Mellow Moss, and Regal Rose Classic Stampin' Pads; Rose grosgrain ribbon; Stampin' Dimensionals; watercolor brush; small flat cellophane bags

[29 A] Loads of Love and Loads of Love Accessories sets; Tailgating wheel; Always Artichoke, Confetti White, Mellow Moss, and Real Red card stock; Basic Black, Blush Blossom, Close to Cocoa, Creamy Caramel, Going Gray, Mellow Moss, and Real Red Classic Stampin' Pads; Always Artichoke Stampin' Around cartridge; Vintage brads; Black hemp twine; Stampin' Dimensionals; watercolor brush

[29 B] Loads of Love set; Always Artichoke, Mellow Moss, Naturals White, and Regal Rose card stock; Always Artichoke, Basic Black, Going Gray, Mellow Moss, Real Red, and Regal Rose Classic Stampin' Pads; Red grosgrain ribbon; Basic eyelets; Stampin' Dimensionals; Crafters' Tool Kit; Aqua Painter

[29 C] Loads of Love set; Time for Trees wheel; Naturals White and Real Red card stock; Accordion book kit, Assortment 4; Basic Black, Close to Cocoa, Mellow Moss, and Real Red Classic Stampin' Pads; Mellow Moss Stampin' Around cartridge; Bold Brights buttons; Red gingham ribbon; Stampin' Dimensionals; watercolor brush; crochet thread

[30 A] Year-Round Fun II and Everyday Flexible Phrases sets; Certainly Celery, Close to Cocoa, and Confetti White card stock; Basic Black, Cameo Coral, Certainly Celery, Close to Cocoa, and More Mustard Classic Stampin' Pads; Taupe grosgrain ribbon; linen thread; Rectangle punch; 1/8" Circle punch

[30 B] Sketch It set; Canvas background stamp; Brocade Blue, Certainly Celery, Close to Cocoa, and Regal Rose card stock; Brocade Blue, Certainly Celery, and Close to Cocoa Classic Stampin' Pads; Vintage brads; Natural hemp twine; Stampin' Dimensionals; 1/16" Circle punch

[30 C] Sketch It set; Certainly Celery, Close to Cocoa, Regal Rose, and Very Vanilla card stock; Certainly Celery, Close to Cocoa, and Regal Rose Classic Stampin' Pads; Rose grosgrain ribbon; Stampin' Dimensionals; 1/8" Circle punch; Small Corner Rounder punch; crimper

[31 A] Sweet Talk and All-Year Cheer I sets; Brocade Blue, Certainly Celery, and Close to Cocoa card stock; Brocade Blue, Certainly Celery, and Rose Red Classic Stampin' Pads; Natural hemp twine; White Circle Aluminum Metal Edge tags; Stampin' Dimensionals; Crafters' Tool Kit

[31 B] Mon Ami and Classic Alphabet sets; Brocade Blue, Certainly Celery, Kraft, and Regal Rose card stock; Brocade Blue, Certainly Celery, and Rose Red Craft Stampin' Pads; Basic Black Stampin' Write marker; Vintage brads; Rose grosgrain ribbon; Stampin' Dimensionals

[31 C] Mon Ami and Collage Alphabet sets; By Definition background stamp; Brocade Blue, Certainly Celery, Regal Rose, and Whisper White card stock; Brocade Blue and Regal Rose Classic Stampin' Pads; Stampin' Dimensionals; sewing machine and thread

[32 A] Loving Hearts, Everyday Flexible Phrases, and Bold Alphabet sets; Almost Amethyst, Confetti White, Old Olive, and Rose Red card stock; Almost Amethyst, Old Olive, and Rose Red Craft Stampin' Pads; Rose Red Stampin' Write marker; linen thread; Stampin' Dimensionals; 1/16" Circle punch; sewing machine and thread

[32 B] Smitten set; By Definition background stamp; Confetti White, Old Olive, and Rose Red card stock; Rose Red Classic Stampin' Pad; Stampin' Dimensionals; Vintage brads; linen thread; Slit punch; 1/16" Circle punch

[32 C] Smitten and Everyday Flexible Phrases set; All Heart wheel; Almost Amethyst, Old Olive, and Regal Rose card stock; Earth Elements Pillar boxes & tags; Lavender Lace and Old Olive Classic Stampin' Pads; Old Olive Classic Stampin' Around cartridge; Rose grosgrain ribbon; Silver eyelets; Wire Works; Crafters' Tool Kit; Stampin' Dimensionals; 1/16" Circle punch

[33 A] Toucan of My Love set; Almost Amethyst, Confetti White, Old Olive, and Rose Red card stock; Basic Black, Close to Cocoa, More Mustard, Old Olive, and Ruby Red Classic Stampin' Pads; Natural hemp twine; Stampin' Dimensionals; staple

[33 B] Happy Hearts, Everyday Flexible Phrases, and Classic Alphabet sets; By Definition background stamp; Almost Amethyst, Regal Rose, Rose Red, and Very Vanilla card stock; Almost Amethyst, Old Olive, and Rose Red Classic Stampin' Pads; Natural hemp twine; Silver brads; Stampin' Dimensionals

[33 C] Happy Hearts and Wonderful Words sets; Rose Red and Very Vanilla card stock; Rose Red and Chocolate Chip Classic Stampin' Pads; Vellum Square Aluminum Metal Edge tags; Soft Subtles I eyelets; Chocolate grosgrain ribbon; Stampin' Dimensionals; Crafters' Tool Kit

[34 A] Spring Fling set; Canvas background stamp; Always Artichoke, Pumpkin Pie, Ruby Red, and Whisper White card stock; Always Artichoke, Pumpkin Pie, and Ruby Red Stampin' Write markers; Black gingham ribbon; Neutrals buttons; Stampin' Dimensionals; crochet thread; sewing machine and thread

[34 B] Never-Ending Joy and Wonderful Words II sets; Always Artichoke and Mellow Moss card stock; Earth Elements tag sheets; Always Artichoke and Ruby Red Craft Stampin' Pads; Basic Black Stampin' Write marker; Moss gingham ribbon; Olive 3/8" organdy ribbon; Vintage brads; 1/16" Circle punch

[34 C] Never-Ending Joy set; Always Artichoke, Barely Banana, and Whisper White card stock; Always Artichoke and Barely Banana Classic Stampin' Pads; Antique Brass Hodgepodge Hardware; White 3/8" organdy ribbon; linen thread; Stampin' Dimensionals; 1/16" Circle punch; watercolor brush

[35 A] Bitty Boos Too and Tidy Alphabet sets; Always Artichoke, Pumpkin Pie, Ruby Red, and Whisper White card stock; Always Artichoke, Pumpkin Pie, and Ruby Red Classic Stampin' Pads; Spring Moss grosgrain ribbon; Natural hemp twine; Stampin' Dimensionals; Crafters' Tool Kit; 1/8" Circle punch

[35 B] Carved & Candlelit and Everyday Flexible Phrases sets; Handsome Hunter, Kraft, Pumpkin Pie, and Whisper White card stock; Basic Black, Handsome Hunter, and Pumpkin Pie Classic Stampin' Pads; Natural hemp twine; Stampin' Dimensionals

[35 C] Bitty Boos Too and Everyday Flexible Phrases sets; Always Artichoke, Barely Banana, Mellow Moss, Pumpkin Pie, and Whisper White card stock; Always Artichoke, Basic Black, and Close to Cocoa Classic Stampin' Pads; Always Artichoke and Pumpkin Pie Stampin' Write markers; Silver brads; twill tape; Stainless Steel Metal Magic tags, Assortment 1; Stampin' Dimensionals; staple; sewing machine and thread

[35 D] Carved & Candlelit and Stencil Alphabet sets; Always Artichoke, Kraft, Mellow Moss, and Whisper White card stock; Oxford Designer Series paper; Always Artichoke, Close to Cocoa, and Pumpkin Pie Classic Stampin' Pads; Aged Copper Hodgepodge Hardware; Spring Moss and Tangerine grosgrain ribbons; Black gingham ribbon; linen thread; Stampin' Dimensionals; window sheets; Write Me a Memory Journaling Fonts CD, Volume 1; Word Window punch; 1/16" and 1/8" Circle punches

[36 A] Trick or Treat and Everyday Flexible Phrases sets; Almost Amethyst, Confetti White, and Really Rust card stock; Confetti White & Kraft tag sheets; Almost Amethyst, Chocolate Chip, Creamy Caramel, Gable Green, and Really Rust Classic Stampin' Pads; Basic Black Craft Stampin' Pad; linen thread; Stampin' Dimensionals

[36 B] Everyday Flexible Phrases, Halloween Backgrounds, and Trick or Treat sets; Confetti White & Kraft Party Favor boxes & tags; Basic Black and Confetti White card stock; Basic Black, Pumpkin Pie, and Really Rust Classic Stampin' Pads; Natural hemp twine

[36 C] Trick or Treat set; Happy Jacks wheel; Almost Amethyst, Confetti White, Gable Green, and Really Rust card stock; Almost Amethyst, Basic Black, and Green Galore Classic Stampin' Pads; Really Rust Stampin' Around cartridge; Vintage brads; 1/16" Circle Punch

[36 D] Trick or Treat and Halloween Backgrounds sets; Almost Amethyst, Confetti White, Kraft, and Really Rust card stock; Really Rust Classic Stampin' Pad;

Almost Amethyst, Creamy Caramel, Gable Green, and Really Rust Stampin' Write markers; Natural hemp twine; Stampin' Dimensionals

[37 A] Home Is Where the Haunt Is and Whimsical Alphabet Upper and Lower sets; Spooky Skyline wheel; Almost Amethyst, Basic Black, Confetti White, Green Galore, and Pumpkin Pie card stock; Basic Black, Green Galore, and White Craft Stampin' Pads; Basic Black Stampin' Write marker; Basic Black Stampin' Around cartridge; Light Orchid grosgrain ribbon; Stampin' Dimensionals; 1/8" Circle punch

[37 B] Web Wishes set; Almost Amethyst, Confetti White, and Really Rust card stock; Almost Amethyst, Basic Black, Gable Green, and Really Rust Classic Stampin' Pads; Antique Brass Hodgepodge Hardware; linen thread; twill tape; Stampin' Dimensionals; watercolor brush; 1/16" Circle punch; sewing machine and thread

[38 A] Frosty set; Kraft, Night of Navy, and Real Red card stock; Night of Navy Classic Stampin' Pad; Watercolor Wonder crayons; Red gingham ribbon; Taupe grosgrain ribbon; Natural hemp twine; Stampin' Dimensionals; staple

[38 B] Crazy for Christmas and All-Year Cheer I sets; Real Red card stock; Pockets & Pieces, Assortment 1; Basic Black, Creamy Caramel, Gable Green, Green Galore, Real Red, and Summer Sun Classic Stampin' Pads; Natural hemp twine; Earth Elements eyelet; Caramel gingham ribbon; 1/2" Circle punch; Crafters' Tool Kit; watercolor brush

[38 C] Crazy for Christmas set; Gable Green, Night of Navy, Real Red, and Very Vanilla card stock; Close to Cocoa, Gable Green, Night of Navy, and Real Red Classic Stampin' Pads; Navy grosgrain ribbon; Stampin' Dimensionals; linen thread; 1/16" Circle punch; watercolor brush

[39 A] Yule Bits & Borders, Everyday Flexible Phrases, Classic Alphabet, and Simple Type Numbers sets; Night of Navy, Real Red, and Very Vanilla card stock; Night of Navy, Real Red, and Very Vanilla Craft Stampin' Pads; Real Red Stampin' Write journaler; Crystal Clear Stampin' Emboss powder; Bold Brights eyelets; Red gingham ribbon; linen thread; Stampin' Dimensionals; 1/8" Circle punch; Crafters' Tool Kit

[39 B] Yule Bits & Borders set; Night of Navy and Very Vanilla card stock; Basic Black, Creamy Caramel, Summer Sun, and Real Red Classic Stampin' Pads; Very Vanilla and Night of Navy Craft Stampin' Pads; Bold Brights Pillar boxes & tags; window sheets; Vintage Brads; Stampin' Dimensionals; Red gingham ribbon; linen thread; watercolor brush

[39 C] Very Merry set; Gable Green and Very Vanilla card stock; Bold Brights pillar boxes & tags; Basic Black, Blush Blossom, Green Galore, Going Gray, Pixie Pink, and Real Red Classic Stampin' Pads; White Square Aluminum Metal Edge tags; Red gingham ribbon; Bold Brights II eyelets; Dazzling Diamonds Stampin' Glitter; Stampin' Dimensionals; Crafters' Tool Kit; sanding blocks; watercolor brush

[40 A] Santa Post set; Print Pattern background stamp; Garden Green, Naturals Ivory, and Real Red card stock; Earths mulberry paper; Basic Black, Close to Cocoa, Garden Green, and Real Red Classic Stampin' Pads; Vintage brads; Natural hemp twine; Red gingham ribbon; watercolor brush

[40 B] Holiday Woodcuts set; Canvas background stamp; Garden Green, Kraft, Real Red, and Very Vanilla card stock; Bold Brights tag sheets; Garden Green, Going Gray, and Real Red Classic Stampin' Pads; Garden Green Stampin' Write marker; Red gingham ribbon; Natural hemp twine; Stampin' Dimensionals; brayer

[41 A] Sparkling Season, Classic Alphabet, and Letterpress Alphabet sets; Confetti White, Garden Green, and Real Red card stock; Pockets & Pieces, Assortment 2; Basic Black, Garden Green, and Real Red Craft Stampin' Pads; Basic Black Stampin' Write journaler; Bold Brights I eyelets; Stampin' Dimensionals; Crafters' Tool Kit

[41 B] Sparkling Season set; Candy Cane Craze wheel; Garden Green, Real Red, and Whisper White card stock; Bold Brights and Whisper White & Very Vanilla tag sheets; Vellum Square Aluminum Metal Edge tags; Basic Black and Real Red Classic Stampin' Pads; Basic eyelets; Brights Fancy Fibers; Stampin' Dimensionals; Crafters' Tool Kit

[41 C] Sparkling Season and Label Classics sets; Funky Firs wheel; Confetti White and Garden Green card stock; Bold Brights Pillar boxes & tags; Real Red Classic Stampin' Pad; Chocolate Chip, Garden Green, and Real Red Stampin' Write markers; Whisper White cartridge & ink refill; Red gingham ribbon; Antique Brass Hodgepodge Hardware; Dazzling Diamonds Stampin' Glitter; Wire Works; Stampin' Dimensionals; 1/16" Circle punch

[42 A] Flaky Friends set; Brocade Blue, Mellow Moss, and Naturals Ivory card stock; Basic Black, Bravo Burgundy, Brocade Blue, Creamy Caramel, and Mellow Moss Classic Stampin' Pads; Silver brads; Silver eyelets; linen thread; Crafters' Tool Kit; watercolor brush

[42 B] Flaky Friends set; Always Artichoke, Bravo Burgundy, Confetti White, and Mellow Moss card stock; Always Artichoke, Basic Black, Bravo Burgundy, Chocolate Chip, and Mellow Moss Classic Stampin' Pads; Vellum Square Aluminum Metal Edge tags; Natural hemp twine; Soft Subtles I eyelets; Stampin' Dimensionals; Crafters' Tool Kit; watercolor brush

[42 C] Flaky Friends set; Star wheel; Confetti Cream and Creamy Caramel card stock; Rich Regals Pillar boxes & tags; Bashful Blue, Basic Black, Bravo Burgundy, Creamy Caramel, and Mellow Moss Classic Stampin' Pads; Bravo Burgundy Stampin' Around cartridge; Stampin' Dimensionals; Antique Brass Hodgepodge Hardware; linen thread; twill tape; watercolor brush; sewing machine and thread

[43 A] Christmas Carolers set; Bravo Burgundy, Mellow Moss, and Naturals Ivory card stock; Heirloom Designer Series paper; Basic Black, Bravo Burgundy, Close to Cocoa, Creamy Caramel, Mellow Moss, and Not Quite Navy Classic Stampin' Pads; Caramel gingham ribbon; Aged Copper Hodgepodge Hardware; linen thread; Stampin' Dimensionals

[43 B] Holiday Print set; Bravo Burgundy, Mellow Moss, and Naturals Ivory card stock; Not Quite Navy and Old Olive Classic Stampin' Pads; Silver brads; Ivory 3/8" organdy ribbon; Dazzling Diamonds Stampin' Glitter; Snowflake punch

[44 A] Merry Minstrels set; Confetti White, Elegant Eggplant, Old Olive, and Ruby Red card stock; Basic Black, Brilliant Blue, Close to Cocoa, Creamy Caramel, Elegant Eggplant, Old Olive, and Ruby Red Classic Stampin' Pads; Aged Copper Hodgepodge Hardware; Chocolate grosgrain ribbon

[44 B] Holiday Wishes set; Confetti White, Old Olive, and Ruby Red card stock; Always Artichoke, Chocolate Chip, and Ruby Red Classic Stampin' Pads; Natural hemp twine; Stampin' Dimensionals; watercolor brush

[45 A] Happy Winter and Everyday Flexible Phrases sets; Chocolate Chip, Elegant Eggplant, Old Olive, and Whisper White card stock; Whisper White & Very Vanilla tag sheets; Chocolate Chip, Elegant Eggplant, and Old Olive Classic Stampin' Pads; White Craft Stampin' Pad; Caramel gingham ribbon; Stampin' Dimensionals; Aqua Painter

[45 B] Ornament Elements set; Elegant Eggplant, Old Olive, Ruby Red, and Whisper White card stock; Earth Elements and Whisper White & Very Vanilla tag sheets; Elegant Eggplant and Ruby Red Craft Stampin' Pads; Basic Black Stampin' Write journaler; Eggplant grosgrain ribbon; Stampin' Dimensionals; linen thread; 1-1/4" Circle punch

[45 C] Ornament Elements set; Elegant Eggplant, Old Olive, Ruby Red, and Whisper White card stock; Old Olive Classic Stampin' Pad; Close to Cocoa, Elegant Eggplant, Old Olive, and Ruby Red Stampin' Write markers; Dazzling Diamonds Stampin' Glitter; Stampin' Dimensionals; watercolor brush; sewing machine and thread

[46 A] Peace Be unto You set; Always Artichoke, Bravo Burgundy, More Mustard, and Naturals Ivory card stock; Always Artichoke, Bravo Burgundy, Close to Cocoa, and Summer Sun Classic Stampin' Pads; Basic Brown and Whisper White Craft Stampin' Pads; Burgundy grosgrain ribbon; Stampin' Dimensionals; watercolor brush

[46 B] Holiday Spirit set; Only Ornaments wheel; Always Artichoke, Bravo Burgundy, More Mustard, and Very Vanilla card stock; Oxford Designers Series vellum; Always Artichoke and More Mustard Classic Stampin' Pads; More Mustard Stampin' Around cartridge; Earth Elements eyelets; Burgundy grosgrain ribbon; Slit punch; Stampin' Dimensionals; Crafters' Tool Kit; sewing machine and thread

[46 C] Holiday Spirit set; Canvas background stamp; Always Artichoke and Confetti Cream card stock; Earth Elements Pillar boxes & tags; Regals mulberry paper; Always Artichoke, Bravo Burgundy, and More Mustard Classic Stampin' Pads; Rich Regals buttons; Natural hemp twine; linen thread; Vintage brads; Stampin' Dimensionals; 1-1/4" Circle punch

[47 A] Madonna and Child set; Always Artichoke, Bravo Burgundy, and Confetti Cream card stock; Regals mulberry paper; Always Artichoke, Blush Blossom, Creamy Caramel, and Mellow Moss Stampin' Pads; VersaMark pad; Gold Glory Stampin' Emboss powder; Gold cord; Stampin' Dimensionals; 1/16" Circle punch

[47 B] Renaissance Angels set; Always Artichoke, Elegant Eggplant, More Mustard, and Naturals Ivory card stock; Always Artichoke, Basic Black, Close to Cocoa, Elegant Eggplant, and More Mustard Classic Stampin' Pads; Ivory 3/8" organdy ribbon; Stampin' Dimensionals

[48 A] Peace & Love set; Glorious Green, Naturals White, and Real Red card stock; Basic Black, Glorious Green, and Real Red Classic Stampin' Pads; Vintage brads; White 3/8" organdy ribbon; Stampin' Dimensionals; brayer

[48 B] Holiday Tag Team set; Glorious Green, Naturals White, Real Red, and Whisper White card stock; Basic Black, Blush Blossom, Glorious Green, Real Red, and Sahara Sand Classic Stampin' Pads; Basic eyelets; Brights Fancy Fibers; Crafters' Tool Kit; watercolor brush

[48 C] Holiday Tag Team and Wonderful Words sets; Glorious Green and Real Red card stock; Whisper White & Very Vanilla Purse boxes & tags; Basic Black, Glorious Green, and Real Red Classic Stampin' Pads; Red 7/8" organdy ribbon; Red grosgrain ribbon; Stampin' Dimensionals; watercolor brush; 1/8" Circle punch; staple

[49 A] Happiest of Holidays and Sincere Salutations sets; Swirling Stars jumbo wheel; Kraft, Naturals Ivory, and Real Red card stock; Basic Black and Real Red Classic Stampin' Pads; Real Red Stampin' Around cartridge; Natural hemp twine; Antique Brass Hodgepodge Hardware; watercolor brush

[49 B] Happiest of Holidays set; Woodcut Holly jumbo wheel; Very Vanilla card stock; Bold Brights Mini Gable boxes & tags; Glorious Green Classic Stampin' Pad; VersaMark pad; Real Red Classic Stampin' Around jumbo cartridge; twill tape; Basic eyelets; Red grosgrain ribbon; Vellum Square Brass Metal Edge tags; Gold Glory Stampin' Emboss powder; Crafters' Tool Kit

[50 A] Cruisin' Christmas set; Always Artichoke, Mellow Moss, Real Red, and Very Vanilla card stock; Basic Black Craft Stampin' Pad; Always Artichoke, Mellow Moss, Real Red, Blush Blossom, and Sahara Sand Classic Stampin' Pads; Vintage brads; Red grosgrain ribbon; watercolor brush

[50 B] 'Tis the Season, Pure & Simple Alphabet Upper, Pure & Simple Alphabet Lower, Classic Alphabet, and Classic Numbers sets; Always Artichoke, Mellow Moss, Real Red, and Very Vanilla card stock; Always Artichoke, Basic Black, Mellow Moss, and Real Red Craft Stampin' Pads; Basic Black Stampin' Write journaler; Black gingham ribbon; Pewter Hodgepodge Hardware; linen thread; watercolor brush; 1/8" Circle punch

[50 C] 'Tis the Season, Word by Word, and Everyday Flexible Phrases sets; Real Red and Very Vanilla card stock; Soft Subtles Mini Gable boxes & tags; Mellow Moss and Real Red Classic Stampin' Pads; Basic eyelets; linen thread; Stampin' Dimensionals; Crafters' Tool Kit

[51 A] Sleigh Full of Toys set; Always Artichoke, Mellow Moss, Real Red, and Very Vanilla card stock; Basic Black, Close to Cocoa, Going Gray, Pretty in Pink, and Real Red Classic Stampin' Pads; Vintage brads; Brights Fancy Fibers; Slit punch; Aqua Painter

[51 B] Sleigh Full of Toys and Sincere Salutations sets; Always Artichoke, Mellow Moss, Real Red, and Very Vanilla card stock; Always Artichoke, Basic Black, Close to Cocoa, Mellow Moss, and Real Red Classic Stampin' Pads; Spring Moss grosgrain ribbon; 1/8" Circle punch; watercolor brush

[51 C] Heavenly Heralds and Expressive Flexible Phrases sets; Always Artichoke, Mellow Moss, Real Red, and Very Vanilla card stock; Oxford Designer Series vellum; Always Artichoke and Basic Black Classic Stampin' Pads; Vintage brads; Red 7/8" organdy ribbon; Olive 3/8" organdy ribbon; Antique Brass Hodgepodge Hardware; linen thread; 1/16" and 1/8" Circle punches

[52 A] Merry set; Brilliant Blue, Glorious Green, Real Red, and Whisper White card stock; Real Red Classic Stampin' Pad; Brilliant Blue, Brocade Blue, Glorious Green, and Real Red Stampin' Write markers; Red grosgrain ribbon; Stampin' Dimensionals; 1-1/4" Circle punch; staple

[52 B] Merry, Label Classics, and Quick Thinking sets; Certainly Celery, Real Red, and Whisper White card stock; Bold Brights pillar boxes & tags; Brilliant Blue, Certainly Celery, and Real Red Classic Stampin' Pads; Silver brads; Silver eyelets; Celery grosgrain ribbon; Stampin' Dimensionals; 1/2" Circle punch; Crafters' Tool Kit

[52 C] Sweet Holidays set; Confetti White and Glorious Green card stock; Bold Brights tag sheets; Basic Black, Glorious Green, Going Gray, Lovely Lilac, Real Red, Ruby Red, and Yoyo Yellow Classic Stampin' Pads; Jet Black StazOn pad; Vintage brads; Red gingham ribbon; Green hemp twine; Bold Brights I eyelets; Stampin' Dimensionals; Crafters' Tool Kit

[53 A] Merry Minis set; Brilliant Blue, Certainly Celery, Real Red, and Whisper White card stock; Brilliant Blue, Certainly Celery, and Real Red Classic Stampin' Pads; Red gingham ribbon; Stampin' Dimensionals; sewing machine and thread

[53 B] Little Holiday Wishes and Whimsical Alphabet Lower sets; Ballet Blue, Brilliant Blue, Real Red, and Whisper White card stock; Ballet Blue, Brilliant Blue, Glorious Green, Real Red, Whisper White, and YoYo Yellow Craft Stampin' Pads; Ballet Blue Stampin' Write journaler; Blue hemp twine; watercolor brush

[54 A] Snowflakes set; Bravo Burgundy, Chocolate Chip, Old Olive, and Whisper White card stock; Bravo Burgundy Classic Stampin' Pad; VersaMark pad; Crystal Clear Stampin' Emboss powder; Natural hemp twine

[54 B] Solemn Stillness and Everyday Flexible Phrases sets; Star Studded wheel; Bravo Burgundy, Bordering Blue, and Whisper White card stock; Earth Elements Pillar boxes & tags; Bordering Blue and Old Olive Classic Stampin' Pads; Old Olive Classic Stampin' Around cartridge; Basic Black Stampin' Write journaler; Natural hemp twine; Earth Elements buttons; Stampin' Dimensionals; sanding blocks

[55 A] It's Snow Time set; Canvas background stamp; Bordering Blue, Bravo Burgundy, Confetti White, and Old Olive card stock; Confetti White & Kraft tag sheets; Basic Black, Bordering Blue, Bravo Burgundy, Old Olive, and Only Orange Classic Stampin' Pads; Vintage brads; Chocolate grosgrain ribbon; Natural hemp twine; Stampin' Dimensionals; watercolor brush; sewing machine and thread

[55 B] It's Snow Time and Alphabits sets; Bordering Blue, Chocolate Chip, Old Olive, Rose Red, and Whisper White card stock; Basic Black, Chocolate Chip, Old Olive, Only Orange, and Rose Red Classic Stampin' Pads; VersaMark pad; Basic Black Stampin' Write marker; Black detail embossing powder; Aged Copper Hodgepodge Hardware; linen thread; Stampin' Dimensionals; bleach

[55 C] It's Snow Time set; Snowman Fun wheel; Bordering Blue, Chocolate Chip, Confetti White, Old Olive, and Rose Red card stock; Confetti White & Kraft tag sheets; Basic Black, Bordering Blue, Close to Cocoa, Old Olive, Only Orange, and Rose Red Classic Stampin' Pads; Old Olive Stampin' Around cartridge; linen thread; Black gingham ribbon; Stampin' Dimensionals; watercolor brush; staple

[56 A] Flower Filled and It's Your Birthday sets; Always Artichoke, Elegant Eggplant, More Mustard, and Whisper White card stock; Always Artichoke, Elegant Eggplant, More Mustard, and Really Rust Craft Stampin' Pads; Natural hemp twine; Earth Elements buttons; Stampin' Dimensionals

[56 B] Bundle Up and Much Appreciated sets; Always Artichoke, Elegant Eggplant, More Mustard, Really Rust, and Whisper White card stock; Whisper White & Very Vanilla tag sheets; Elegant Eggplant and Really Rust Classic Stampin' Pads; Always Artichoke, Elegant Eggplant, and Really Rust Stampin' Write markers; Eggplant grosgrain ribbon; linen thread; Stampin' Dimensionals

[57 A] Always on My Mind set; Cheesecloth background stamp; Always Artichoke, Confetti White, More Mustard, and Really Rust card stock; Confetti White & Kraft tag sheets; Chocolate Chip and More Mustard Classic Stampin' Pads; Vintage brads; Mustard grosgrain ribbon; Stampin' Dimensionals; Watercolor pencils; 1/8" Circle punch; watercolor brush; sewing machine and thread

[57 B] Always on My Mind and Simple Sayings II sets; French Script background stamp; Always Artichoke, Elegant Eggplant, and More Mustard card stock; White vellum card stock; watercolor paper; More Mustard Classic Stampin' Pad; Jet Black StazOn pad; Eggplant grosgrain ribbon; Watercolor pencils; 1/8" Circle punch; Aqua Painter

[57 C] Always on My Mind set; Canvas and French Script background stamps; Always Artichoke, Confetti White, and Elegant Eggplant card stock; Basic Black, Bordering Blue, Close to Cocoa, Elegant Eggplant, and Going Gray Classic Stampin' Pads; Olive 3/8" organdy ribbon; Silver cord; Dazzling Diamonds Stampin' Glitter; Slit and 1/8" Circle punches; watercolor brush; sewing machine and thread

[58 A] Sparkling Summer, Classic Alphabet, and Simple Type Alphabet sets; Geometric background stamp; Green Galore, Pink Passion, Only Orange, and Whisper White card stock; Basic Black, Green Galore, Only Orange, and Pink Passion Classic Stampin' Pads; Bold Brights I and II eyelets; Crafters' Tool Kit; watercolor brush

[58 B] Sparkling Summer, Alphadots, Pure & Simple Alphabet Upper, and Fine Frames sets; Canvas background stamp; Pink Passion, Only Orange, Green Galore, and Confetti White card stock; Confetti White & Kraft tag sheets; Only Orange, Green Galore, Pink Passion, and Basic Black Classic Stampin' Pads; Basic Black Stampin' Write journaler; Black gingham ribbon; Vintage brads; Natural hemp twine; Stampin' Dimensionals; staple; watercolor brush

[58 C] Sparkling Summer and All-Year Cheer I sets; Green Galore, Only Orange, Pink Passion, and Whisper White card stock; Basic Black, Green Galore, Only Orange, and Pink Passion Classic Stampin' Pads; White Square Aluminum Metal Edge tags; Apple Green grosgrain ribbon; Stampin' Dimensionals; crochet thread; 1/8" and 1/16" Circle punches; watercolor brush

[59 A] Seaside Sketches set; Brocade Blue, Confetti White, and Only Orange card stock; White vellum card stock; Basic Black, Blush Blossom, Brocade Blue, Close to Cocoa, Only Orange, and Tempting Turquoise Classic Stampin' Pads; Silver brads; Natural hemp twine; watercolor brush

[59 B] Some Like It Hot and Expressive Flexible Phrases sets; Brocade Blue, Green Galore, Only Orange, and Whisper White card stock; Brocade Blue, Only Orange, and Pink Passion Classic Stampin' Pads; Apple Green grosgrain ribbon; Metallic Wire Works; 1/8" and 1-1/4" Circle punches; sewing machine and thread

[60 A] Window on the World set; Simple Stripes background stamp; Brocade Blue, Close to Cocoa, Confetti White, and Mellow Moss card stock; Always Artichoke, Brocade Blue, Close to Cocoa, and Summer Sun Classic Stampin' Pads; Bluebird grosgrain ribbon; linen thread; Stampin' Dimensionals; watercolor brush

[60 B] Little Layers II and All-Year Cheer I sets; Mellow Moss and Rose Red card stock; Basic Black and Mellow Moss Classic Stampin' Pads; Bashful Blue, Mellow Moss, and Rose Red Stampin' Write markers; White Square Aluminum Metal Edge tags; Spring Moss grosgrain ribbon; Bold Brights II eyelets; Stampin' Dimensionals; Crafters' Tool Kit

[61 A] Summer by the Sea set; Brocade Blue, Close to Cocoa, Confetti White, and Regal Rose card stock; Confetti White & Kraft tag sheets; Brocade Blue, Close to Cocoa, Mellow Moss, Regal Rose, and Summer Sun Classic Stampin' Pads; Light Blue gingham ribbon; Stampin' Dimensionals; 1/8" and 1/2" Circle punches; watercolor brush

[61 B] Summer by the Sea, Expressive Flexible Phrases, Whimsical Alphabet Lower, and Whimsical Numbers sets; Canvas background stamp; Brocade Blue, Close to Cocoa, Confetti White, and Mellow Moss card stock; Basic Brown, Close to Cocoa, Mellow Moss, More Mustard, and Ruby Red Craft Stampin' Pads; Vintage brads; French Blue grosgrain ribbon; Natural hemp twine; window sheets; Stampin' Dimensionals; 1/8" Circle punch

[62 A] Little Somethings set; Pindot wheel; Bravo Burgundy, Creamy Caramel, Confetti Cream, and Not Quite Navy card stock; Basic Black, Bravo Burgundy, and Going Gray Classic Stampin' Pads; Bravo Burgundy Stampin' Around cartridge; Rich Regals buttons; linen thread; Natural hemp twine; Stampin' Dimensionals; 1/8" and 1-1/4" Circle punches; watercolor brush

[62 B] Fall Whimsy, It's a Date, and Sincere Salutations sets; Creamy Caramel, Naturals Ivory, and Old Olive card stock; Rich Regals Petal card & tags; Bravo Burgundy, More Mustard, and Old Olive Classic Stampin' Pads; Burgundy grosgrain ribbon; linen thread; Earth Elements eyelets; Stampin' Dimensionals; Crafters' Tool Kit; 1/2" Circle punch

[62 C] Fall Whimsy and All-Year Cheer III sets; Bravo Burgundy, Naturals Ivory, and Really Rust card stock; Earth Elements Pillar boxes & tags; Bravo Burgundy, More Mustard, Old Olive, and Really Rust Classic Stampin' Pads; More Mustard, Old Olive, and Really Rust Stampin' Write markers; Natural hemp twine; Mustard grosgrain ribbon; Stampin' Dimensionals; 1/8" Circle punch; watercolor brush

[63 A] A Tree for All Seasons and Everyday Flexible Phrases sets; Confetti Cream and Old Olive card stock; Bravo Burgundy, Night of Navy, Old Olive, and Really Rust Classic Stampin' Pads; twill tape; Earth Elements and Rich Regals eyelets; 1-3/8" Square punch; Crafters' Tool Kit

[63 B] Sweet Seasons and Wonderful Words II sets; Canvas background stamp; Bravo Burgundy, Creamy Caramel, and Naturals Ivory card stock; Basic Black, Bravo Burgundy, Close to Cocoa, Creamy Caramel, More Mustard, and Night of Navy Classic Stampin' Pads; Cream grosgrain ribbon; watercolor brush

[63 C] Sweet Seasons and Everyday Flexible Phrases sets; Bravo Burgundy, Confetti Cream, Creamy Caramel, and Really Rust card stock; Basic Black, Bravo Burgundy, Brocade Blue, Chocolate Chip, Creamy Caramel, Old Olive, and Really Rust Classic Stampin' Pads; Natural hemp twine; Vintage brads; watercolor brush

[64 A] Fun Filled and Expressive Flexible Phrases sets; Bashful Blue, Certainly Celery, and Confetti White card stock; Bashful Blue, Certainly Celery, and Lavender Lace Classic Stampin' Pads; Spring Moss grosgrain ribbon; Stampin' Dimensionals; sewing machine and thread

[64 B] L'Chayim and It's a Date sets; Night of Navy and Sahara Sand card stock; Saddle Stitch book kit, Assortment 1; Bordering Blue, Brocade Blue, and Night of Navy Classic Stampin' Pads; twill tape; Pewter Hodgepodge Hardware; linen thread

[64 C] L'Chayim set; Bashful Blue, Lavender Lace, Night of Navy, and Sahara Sand card stock; Lavender Lace and Night of Navy Classic Stampin' Pads; VersaMark pad; Silver brads; Silver cord; Stampin' Dimensionals; Sterling Silver Stampin' Emboss powder; Slit punch; watercolor brush

[65 A] Little Layers Plus and Everyday Flexible Phrases sets; Bashful Blue, Confetti White, and Lavender Lace card stock; Lavender Lace and Night of Navy Classic Stampin' Pads; Natural hemp twine; Stampin' Dimensionals; 1/8" Circle punch

[65 B] It All Adds Up set; Canvas background stamp; Bashful Blue, Certainly Celery, Confetti White, and Lavender Lace card stock; Bashful Blue, Certainly Celery, and Lavender Lace Classic Stampin' Pads; Light Blue gingham ribbon; Stampin' Dimensionals

[65 C] It All Adds Up and It's Your Birthday sets; Bashful Blue, Certainly Celery, Confetti White, Lavender Lace, and Sahara Sand card stock; Bashful Blue, Certainly Celery, and Lavender Lace Classic Stampin' Pads; Celery grosgrain ribbon; linen thread; Soft Subtles II eyelets; Stampin' Dimensionals; Crafters' Tool Kit; 1/16" Circle punch; sewing machine and thread

[66 A] Stipple Celebrations and Everyday Flexible Phrases sets; Kraft, Naturals Ivory, and Ruby Red card stock; Chocolate Chip and Ruby Red Classic Stampin' Pads; Silver eyelets; Caramel gingham ribbon; linen thread; Stampin' Dimensionals; Crafters' Tool Kit

[66 B] Stipple Celebrations, Everyday Flexible Phrases, and Simple Type Alphabet sets; Kraft, Naturals Ivory, and Ruby Red card stock; Chocolate Chip, More Mustard, Old Olive, and Ruby Red Craft Stampin' Pads; Basic Black Stampin' Write journaler; Caramel gingham ribbon; Earth Elements buttons; Stampin' Dimensionals

[67 A] Little Layers and Everyday Flexible Phrases sets; Lovely Ladybugs wheel; Close to Cocoa, Kraft, and Ruby Red card stock; Chocolate Chip Classic Stampin' Pad; Ruby Red and Whisper White Craft Stampin' Pads; Chocolate Chip Stampin' Around cartridge; Vintage brads; linen thread; Chocolate grosgrain ribbon; Caramel gingham ribbon; Stampin' Dimensionals; 1/16" and 1-3/8" Circle punches

[67 B] Shapes & Shadows, Everyday Flexible Phrases, Newsprint Numbers, and Classic Alphabet sets; Chocolate Chip, Kraft, Ruby Red, and Whisper White card stock; Confetti White & Kraft tag sheets; Chocolate Chip, Close to Cocoa, More Mustard, and Ruby Red Classic Stampin' Pads; Ruby Red Classic ink refill; Basic Black Stampin' Write marker; linen thread; Gold brads; sewing machine and thread

[67 C] Shapes & Shadows, Classic Numbers, and Pure & Simple Alphabet Upper sets; Kraft, More Mustard, Old Olive, and Ruby Red card stock; Chocolate Chip, More Mustard, and Ruby Red Craft Stampin' Pads; Basic Black Stampin' Write journaler; Gold brad; Natural hemp twine

[68 A] Nice & Easy Notes sets; Apricot Appeal, Cameo Coral, Certainly Celery, Confetti White card stock; Apricot Appeal, Basic Black, Cameo Coral, Close to Cocoa, and Green Galore Classic Stampin' Pads; White 3/8" organdy ribbon; Silver brads; Stampin' Dimensionals; watercolor brush; 1/8" Circle and Slit punches

[68 B] Nice & Easy Notes and Everyday Flexible Phrases sets; Apricot Appeal, Bashful Blue, Certainly Celery, and Confetti White card stock; Apricot Appeal, Bashful Blue, Basic Black, Certainly Celery, Close to Cocoa, and Going Gray Classic Stampin' Pads; Light Blue gingham ribbon; White grosgrain ribbon; linen thread; Stampin' Dimensionals; 1/16" Circle punch; watercolor brush

[68 C] Simple Wishes set; Canvas background stamp; Apricot Appeal, Cameo Coral, Certainly Celery, and Confetti White card stock; Apricot Appeal, Basic Black, Cameo Coral, Certainly Celery, and Green Galore Classic Stampin' Pads; Natural hemp twine; White Square Aluminum Metal Edge tag; Stampin' Dimensionals; watercolor brush; staple; sewing machine and thread

[69 A] Greetings Galore set; Regal Rose, Bashful Blue, Confetti White, and Regal Rose card stock; Bashful Blue, Basic Black, and Regal Rose Classic Stampin' Pads; Black gingham ribbon; Vintage brads; Stampin' Dimensionals; Crafters' Tool Kit; watercolor brush

[69 B] Mini Medleys and Newsprint Alphabet sets; Polka Dot Blocks wheel; Bashful Blue, Certainly Celery, and Confetti White card stock; Brocade Blue and Whisper White Craft Stampin' Pads; VersaMark pad; Whisper White Craft Stampin' Around cartridge; Crystal Clear Stampin' Emboss Powder; Basic Black Stampin' Write journaler; Celery grosgrain ribbon; Silver brads

[70 A] Favorite Teddy Bear and Everyday Flexible Phrases set; Simple Stripes background stamp; Brocade Blue, Confetti White, Elegant Eggplant, and Kraft card stock; Basic Brown and Brocade Blue Classic Stampin' Pads; Brocade Blue Stampin' Write marker; Watercolor Wonder crayons; Natural hemp twine; Stampin' Dimensionals; 1/16" Circle punch; watercolor brush

[70 B] Favorite Teddy Bear set; Confetti White, Bashful Blue, Elegant Eggplant, and More Mustard card stock; Bashful Blue, Basic Black, Elegant Eggplant, and More Mustard Classic Stampin' Pads; Bashful Blue Stampin' Write marker; Gold hemp twine; Stampin' Dimensionals; 1/16" Circle punch; watercolor brush

[70 C] Favorite Teddy Bear set; Paw Tracks wheel; Bashful Blue and More Mustard card stock; Confetti White & Kraft tag sheets; watercolor paper; Chocolate Chip Classic Stampin' Pad; Chocolate Chip Stampin' Around cartridge; Watercolor Wonder crayons; Natural hemp twine; Stampin' Dimensionals; watercolor brush; 1/16" Circle punch

[71 A] The Fine Print set; By Definition and Canvas background stamps; Brocade Blue, Confetti White, and More Mustard card stock; Basic Brown, Brocade Blue, and More Mustard Classic Stampin' Pads; White Craft Stampin' Pad; Watercolor Wonder crayons; Natural hemp twine; Stampin' Dimensionals; crimper; watercolor brush

[71 B] Nice & Narrow set; Certainly Celery, Confetti White, Elegant Eggplant, and More Mustard card stock; Regals mulberry paper; Basic Brown, Certainly Celery, Elegant Eggplant, and More Mustard Classic Stampin' Pads; More Mustard Craft Stampin' Pad; linen thread; 1/2" and 1/8" Circle punches; Aqua Painter

[71 C] Nice & Narrow set; Double-Line Stitched Plaid wheel; Certainly Celery, Confetti White, and Elegant Eggplant card stock; Rich Regals Mini Gable boxes & tags; Confetti White & Kraft tag sheets; Basic Brown, Certainly Celery, and Elegant Eggplant Classic Stampin' Pads; Brocade Blue Classic Stampin' Around cartridge; linen thread; Bold Brights buttons; Stampin' Dimensionals; watercolor brush; sanding block

[72 A] Mini Messages set; Certainly Celery, Lovely Lilac, Rose Red, and Whisper White card stock; Rose Red Classic Stampin' Pad; White Circle Aluminum Metal Edge tags; Silver brads; Spring Moss grosgrain ribbon; Stampin' Dimensionals

[72 B] Mini Messages set; Certainly Celery, Rose Red, and Whisper White card stock; Bold Brights Mini Gable boxes & tags; Lovely Lilac and Rose Red Classic Stampin' Pads; Silver eyelet; White Circle Aluminum Metal Edge tags; Light Orchid grosgrain ribbon; Bold Brights buttons; Stampin' Dimensionals; Crafters' Tool Kit; 1-1/4" Circle punch

[72 C] Feathered Friends set; Print Pattern background stamp; Certainly Celery, Confetti White, Kraft, and Rose Red card stock; Always Artichoke, Ballet Blue, Basic Black, Close to Cocoa, Lovely Lilac and Rose Red Classic Stampin' Pads; Celery grosgrain ribbon; Pewter Hodgepodge Hardware; Stampin' Dimensionals; watercolor brush

stampin' supplies

[73 A] Figures of Speech and Everyday Flexible Phrases sets; Certainly Celery, Rose Red, and Whisper White card stock; Rose Red Classic Stampin' Pad; 1/2" Circle, 1-1/4" Square, and 1-3/8" Square punches; Silver brads; Silver eyelets; Spring Moss grosgrain ribbon; Crafters' Tool Kit; window sheets; sewing machine and thread

[73 B] Figures of Speech set; Certainly Celery, Lavender Lace, and Rose Red card stock; watercolor paper; Basic Black, Certainly Celery, Lavender Lace, Rose Red, and Summer Sun Classic Stampin' Pads; Crystal Effects; Crystal Clear Stampin' Emboss powder; Silver cord; Silver brads; Light Orchid grosgrain ribbon; Vellum Square Aluminum Metal Edge tag; Stampin' Dimensionals; 1/8" Circle punch; 1-3/8" Square punch; crimper

[73 C] Quick & Cute set; Lavender Lace, Lovely Lilac, Rose Red, and Whisper White card stock; Lovely Lilac and Rose Red Stampin' Write markers; Stainless Steel Metal Magic tags, Assortment 1; Light Orchid grosgrain ribbon; Stampin' Dimensionals; 1-1/4" Square punch; sewing machine and thread

[74 A] Mini Mates and Everyday Flexible Phrases sets; Brocade Blue, Kraft, Mellow Moss, Rose Red, and Very Vanilla card stock; Basic Black, Creamy Caramel, and Rose Red Classic Stampin' Pads; Chocolate Chip, Creamy Caramel, Mellow Moss, and Rose Red Stampin' Write markers; Black gingham ribbon; Soft Subtles buttons; Soft Subtles I eyelets; linen thread; Crafters' Tool Kit; 1-1/4" and 1-3/8" Circle punches; Mini Envelope template; brayer

[74 B] Mini Mates set; Elegant Eggplant, Mellow Moss, and Rose Red card stock; Elegant Eggplant, Mellow Moss, and Rose Red Stampin' Write markers; White Square Aluminum Metal Edge tags; Purple hemp twine; linen thread; Crafters' Tool Kit

[74 C] Tags & More set; Rose Red and Very Vanilla card stock; Bashful Blue, Elegant Eggplant, Mellow Moss, More Mustard, and Rose Red Stampin' Write Markers; Soft Subtles Bloomin' boxes & tags; French Blue grosgrain ribbon; Metallic Wire Works; Stampin' Dimensionals; Rectangle punch; 1/16" Circle punch

[75 A] Something to Celebrate set; Brocade Blue, Elegant Eggplant, Rose Red, and Very Vanilla card stock; Basic Black, Brocade Blue, Elegant Eggplant, Mellow Moss, Night of Navy, and Regal Rose Classic Stampin' Pads; Bluebird grosgrain ribbon; Silver brads; Silver cord; Crafters' Tool Kit; watercolor brush

[75 B] Something to Celebrate set; Brocade Blue, Rose Red, and Very Vanilla card stock; Soft Subtles Mini Gable boxes & tags; Barely Banana, Basic Black, Brocade Blue, Mellow Moss, Perfect Plum, and Rose Red Classic Stampin' Pads; French Blue grosgrain ribbon; Soft Subtles buttons; Dazzling Diamonds Stampin' Glitter; Stampin' Dimensionals; sanding blocks; watercolor brush; sewing machine and thread

[75 C] Good Times set; Brocade Blue, Elegant Eggplant, Kraft, Mellow Moss, and Rose Red card stock; Regals mulberry paper; Brocade Blue Classic Stampin' Pad; VersaMark pad; Crystal Clear Stampin' Emboss powder; French Blue grosgrain ribbon; Wire Works; Stampin' Dimensionals; Convex Square punch

[76 A] Simply Sweet and Wonderful Words II sets; Confetti White, Ballet Blue, Barely Banana, Old Olive, and Ruby Red card stock; Ballet Blue, Basic Brown, More Mustard, Old Olive, and Ruby Red Classic Stampin' Pads; Natural hemp twine; twill tape; Stampin' Dimensionals; 1/8" and 1/2" Circle punches; watercolor brush

[76 B] Sketch an Event, Classic Alphabet, and Stencil Alphabet sets; By Definition background stamp; Barely Banana, Close to Cocoa, Naturals Ivory, Old Olive, and Ruby Red card stock; Chocolate Chip, Ruby Red, and So Saffron Craft Stampin' Pads; Chocolate grosgrain ribbon; Natural hemp twine; Vintage brads; Stampin' Dimensionals; 1/2" Circle punch; 1-1/2" Square punch

[77 A] It's a Party set; Ballet Blue, Barely Banana, Confetti White, and Old Olive card stock; Basic Brown, Ballet Blue, Barely Banana, and Rose Red Classic Stampin' Pads; Bluebird grosgrain ribbon; Stampin' Dimensionals; 1/8" Circle punch; crimper; watercolor brush

[77 B] It's a Party set; Linograph background stamp; Ballet Blue, Barely Banana, Old Olive, Ruby Red, and Whisper White card stock; Old Olive Classic Stampin' Pad; Ballet Blue, Old Olive, and Ruby Red Stampin' Write markers; Cream grosgrain ribbon; Natural hemp twine; Stampin' Dimensionals; Earth Elements eyelets; Crafters' Tool Kit; 1/2" Circle punch

[77 C] Let's Party and All-Year Cheer I sets; Ballet Blue, Old Olive, Ruby Red, and Very Vanilla card stock; Whisper White & Very Vanilla tag sheets; Ballet Blue, Old Olive, and Ruby Red Stampin' Write markers; Silver eyelets; Natural hemp twine; crochet thread; watercolor brush; Crafters' Tool Kit; 1/2" Circle punch

[78 A] Birthday Best set; Confetti White, Only Orange, and Real Red card stock; Sassy Designer Series paper; Basic Black, Green Galore, Only Orange, and Regal Rose Classic Stampin' Pads; Basic Black Stampin' Write marker; linen thread; 1/16" Circle punch; staples; watercolor brush

[78 B] Birthday Best set; Basic Black, Real Red, and Whisper White card stock; Whisper White & Very Vanilla tag sheets; Basic Black, Green Galore, Only Orange, and Real Red Classic Stampin' Pads; Basic Black Stampin' Write marker; Silver brads; crochet thread; sewing machine and thread; watercolor brush

[78 C] Simple Somethings and Everyday Flexible Phrases sets; Crosshatch background stamp; Only Orange and Real Red card stock; Basic Black, Only Orange, Real Red, and Yoyo Yellow Classic Stampin' Pads; Whisper White & Very Vanilla tag sheets; White Square Aluminum Metal Edge tags; Red grosgrain ribbon; Stampin' Dimensionals; watercolor brush

[78 D] Simple Somethings, All-Year Cheer II, and Newsprint Alphabet sets; Hot to Dot wheel; Basic Black, Confetti White, and Green Galore card stock; Basic Black, Green Galore, Lovely Lilac, Only Orange, and Real Red Classic Stampin' Pads; White Craft Stampin' Pad; Basic Black Stampin' Write marker; Black gingham ribbon; Stampin' Dimensionals; 1-3/8" Square punch; watercolor brush

[79 A] Framed Greetings set; Basic Black, Green Galore, Naturals White, and Real Red card stock; Sassy Designer Series paper; Basic Black, Green Galore, Lavender Lace, Only Orange, and Real Red Classic Stampin' Pads; Vellum Square Aluminum Metal Edge tags; Basic eyelets; Wire Works; Apple Green grosgrain ribbon; Brights beads; Stampin' Dimensionals; blender pen; Crafters' Tool Kit; 1/16" Circle punch

[79 B] Framed Greetings set; Basic Black, Naturals White, Only Orange, and Real Red card stock; Vellum Circle Aluminum Metal Edge tags; Basic Black, Only Orange, and Real Red Classic Stampin' Pads; Basic Black and Real Red Classic ink refills; Bold Brights II eyelets; Stampin' Dimensionals; Crafters' Tool Kit; 1/8" Circle punch; crochet thread; watercolor brush

[79 C] Little Hellos set; Basic Black, Green Galore, and Only Orange card stock; Whisper White & Very Vanilla tag sheets; Basic Black, Green Galore, and Only Orange Classic Stampin' Pads; Basic Black Stampin' Write marker; Apple Green grosgrain ribbon; Stampin' Dimensionals; watercolor brush

[80 A] Simple Sketches set; Bravo Burgundy, Mellow Moss, and Sahara Sand card stock; Always Artichoke, Bravo Burgundy, and Mellow Moss Classic Stampin' Pads; Whisper White Craft Stampin' Pad; Caramel gingham ribbon; Earth Elements eyelet; linen thread; Crafters' Tool Kit; watercolor brush

[80 B] A Greeting for All Reasons set; Bravo Burgundy, Mellow Moss, and Sahara Sand card stock; Bravo Burgundy Classic Stampin' Pad; VersaMark pad; Gold Glory Stampin' Emboss powder; Gold brads; Stampin' Dimensionals; Gold cord

[81 A] Happy Occasions and All-Year Cheer I sets; Leaves & Swirls jumbo wheel; Bravo Burgundy, Confetti White, Mellow Moss, and Sahara Sand card stock; Bravo Burgundy jumbo cartridge; VersaMark pad; Gold detail embossing powder; Olive 3/8" organdy ribbon; 1/8" Circle punch; Stampin' Dimensionals

[81 B] Happy Occasions set; Leaves & Swirls jumbo wheel; Bravo Burgundy and Whisper White card stock; White mulberry paper; Burgundy 7/8" organdy ribbon; Pewter Hodgepodge Hardware; 1/8" Circle punch

[82 A] Smile set; Gable Green, Regal Rose, and Whisper White card stock; Soft Subtles Mini Gable boxes & tags; Regal Rose and Tempting Turquoise Classic Stampin' Pads; Silver brads; Stampin' Dimensionals; 1/16" and 1/2" Circle punches

[82 B] Perfect Party and Simple Type Alphabet, and Simple Type Numbers sets; Gable Green, Tempting Turquoise, and Whisper White card stock; Gable Green and Tempting Turquoise Craft Stampin' Pads; Silver eyelets; Turquoise grosgrain ribbon; Stampin' Dimensionals; 1/8" Circle punch; Crafters' Tool Kit; crochet thread

[83 A] Smile and Smile Some More sets; Gable Green, Pretty in Pink, Tempting Turquoise, and Whisper White card stock; Pretty in Pink Classic Stampin' Pad; Stainless Steel Metal Magic tags, Assortment 1; Rose grosgrain ribbon; Silver eyelets; Stampin' Dimensionals; Small Corner Rounder punch; Crafters' Tool Kit

[83 B] Surprise! set; Gable Green, Pretty in Pink, Tempting Turquoise, and Whisper White card stock; Pretty in Pink Classic Stampin' Pad; Silver eyelets; Rose grosgrain ribbon; Stampin' Dimensionals; 1/8" and 1/2" Circle punches; Crafters' Tool Kit; crimper; staple

[84 A] Happy Birthday Greetings and Everyday Flexible Phrase sets; Bashful Blue, Certainly Celery, and Night of Navy card stock; Certainly Celery and Night of Navy Classic Stampin' Pads; Certainly Celery Classic ink refill; Night of Navy Stampin' Write marker; Silver brads; Light Blue gingham ribbon; Celery, Navy, and Spring Moss grosgrain ribbon; 1/8" Circle punch

[84 B] Sweet Treats and It's Your Birthday sets; Whimsical Blossoms wheel; Certainly Celery and Confetti White card stock; Soft Subtles Pillar boxes & tags; Bashful Blue, Basic Black, Certainly Celery, Lavender Lace, and Summer Sun Classic Stampin' Pads; Lavender Lace Classic Stampin' Around cartridge; Silver brads; Soft Subtles II eyelets; Celery grosgrain ribbon; Stampin' Dimensionals; 1-1/4" and 1/4" Circle punches; Crafters' Tool Kit; watercolor brush; crochet thread

[85 A] Pretty Princess set; Bashful Blue, Certainly Celery, Confetti White, and Lavender Lace card stock; Bashful Blue, Basic Black, Certainly Celery, Chocolate Chip, Lavender Lace, More Mustard, Orchid Opulence, and Pretty in Pink Classic Stampin' Pads; Orchid 3/8" organdy ribbon; Earth Elements beads; Stampin' Dimensionals; watercolor brush

[85 B] Pretty Princess and All-Year Cheer II sets; Confetti White and Lavender Lace card stock; Soft Subtles Bloomin' boxes & tags; Bashful Blue, Basic Black, and Lavender Lace Classic Stampin' Pads; Basic Black Stampin' Write marker; Orchid 3/8" organdy ribbon; Dazzling Diamonds Stampin' Glitter; Stampin' Dimensionals; 1/8" and 1/16" Circle punches

[85 C] Tassel Time set; Bashful Blue, Certainly Celery, Confetti White, Night of Navy, and Old Olive card stock; Certainly Celery and Night of Navy Classic Stampin' Pads; Natural hemp twine; Rich Regals eyelets; Stampin' Dimensionals; Crafters' Tool Kit; watercolor brush

[86 A] Special Day set; Elegant Eggplant, Lavender Lace, and Pale Plum card stock; Lavender Lace Classic Stampin' Pad; Elegant Eggplant Stampin' Write marker; Silver cord; Wire Works; Silver brads; Stampin' Dimensionals; Folk Heart punch; 1/16" Circle punch

[86 B] Happily Ever After set; Confetti White, Elegant Eggplant, and Pale Plum card stock; White vellum card stock; Basic Black, Certainly Celery, Elegant Eggplant, and Yoyo Yellow Classic Stampin' Pads; Elegant Eggplant Stampin' Write marker; Dazzling Diamonds Stampin' Glitter; Silver cord; White 3/8" organdy ribbon; Stampin' Dimensionals; 1/8" Circle punch; watercolor brush

[86 C] Happily Ever After set; Confetti White and Elegant Eggplant card stock; Elegant Eggplant Classic Stampin' Pad; Almost Amethyst Craft Stampin' Pad; 3/8" White organdy ribbon; Silver cord; 1/8" Circle punch

[87 A] Life's Special Moments set; Certainly Celery, Confetti White, Elegant Eggplant, and Pale Plum card stock; White mulberry paper; Basic Black, Elegant Eggplant, Mellow Moss, and Pale Plum Classic Stampin' Pads; White 3/8" organdy ribbon; 1/8" Circle punch; watercolor brush

[87 B] Birthday Banter set; Certainly Celery, Confetti White, Elegant Eggplant, Lavender Lace card stock; Basic Black, Certainly Celery, and Elegant Eggplant Classic Stampin' Pads; Lavender Lace Craft Stampin' Pad; twill tape; Stainless Steel Metal Magic tags, Assortment 2; Stampin' Dimensionals; sanding blocks

[87 C] Birthday Banter set; Confetti White, Elegant Eggplant, Lavender Lace, and Pale Plum card stock; Basic Black, Certainly Celery, Lavender Lace, Pale Plum, and Yoyo Yellow Classic Stampin' Pads; Metallic Wire Works; Basic eyelets; Black gingham ribbon; Stampin' Dimensionals; Crafters' Tool Kit; watercolor brush

[88 A] Baby Talk and Alphadots sets; Barely Banana, Bashful Blue, and Confetti White card stock; Barely Banana, Basic Black, Brocade Blue, Going Gray, and More Mustard Craft Stampin' Pads; Basic Black Stampin' Write journaler; Light Blue gingham ribbon; Soft Subtles buttons; Soft Subtles I eyelets; Stampin' Dimensionals; Crafters' Tool Kit; 1/16" Circle punch; sanding blocks; crochet thread

[88 B] Baby Talk set; Bashful Blue and Mellow Moss card stock; Pool Party Designer Series vellum; Basic Black and Brocade Blue Classic Stampin' Pads; twill tape; Vintage brads; 1/16" Circle punch; Crafters' Tool Kit; crochet thread

[88 C] Welcome, Little One and Everyday Flexible Phrases sets; Bashful Blue card stock; Soft Subtles and Confetti White & Kraft tag sheets; Pool Party Designer Series vellum; Bashful Blue, Basic Black, Basic Brown, Blush Blossom, Mellow Moss, and Pretty in Pink Classic Stampin' Pads; Bashful Blue Classic ink refill; Light Blue gingham ribbon; Soft Subtles I and II eyelets; Regals Fancy Fibers; linen thread; Stampin' Dimensionals; Crafters' Tool Kit; watercolor brush; crochet thread

[89 A] Swell News, All-Year Cheer II, and Everyday Flexible Phrases sets; Bashful Blue and Confetti White card stock; Confetti White & Kraft tag sheets; Bashful Blue, Basic Black, Creamy Caramel, Old Olive, Pixie Pink, and Summer Sun Classic Stampin' Pads; Light Blue gingham ribbon; watercolor brush; crochet thread

[89 B] Swell News set; Barely Banana and Mellow Moss card stock; Confetti White & Kraft tag sheets; Blush Blossom, Old Olive, Pixie Pink, and Yoyo Yellow Classic Stampin' Pads; Basic Brown Classic Stampin' Pad; Cream grosgrain ribbon; Soft Subtles I eyelets; Stampin' Dimensionals; Crafters' Tool Kit; watercolor brush; crochet thread; safety pin

[89 C] Maternal Instincts set; Confetti White and Mellow Moss card stock; Always Artichoke and Basic Black Classic Stampin' Pads; Watercolor pencils; Subtles mulberry paper; Gold cord

[90 A] Bubble Queen set; Certainly Celery, Confetti White, Pink Passion, and So Saffron card stock; Basic Black, Blush Blossom, More Mustard, Old Olive, and So Saffron Classic Stampin' Pads; Basic Black Stampin' Write marker; Cream grosgrain ribbon; Stampin' Dimensionals; 1/8" Circle punch; crimper

[90 B] Cool Cat set; Cool wheel; Certainly Celery, Pink Passion, So Saffron, and Whisper White card stock; Basic Black Craft Stampin' Pad; Pink Passion and So Saffron Classic Stampin' Pads; Basic Black and Pink Passion Stampin' Write markers; Vintage brads; Stampin' Dimensionals; Crafters' Tool Kit

[90 C] Cool Cat and All-Year Cheer I sets; Orchid Opulence and Whisper White card stock; Basic Black, Orchid Opulence, and Pink Passion Classic Stampin' Pads; Celery grosgrain ribbon; Double Circle and 1-3/8" Circle punches

[90 D] Cool Cat and Pure & Simple Alphabet Lower sets; Certainly Celery, Orchid Opulence, Pink Passion, and So Saffron card stock; Certainly Celery, Pink Passion, and So Saffron Classic Stampin' Pads; VersaMark pad; linen thread; Light Orchid grosgrain ribbon; Stampin' Dimensionals; 1/8" Circle punch; Crystal Clear Stampin' Emboss powder; sewing machine and thread; stipple brush

[91 A] Do the Hula and Everyday Flexible Phrases sets; Certainly Celery, Orchid Opulence, Pink Passion, and Whisper White card stock; Confetti White & Kraft tag sheets; Basic Black, Certainly Celery, Creamy Caramel, More Mustard, Orchid Opulence, and Pink Passion Classic Stampin' Pads; twill tape; linen thread; Vintage brads; Light Pink gingham ribbon; Stampin' Dimensionals

[91 B] Just Beakause set; Island wheel; Confetti White, Certainly Celery, Orchid Opulence, and So Saffron card stock; Basic Black and So Saffron Classic Stampin' Pads; Basic Black, Certainly Celery, Orchid Opulence, and So Saffron Stampin' Write markers; Orchid Opulence Stampin' Around cartridge; linen thread; Stampin' Dimensionals; 1/16" Circle punch; watercolor brush

[92 A] Computer Quips set; Ballet Blue, Confetti White, Mellow Moss, and Real Red card stock; Ballet Blue, Basic Black, Lovely Lilac, Mellow Moss, Only Orange, and Real Red Classic Stampin' Pads; Stampin' Dimensionals; Aqua Painter; sewing machine and thread

[92 B] Love Ya Bunches set; By Definition background stamp; Ballet Blue, Confetti White, Lovely Lilac, and Real Red card stock; Basic Black, Ballet Blue, Lovely Lilac, Mellow Moss, Ruby Red, and Yoyo Yellow Classic Stampin' Pads; Basic Black, Mellow Moss, and Real Red Stampin' Write markers; Bold Brights I eyelets; linen thread; 1/16" and 1/2" Circle punches; Crafters' Tool Kit

[93 A] Celebrate in Style set; Confetti White, Lovely Lilac, Mellow Moss, and Real Red card stock; Ballet Blue, Basic Black, Close to Cocoa, Creamy Caramel, Lovely Lilac, Mellow Moss, and Real Red Classic Stampin' Pads; linen thread; Pewter Hodgepodge Hardware; Crafters' Tool Kit

[93 B] Going Out in Style set; Millinery wheel; Confetti White, Lovely Lilac, and Real Red card stock; Ballet Blue, Basic Black, Blush Blossom, Lovely Lilac, Mellow Moss, Real Red, and Yoyo Yellow Classic Stampin' Pads; Lovely Lilac Jumbo Stampin' Around cartridge; Brights beads; Vintage brad; Stampin' Dimensionals; watercolor brush

[94 A] A Good Sign, Everyday Flexible Phrases, and Wonderful Weaves sets; Word by Word background stamp; Chocolate Chip, Confetti White, Kraft, and Ruby Red card stock; Chocolate Chip, Creamy Caramel, and Ruby Red Classic Stampin' Pads; Earth Elements Mini Gable boxes and tags; Chocolate grosgrain ribbon; Natural hemp twine; Stampin' Dimensionals; sponge daubers

[94 B] I Like Your Style set; Always Artichoke, Brocade Blue, Confetti White, and Ruby Red card stock; Always Artichoke, Brocade Blue, and Real Red Classic Stampin' Pads; Bluebird grosgrain ribbon; Silver eyelets; Stampin' Dimensionals; Slit punch; Crafters' Tool Kit

[95 A] Best of Cluck set; Chocolate Chip, Ruby Red, and Whisper White card stock; Weathered Timeworn Collection paper; Basic Black, Chocolate Chip, Creamy Caramel, More Mustard, and Ruby Red Classic Stampin' Pads; Natural hemp twine; Stampin' Dimensionals; watercolor brush

[95 B] Best of Cluck and Wonderful Weaves sets; Always Artichoke, Chocolate Chip, Confetti White, and Kraft card stock; Always Artichoke and Chocolate Chip Classic Stampin' Pads; Stampin' Pastels; twill tape; Aged Copper Hodgepodge Hardware; Stampin' Dimensionals

[95 C] Right at Home set; Canvas background stamp; Always Artichoke, Brocade Blue, Chocolate Chip, Confetti White, and Kraft card stock; Always Artichoke, Basic Black, Brocade Blue, Chocolate Chip, Going Gray, and More Mustard Classic Stampin' Pads; Pewter Hodgepodge Hardware; linen thread; Stampin' Dimensionals; 1/16" Circle punch; watercolor brush

[96 A] A Little Love set; Naturals Ivory, Pumpkin Pie, and Sahara Sand card stock; Sahara Sand Classic Stampin' Pad; Basic Black, Mellow Moss, More Mustard, and Pumpkin Pie Stampin' Write markers; Neutrals Fancy Fibers; Basic eyelets; Crafters' Tool Kit; Aqua Painter

[96 B] Wanda's Wit & Wisdom set; Always Artichoke, Naturals Ivory, Pumpkin Pie, and So Saffron card stock; Basic Black Classic Stampin' Pad; Stampin' Pastels; Soft Subtles eyelets; Black gingham ribbon; Crafters' Tool Kit; 1/2" Circle punch

[96 C] Wanda's Wit & Wisdom set; Crosshatch background stamp; Always Artichoke, Naturals Ivory, Pumpkin Pie, and So Saffron card stock; Always Artichoke and Basic Black Classic Stampin' Pads;; Stampin' Pastels; Natural hemp twine; Earth Elements buttons; sanding blocks

[97 A] Words by Wilson set; Always Artichoke, Naturals Ivory, Pumpkin Pie, and Sahara Sand card stock; Always Artichoke, Basic Black, Going Gray, and Pumpkin Pie Classic Stampin' Pads; linen thread; Basic eyelets; Crafters' Tool Kit; watercolor brush

[97 B] Words by Wilson set; Always Artichoke, Confetti Cream, Pumpkin Pie, and So Saffron card stock; Always Artichoke, Basic Black, Pumpkin Pie, Sahara Sand, and So Saffron Classic Stampin' Pads; Natural hemp twine; Vintage brads; 1/8" Circle punch; watercolor brush

[97 C] Espress Yourself set; Always Artichoke, Naturals Ivory, Pumpkin Pie, and So Saffron card stock; Always Artichoke, More Mustard, and Pumpkin Pie Classic Stampin' Pads; Natural hemp twine; Vintage brads; twill tape; Stampin' Dimensionals

[98 A] Oh So Sweet set; Chocolate Chips wheel; Chocolate Chip, Kraft, Old Olive, Ruby Red, and Very Vanilla card stock; Chocolate Chip, Old Olive, and Ruby Red Stampin' Write markers; Chocolate Chip Stampin' Around cartridge; Natural hemp twine; 1/8" Circle punch; 1-1/4", and 1-3/8" Square punches

[98 B] Oh So Sweet set; Chocolate Chip and Very Vanilla card stock; Earth Elements Pillar boxes & tags; Ruby Red Classic Stampin' Pad; Chocolate Chip, Old Olive, and Ruby Red Stampin' Write markers; Chocolate grosgrain ribbon; Stampin' Dimensionals; 1/2" and 1/8" Circle punches

[98 C] Jazzed Up set; Jazz wheel; Brocade Blue, Chocolate Chip, Old Olive, and Really Rust card stock; Brocade Blue and Old Olive Classic Stampin' Pads; Brocade Blue Stampin' Around cartridge; Chocolate grosgrain ribbon; linen thread; Stainless Steel Metal Magic tags, Assortment 1; Stampin' Dimensionals; Slit punch; sewing machine and thread

[99 A] What's for Dinner and Classic Alphabet sets; Confetti White, Old Olive, and Ruby Red card stock; Chocolate Chip, More Mustard, Old Olive, Pumpkin Pie, and Ruby Red Classic Stampin' Pads; Vintage brads; linen thread; Stampin' Dimensionals; 1/2" Circle punch; watercolor brush

[99 B] Under the Weather set; Chocolate Chip, Ruby Red, and Very Vanilla card stock; Chocolate Chip and Ruby Red Classic Stampin' Pads; Brocade Blue, Chocolate Chip, and Ruby Red Stampin' Write markers; French Blue grosgrain ribbon; Metallic Wire Works; Stampin' Dimensionals; 1/16" Circle punch; sewing machine and thread

[100 A] Frolicking Frogs and Expressive Flexible Phrases sets; Kraft, Old Olive, Ruby Red, and Very Vanilla card stock; Always Artichoke, Basic Black, Chocolate Chip, Old Olive, and Ruby Red Classic Stampin' Pads; Creamy Caramel Classic refill; Earth Elements eyelets; Black gingham ribbon; Crafters' Tool Kit; watercolor brush

[100 B] Frolicking Frogs and All-Year Cheer II sets; Always Artichoke, Confetti Cream, Kraft, Old Olive, and Ruby Red card stock; Always Artichoke, Bashful Blue, Basic Black, Ruby Red, and So Saffron Classic Stampin' Pads; Vintage brads; Spring Moss grosgrain ribbon; twill tape; linen thread; Stampin' Dimensionals; 1/8" and 1/16" Circle punches

[100 C] All the Best, Quick Thinking, It's a Date, and Stencil Alphabet sets; Chocolate Chip, Kraft, Naturals Ivory, Old Olive, Ruby Red, and Very Vanilla card stock; Chocolate Chip, Old Olive, and Ruby Red Craft Stampin' Pads; Basic Black Stampin' Write marker; twill tape; linen thread; Aged Copper Hodgepodge Hardware; 1/16" and 1/4" Circle punches

[101 A] Say Something Mice set; Linograph background stamp; Chocolate Chip, Confetti Cream, Kraft, Old Olive, and Ruby Red card stock; Always Artichoke, Basic Black, Chocolate Chip, Going Gray, and Ruby Red Classic Stampin' Pads; Earth Elements eyelets; twill tape; Aged Copper Hodgepodge Hardware; Crafters' Tool Kit; watercolor brush

[101 B] Say Something Mice and Expressive Flexible Phrases sets; Floral background stamp; Certainly Celery, Ruby Red, and Very Vanilla card stock; Always Artichoke, Basic Black, Certainly Celery, Going Gray, Ruby Red, and So Saffron Classic Stampin' Pads; Bold Brights buttons; linen thread; White Square Aluminum Metal Edge tags; Celery grosgrain ribbon; 1/16" Circle punch; watercolor brush; Crafters' Tool Kit

[101 C] All Natural set; Chocolate Chip, Kraft, Naturals Ivory, Old Olive, and Very Vanilla card stock; Confetti White & Kraft tag sheets; Basic Black, Certainly Celery, Old Olive, and Ruby Red Classic Stampin' Pads; twill tape; linen thread; Earth Elements buttons; Aged Copper Hodgepodge Hardware; stipple brush; watercolor brush

[102 A] Wisecracks and Fresh Fillers sets; Brilliant Blue, Confetti White, Old Olive, and Rose Red card stock; Basic Black, Blush Blossom, Brilliant Blue, Chocolate Chip, More Mustard, Old Olive, Regal Rose, and Rose Red Classic Stampin' Pads; Earth Elements buttons; linen thread; Stampin' Dimensionals; watercolor brush

[102 B] Paris in the Spring and Everyday Flexible Phrases sets; Springtime wheel; Brilliant Blue, Confetti White, Old Olive, and Rose Red card stock; Old Olive Classic Stampin' Pad; Brilliant Blue, Going Gray, More Mustard, Old Olive, and Ruby Red Stampin' Write markers; Natural hemp twine; Silver brads; Stainless Steel Metal Magic tags, Assortment 1; Stampin' Dimensionals; 1/16" Circle punch; blender pen; sewing machine and thread

[103 A] Favorite Friends and Tidy Alphabet sets; Going Gray, More Mustard, Old Olive, and Rose Red card stock; Confetti White & Kraft tag sheets; Always Artichoke, Basic Black, Creamy Caramel, Going Gray, More Mustard, and Rose Red Classic Stampin' Pads; Black gingham ribbon; linen thread; 1/8" Circle punch; watercolor brush; stapler

[103 B] And Everything Nice set; Confetti White, More Mustard, and Old Olive card stock; Basic Black, Blush Blossom, Creamy Caramel, Old Olive, Pink Passion, and Summer Sun Classic Stampin' Pads; More Mustard Stampin' Write marker; Silver brads; Mustard grosgrain ribbon; Ivory 3/8" organdy ribbon; Stampin' Dimensionals; watercolor brush

[104 A] Please Be Seated set; Linograph background stamp; Bordering Blue, Naturals White, and Ruby Red card stock; watercolor paper; Always Artichoke, Basic Black, Bordering Blue, and Ruby Red Classic Stampin' Pads; Jet Black StazOn pad; Pewter Hodgepodge Hardware; linen thread; Crafters' Tool Kit; watercolor brush

[104 B] Please Be Seated and Newsprint Alphabet sets; Print Pattern background stamp; Ruby Red and Very Vanilla card stock; Confetti White & Kraft Mini Gable boxes & tags; Basic Black and Ruby Red Classic Stampin' Pads; Vintage brads; linen thread; 1/16" Circle punch; watercolor brush

[104 C] Sweet of You set; Bordering Blue, Ruby Red, Barely Banana, and Confetti Cream card stock; Barely Banana, Bordering Blue, Old Olive, and Ruby Red Classic Stampin' Pads; Jet Black StazOn pad; White Square Aluminum Metal Edge tags; Cream grosgrain ribbon; Stampin' Dimensionals; watercolor brush

[104 D] Sweet of You and All-Year Cheer II sets; Basic Black, Mellow Moss, Ruby Red, and Very Vanilla card stock; Whisper White & Very Vanilla tag sheets; Always Artichoke, Bordering Blue, Creamy Caramel, Mellow Moss, and Ruby Red Classic Stampin' Pads; Jet Black StazOn pad; VersaMark pad; Crystal Clear Stampin' Embossing powder; Vintage brads; Black gingham ribbon; watercolor brush; brayer

[105 A] Farm Fever and Quick Thinking sets; Print Pattern background stamp; Bordering Blue, Mellow Moss, Ruby Red, and Very Vanilla card stock; Bordering Blue, Close to Cocoa, Mellow Moss, More Mustard, Pretty in Pink, and Ruby Red Classic Stampin' Pads; Jet Black StazOn pad; Spring Moss grosgrain ribbon; Moss gingham ribbon; Silver brads; 1/8" and 1/2" Circle punches; Aqua Painter; staples

[105 B] Sweet Songbirds and Expressive Flexible Phrases; Barely Banana, Basic Black, Bordering Blue, Kraft, Naturals Ivory, and Ruby Red card stock; Barely Banana, Bordering Blue, and Ruby Red Classic Stampin' Pads; Jet Black StazOn pad; Black gingham ribbon; watercolor brush

[106 A] All God's Children and Beyond the Basics sets; Barely Banana, Cameo Coral, and Certainly Celery card stock; Cameo Coral, Certainly Celery, Creamy Caramel, Close to Cocoa, and Summer Sun Classic Stampin' Pads; Jet Black StazOn pad; Natural hemp twine; linen thread; White Square Brass Metal Edge tags; Neutrals buttons; Stampin' Dimensionals; watercolor brush; sponge

[106 B] All God's Children set; Blush Blossom, Certainly Celery, Chocolate Chip, and Confetti White card stock; Basic Black, Certainly Celery, More Mustard, Regal Rose, and Summer Sun Classic Stampin' Pads; Natural hemp twine; Crafters' Tool Kit; 1-1/4" Square punch; 1/16" and 1/2" Circle punches; watercolor brush

[106 C] Symbols of Salvation set; Barely Banana and Chocolate Chip card stock; VersaMark pad; Gold Glory Stampin' Emboss powder; Stampin' Pastels; Gold cord; Basic eyelets; Crafters' Tool Kit; sponge daubers

[106 D] Symbols of Salvation set; Blush Blossom card stock; watercolor paper; Close to Cocoa, Garden Green, Pretty in Pink, Summer Sun, and Tempting Turquoise Classic Stampin' Pads; Timber Brown StazOn pad; White 3/8" organdy ribbon; watercolor brush

[107 A] A New Little Someone and Everyday Flexible Phrases sets; Barely Banana, Blush Blossom, Cameo Coral, Confetti White, and Certainly Celery card stock; Barely Banana, Cameo Coral, and Certainly Celery Classic Stampin' Pads; Jet Black StazOn pad; Soft Subtles I eyelets; Celery grosgrain ribbon; Crafters' Tool Kit; watercolor brush

[107 B] A New Little Someone, Everyday Flexible Phrases, and Simple Type Alphabet sets; Wash Day wheel; Certainly Celery, Chocolate Chip, Confetti White, and So Saffron card stock; Confetti White & Kraft tag sheets; Basic Brown Classic Stampin' Pad; Basic Black Stampin' Around cartridge; Basic Black Stampin' Write journaler; Stampin' Pastels; Neutrals Fancy Fibers; Stampin' Dimensionals; blender pen; stamping sponges; safety pins

[108 A] I'm Here and Letterpress Alphabet sets; Confetti White and Regal Rose card stock; Slumber Party Designer Series vellum; Whisper White & Very Vanilla tag sheets; Basic Black Classic Stampin' Pad; Regal Rose Craft Stampin' Pad; Basic Black Stampin' Write marker; Light Pink grosgrain ribbon; linen thread; Soft Subtles I eyelets; Stampin' Dimensionals; Crafters' Tool Kit; 1/4" Circle punch; staples

[108 B] I'm Here, Classic Alphabet, and Classic Numbers sets; Bashful Blue, Confetti Cream, Kraft, and Very Vanilla card stock; Whisper White & Very Vanilla tag sheets; Bashful Blue and Close to Cocoa Classic Stampin' Pads; Soft Subtles II eyelets; Stampin' Dimensionals; linen thread; Crafters' Tool Kit; 1/4" Circle punch; watercolor brush; sewing machine and thread

[109 A] Buggies & Booties set; Confetti White, Kraft, and Pretty in Pink card stock; White vellum card stock; Close to Cocoa, Going Gray, and Pretty in Pink Classic Stampin' Pads; Jet Black StazOn pad; Light Pink gingham ribbon; Stampin' Dimensionals; 1/8" Circle punch; watercolor brush

[109 B] Baby Firsts and All-Year Cheer II sets; French Script background stamp; Kraft, Pretty in Pink, and Very Vanilla card stock; Bashful Blue, Blush Blossom, and Pretty in Pink Classic Stampin' Pads; Jet Black StazOn pad; French Blue grosgrain ribbon; Light Blue gingham ribbon; linen thread; Basic eyelets; Stampin' Dimensionals; 1/16" Circle punch; Crafters' Tool Kit; watercolor brush

[110 A] Toy Box and It's Your Birthday sets; Bashful Blue, and Certainly Celery card stock; Bashful Blue, Certainly Celery, Going Gray, and More Mustard Classic Stampin' Pads; Jet Black StazOn pad; White Square Aluminum Metal Edge tags; Black gingham ribbon; Natural hemp twine; Stampin' Dimensionals; 1/16" Circle punch; sewing machine and thread; watercolor brush

[110 B] Buttons, Bows & Twinkletoes and Everyday Flexible Phrases sets; Bashful Blue, Confetti White, Pretty in Pink, and Regal Rose card stock; Bashful Blue, Blush Blossom, Garden Green, More Mustard, Pretty in Pink, Rose Red, and Sahara Sand Classic Stampin' Pads; Jet Black StazOn pad; Pink grosgrain ribbon; Stampin' Dimensionals; Rectangle punch; watercolor brush

[110 C] Buttons, Bows & Twinkletoes, Everyday Flexible Phrases, and Tidy Alphabet sets; Certainly Celery, Confetti White, Pretty in Pink, and Regal Rose card stock; Always Artichoke and Rose Red Craft Stampin' Pads; Spring Moss grosgrain ribbon; Stampin' Dimensionals; Write Me a Memory Journaling Fonts CD, Volume II; crochet thread

[111 A] Teacher's Aid set; Pretty in Pink, Regal Rose, and Rose Red card stock; Going Gray, More Mustard, Regal Rose, and Rose Red Classic Stampin' Pads; Jet Black StazOn pad; Silver brads; Silver eyelets; Red hemp twine; Crafters' Tool Kit; watercolor brush

[111 B] Charming Children and It's Your Birthday sets; Bashful Blue, Certainly Celery, Pretty in Pink, and Regal Rose card stock; Confetti White & Kraft tag sheets; Certainly Celery, Close to Cocoa, Creamy Caramel, and Pretty in Pink Classic Stampin' Pads; Timber Brown StazOn pad; Soft Subtles I eyelets; Celery grosgrain ribbon; Stampin' Dimensionals; Crafters' Tool Kit; 1-1/4" Square punch

[111 C] Charming Children and Words of Wisdom sets; Bashful Blue, Certainly Celery, and Confetti White card stock; Bashful Blue, Blush Blossom, Certainly Celery, Close to Cocoa, More Mustard, and Pretty in Pink Classic Stampin' Pads; Jet Black StazOn pad; Natural hemp twine; Soft Subtles II eyelets; Crafters' Tool Kit; 1-1/4" Circle punch; watercolor brush

[112 A] Travel Time and All-Year Cheer II sets; Apricot Appeal, Bashful Blue, Certainly Celery, Lovely Lilac, and Whisper White card stock; Basic Black Classic Stampin' Pad; Watercolor pencils; White eyelets; Natural hemp twine; Crafters' Took Kit; 1/8" Circle punch; crimper; blender pen

[112 B] Travel Time and Whimsical Alphabet Upper and Lower sets; Apricot Appeal, Basic Black, Certainly Celery, Lovely Lilac, and Whisper White card stock; Basic Black Craft Stampin' Pad; Basic Black Stampin' Write journaler; Watercolor pencils; Vintage brads; Stampin' Dimensionals; blender pen

[113 A] Time for Fun, Everyday Flexible Phrases, Phrase Starters II, and Simple Type Numbers sets; Carnival jumbo wheel; Apricot Appeal, Bashful Blue, Certainly Celery, Lovely Lilac, and Whisper White card stock; Basic Black and Lovely Lilac Craft Stampin Pads; Lovely Lilac Stampin' Around jumbo cartridge; Basic Black Stampin' Write journaler; Watercolor pencils; Stampin' Dimensionals; crochet thread; 1/16" Circle punch; blender pen

[113 B] At the Races and It's Your Birthday sets; Making Tracks wheel; Bashful Blue, Basic Black, Certainly Celery, and Whisper White card stock; Apricot Appeal, Bashful Blue, Basic Black, and Certainly Celery Classic Stampin' Pads; Certainly Celery Stampin' Around cartridge; Vintage brads; Natural hemp twine; Stampin' Dimensionals; 1/16" Circle punch; Aqua Painter

[114 A] Girlfriends set; Cameo Coral, Certainly Celery, Confetti White, and Tempting Turquoise card stock; Basic Black, Blush Blossom, Cameo Coral, Creamy Caramel, and Tempting Turquoise Classic Stampin' Pads; Silver brads; Natural hemp twine; Stampin' Dimensionals; watercolor brush; 1/16" Circle punch

[114 B] Girlfriends and Everyday Flexible Phrases sets; Cameo Coral, Certainly Celery, Confetti White, and Tempting Turquoise card stock; Tempting Turquoise Craft Stampin' Pad; Cameo Coral, Certainly Celery, and Tempting Turquoise Stampin' Write markers; Basic Black Stampin' Write journaler; Natural hemp twine; Stampin' Dimensionals; 1/16" Circle punch; watercolor brush

[114 C] Girlfriend Accessories set; Certainly Celery, Confetti White, and Regal Rose card stock; White vellum; Barely Banana, Basic Black, Certainly Celery, and Regal Rose Classic Stampin' Pads; Certainly Celery Stampin' Write marker; watercolor brush; Cream grosgrain ribbon; staple

[115 A] Lively Little Ones and Tiny Talk sets; Cameo Coral, Certainly Celery, and Tempting Turquoise card stock; Basic Black, Blush Blossom, Cameo Coral, Certainly Celery, Close to Cocoa, More Mustard, Summer Sun, and Tempting Turquoise Classic Stampin' Pads; Turquoise grosgrain ribbon; Stampin' Dimensionals; Crafters' Tool Kit; watercolor brush; sewing machine and thread

[115 B] En Pointe set; Cameo Coral, Certainly Celery, and Confetti White card stock; watercolor paper; Basic Black, Blush Blossom, Cameo Coral, Certainly Celery, and Creamy Caramel Classic Stampin' Pads; Celery grosgrain ribbon; Stampin' Dimensionals; watercolor brush

[116 A] All Wrapped Up, Everyday Flexible Phrases, and Simple Sayings II sets; Night of Navy, Old Olive, and Very Vanilla card stock; Night of Navy and Old Olive Classic Stampin' Pads; Rich Regals eyelets; Natural hemp twine; linen thread; Stampin' Dimensionals; Crafters' Tool Kit; 1/16" Circle punch; crochet thread; stipple brush; crimper

[116 B] All Wrapped Up, All Wrapped Up Accessories, and Season's Greetings sets; Night of Navy, Old Olive, Ruby Red, and Very Vanilla card stock; Night of Navy, Old Olive, and Ruby Red Classic Stampin' Pads; linen thread; Navy grosgrain ribbon; Stampin' Dimensionals

[116 C] Totally Cool set; Night of Navy, Old Olive, and Very Vanilla card stock; Night of Navy and Old Olive Classic Stampin' Pads; Navy grosgrain ribbon; Stampin' Dimensionals

[117 A] Pocket Fun set; Just Jeans background stamp; Night of Navy, Old Olive, and Very Vanilla card stock; Night of Navy and Old Olive Classic Stampin' Pads; Night of Navy and Old Olive Stampin' Write journalers; Vintage brads; Navy grosgrain ribbon; twill tape; Stampin' Dimensionals; Small Corner Rounder, 1/8", and 1/16" Circle punches; crimper

[117 B] Treat Yourself set; Night of Navy, Old Olive, Ruby Red, and Very Vanilla card stock; Old Olive Classic Stampin' Pad; More Mustard, Night of Navy, Old Olive, and Ruby Red Stampin' Write markers; Natural hemp twine; Rich Regals eyelets; Stampin' Dimensionals; 1/16" Circle punch; Crafters' Tool Kit

[117 C] Treat Yourself set; Night of Navy, Ruby Red, and Very Vanilla card stock; Night of Navy, Old Olive, and Ruby Red Classic Stampin' Pads; Earth Elements eyelets; Red grosgrain ribbon; Stampin' Dimensionals; Crafters' Tool Kit

[118 A] Sporting Goods, Expressive Flexible Phrases, Stencil Alphabet, and Stencil Numbers sets; Handsome Hunter, Kraft, Night of Navy, Really Rust and Whisper White card stock; Basic Black, Handsome Hunter, and Really Rust Craft Stampin' Pads; Jet Black StazOn pad; Silver brads; Write Me a Memory Journaling Fonts CD, Volume II; window sheets; watercolor brush; staple

[118 B] Sporting Goods and Everyday Flexible Phrases sets; Sports Fan wheel; Canvas background stamp; Handsome Hunter, Kraft, Really Rust, and Whisper White card stock; Basic Black, Creamy Caramel, Night of Navy, and Really Rust Classic Stampin' Pads; Silver eyelets; Silver brads; White Square Aluminum Metal Edge tags; Stampin' Dimensionals; Crafters' Tool Kit

[119 A] Good Sport and Pure & Simple Type Alphabet Upper sets; Handsome Hunter, Kraft, Night of Navy, and Whisper White card stock; Pockets & Pieces, Assortment 2; White vellum card stock; Creamy Caramel, Going Gray, and Night of Navy Craft Stampin' Pads; Silver eyelets; Natural hemp twine; Navy grosgrain ribbon; Write Me a Memory Journaling Fonts CD, Volume 1; Stampin' Dimensionals; Crafters' Tool Kit

[119 B] Power Up and It's Your Birthday sets; Builder Bits wheel; Confetti White, Handsome Hunter, Night of Navy, and Really Rust card stock; Confetti White & Kraft tag sheets; Stainless Steel Metal Magic tags, Assortment 1; Basic Black, Creamy Caramel, Going Gray, Handsome Hunter, and Night of Navy Classic Stampin' Pads; Really Rust Stampin' Around cartridge; Navy grosgrain ribbon; linen thread; 1/8" Circle punch; Stampin' Dimensionals

[120 A] It's a Cheer Thing set; More Mustard, Naturals Ivory, Night of Navy, and Old Olive card stock; Basic Black, Blush Blossom, More Mustard, Night of Navy, and Old Olive Classic Stampin' Pads; Mustard and Navy grosgrain ribbon; Black gingham ribbon; Stampin' Dimensionals; 1/8" Circle punch

[120 B] Crayon Kids and Expressive Flexible Phrases sets; Kraft, More Mustard, Old Olive, and Very Vanilla card stock; White Squares Aluminum Metal Edge tags; Creamy Caramel, More Mustard, and Old Olive Classic Stampin' Pads; Red grosgrain ribbon; Stampin' Dimensionals; Wire Works; Slit punch; 1/16" and 1/8" Circle punches; sewing machine and thread

[121 A] Love without End set; Kraft, More Mustard, Night of Navy, Old Olive, Ruby Red, and Very Vanilla card stock; More Mustard, Night of Navy, Old Olive, and Ruby Red Stampin' Write markers; Natural hemp twine; 1/16" Circle punch

[121 B] Love without End set; Kraft and Old Olive card stock; Night of Navy, Old Olive, and Ruby Red Classic Stampin' Pads; Navy 3/8" organdy ribbon; Natural hemp twine; Stainless Steel Metal Magic tags, Assortment 1; Stampin' Dimensionals; 1/2" Circle punch

[121 C] Petal Pushers set; More Mustard, Ruby Red, and Very Vanilla card stock; White vellum card stock; More Mustard, Old Olive, and Ruby Red Classic Stampin' Pads; Mustard grosgrain ribbon; Pewter Hodgepodge Hardware; Stampin' Dimensionals; crimper

[121 D] Petal Pushers set; Linograph background stamp; Kraft, More Mustard, Night of Navy, Old Olive, and Very Vanilla card stock; More Mustard, Night of Navy, Old Olive, and Ruby Red Classic Stampin' Pads; Very Vanilla Craft Stampin' Pad; Natural hemp twine; Vintage brads; Navy grosgrain ribbon; Stampin' Dimensionals; Crafters' Tool Kit

[122 A] Gladsome Garden and All-Year Cheer I sets; Confetti White, Pink Passion, and Real Red card stock; Green Galore, Only Orange, and Real Red Classic Stampin' Pads; VersaMark pad; Winter White Stampin' Emboss powder; Silver brads; Natural Magic Mesh; Stampin' Dimensionals; Crafters' Tool Kit; watercolor brush

[122 B] Gladsome Garden and Everyday Flexible Phrases sets; Confetti White and Only Orange card stock; Confetti White & Kraft Bloomin' boxes & tags; Sassy Designer Series paper; Green Galore and Pink Passion Classic Stampin' Pads; Vintage brads; Apple Green grosgrain ribbon; Stampin' Dimensionals; watercolor brush

[123 A] Buds & Blossoms, Everyday Flexible Phrases, and Pure & Simple Alphabet sets; Green Galore, Pink Passion, and Whisper White card stock; Sassy Designer Series paper; Green Galore, Only Orange, and Pink Passion Classic Stampin' Pads; Bold Brights II eyelets; White Square Aluminum Metal Edge tags; Apple Green grosgrain ribbon; linen thread; Stampin' Dimensionals; Crafters' Tool Kit; watercolor brush

[123 B] Buds & Blossoms and Tidy Alphabet sets; Bold Blooms jumbo wheel; Confetti White, Green Galore, Only Orange, and Pink Passion card stock; Green Galore, Only Orange, Pink Passion, and Real Red Craft Stampin' Pads; Whisper White Stampin' Around cartridge; Basic Black Stampin' Write journaler; Stampin' Dimensionals; 1/16" Circle punch; Crafters' Tool Kit

[124 A] Bloomin' Wonderful, Alphabits, and Headline Alphabet sets; Confetti White, More Mustard, Night of Navy, Old Olive, Ruby Red card stock; Pockets & Pieces boxes & tags, Assortment 2; Confetti White & Kraft tag sheets; More Mustard, Night of Navy, Old Olive, and Ruby Red Craft Stampin' Pads; Basic Black Stampin' Write marker; Night of Navy Stampin' Write journaler; Natural Magic Mesh; linen thread; Red gingham ribbon; Stampin' Dimensionals; staple; brayer

[124 B] Bloomin' Wonderful and Cheery Chat sets; Whirly Twirly wheel; Confetti White, Kraft, Night of Navy, and Old Olive card stock; More Mustard and Ruby Red Craft Stampin' Pads; Creamy Caramel Classic Stampin' Pad; Old Olive Stampin' Around cartridge; Natural hemp twine; Stampin' Dimensionals; Word Window and 1/8" Circle punches

[125 A] All I Have Seen set; Fine Lace background stamp; Confetti White, More Mustard, Night of Navy, and Ruby Red card stock; Chocolate Chip, More Mustard, and Old Olive Classic Stampin' Pads; Ruby Red Stampin' Write marker; Antique Brass Hodgepodge Hardware; twill tape; Slit punch

[125 B] Heartfelt Thanks and Expressive Flexible Phrases sets; Watercolor Joy wheel; Confetti White, More Mustard, Night of Navy, Old Olive, and Ruby Red card stock; More Mustard and Night of Navy Classic Stampin' pads; Old Olive and Ruby Red Stampin' Write markers; Ruby Red Stampin' Around cartridge; linen thread; Stampin' Dimensionals; watercolor brush; 1/16" Circle punch; sewing machine and thread

[126 A] Daisy, Wonderful Words II, and Stencil Alphabet sets; Gable Green, Night of Navy, Rose Red, So Saffron, and Very Vanilla card stock; Gable Green, Night of Navy, Rose Red, and So Saffron Craft Stampin' Pads; Night of Navy Stampin' Write journaler; Write Me a Memory Journaling Fonts CD, Volume II; Navy grosgrain ribbon; Stampin' Dimensionals; sewing machine and thread

[126 B] Daisy and Everyday Flexible Phrases sets; Whisper White & Very Vanilla Petal boxes & tags; Barely Banana and Night of Navy Classic Stampin' Pads; VersaMark pad; Soft Subtles I eyelets; Ivory 3/8" organdy ribbon; Crystal Clear Stampin' Emboss powder; stamping sponges; Crafters' Tool Kit

[126 C] Watercolor Minis and Wonderful Words II sets; Rose Red and Very Vanilla card stock; White vellum paper; Basic Black, Green Galore, Night of Navy, Rose Red, and Summer Sun Classic Stampin' Pads; Cream grosgrain ribbon; Ivory 3/8" organdy ribbon; Double Circle punch

[127 A] Petal Prints, Alphabits, and Newsprint Alphabet sets; Pocket & Pieces, Assortment 1; Rich Regals and Whisper White & Vanilla tag sheets; Night of Navy and Rose Red Classic Stampin Pads; linen thread; Neutrals Fancy Fibers; 1/4" Circle punch

[127 B] Petal Prints and All-Year Cheer III sets; Barely Banana, Night of Navy, Rose Red, and Very Vanilla card stock; Apricot Appeal, Green Galore, Night of Navy, and Rose Red Classic Stampin' Pads; Apricot grosgrain ribbon; Stampin' Dimensionals; watercolor brush

[128 A] Stipple Rose and Sincere Salutations sets; Elegant Eggplant and Naturals Ivory card stock; Regals mulberry paper; Basic Black, Certainly Celery, and Elegant Eggplant Classic Stampin' Pads; Very Vanilla Craft Stampin' Pad; VersaMark pad; Ivory 3/8" organdy ribbon; 1/8" Circle punch; watercolor brush

[128 B] Burst into Bloom and Everyday Flexible Phrases sets; Apricot Appeal and Certainly Celery card stock; Whisper White & Very Vanilla tag sheets; Apricot Appeal, Certainly Celery, and Pumpkin Pie Classic Stampin' Pads; Celery grosgrain ribbon; Bold Brights II eyelets; Brights beads; 1/2" Circle punch; Crafters' Tool Kit

[128 C] Perfect Petals and Wonderful Words sets; Apricot Appeal, Elegant Eggplant, and Naturals Ivory card stock; Certainly Celery, Elegant Eggplant, and Pumpkin Pie Classic Stampin' Pads; Copper cord; Vintage brads; Stampin' Dimensionals; watercolor brush

[129 A] Roses in Winter set; Apricot Appeal, Certainly Celery, and Naturals Ivory card stock; Apricot Appeal, Elegant Eggplant, Old Olive, and Pumpkin Pie Classic Stampin' Pads; Celery grosgrain ribbon

[129 B] Flower Garden and Label Classics sets; Floral background stamp; Certainly Celery and Naturals Ivory card stock; Basic Black and Certainly Celery Craft Stampin' Pads; Celery 7/8" organdy ribbon; Stampin' Dimensionals; Watercolor pencils; watercolor brush

[130 A] Simple Florals, Much Appreciated, and Wonderful Weaves sets; Mellow Moss, Naturals Ivory, and Not Quite Navy card stock; Basic Black, Close to Cocoa, Creamy Caramel, Not Quite Navy, and Summer Sun Classic Stampin' Pads; Soft Subtles buttons; linen thread; 1/16" Circle punch; watercolor brush; sanding blocks

[130 B] In Full Bloom and Everyday Flexible Phrases sets; Bloomin' wheel; Always Artichoke, More Mustard, and Naturals Ivory card stock; Always Artichoke, Basic Black, More Mustard, and Not Quite Navy Classic Stampin' Pads; Squares eyelets; Earths Fancy Fibers; Stampin' Dimensionals; Crafters' Tool Kit; watercolor brush

[131 A] Delicate Dandelions set; Always Artichoke, Naturals Ivory, and So Saffron card stock; Always Artichoke, Basic Black, Going Gray, Summer Sun, and Yoyo Yellow Classic Stampin' Pads; Ivory 3/8" organdy ribbon; Stampin' Dimensionals; watercolor brush

[131 B] Delicate Dandelions set; Cheesecloth background stamp; Always Artichoke, Naturals Ivory, and Not Quite Navy card stock; White vellum card stock; Always Artichoke and Not Quite Navy Classic Stampin' Pads; Not Quite Navy Craft Stampin' Pad; Moss gingham ribbon; Aged Copper Hodgepodge Hardware

[131 C] Terrific Tulips and Sincere Salutations sets; Fine Lace background stamp; More Mustard, So Saffron, and Very Vanilla card stock; Earths mulberry paper; Mellow Moss, More Mustard, and So Saffron Classic Stampin' Pads; Mustard grosgrain ribbon; Stampin' Dimensionals

[132 A] Delightful Doodles and Everyday Flexible Phrases sets; By Definition background stamp; Bashful Blue, Certainly Celery, Confetti White, and Regal Rose card stock; Regal Rose Classic Stampin' Pad; Bashful Blue, Certainly Celery, and Regal Rose Stampin' Write markers; linen thread; window sheets; Soft Subtles buttons; Stampin' Dimensionals; 1/2" Circle punch; sewing machine and thread

[132 B] Fresh Flowers and Everyday Flexible Phrases; Blossoms & Bugs wheel; Bashful Blue, Certainly Celery, and Confetti White card stock; White vellum card stock; Bashful Blue, Certainly Celery, and Regal Rose Classic Stampin' Pads; Certainly Celery Stampin' Around cartridge; Soft Subtles button; Light Blue gingham ribbon; linen thread; Stampin' Dimensionals; sanding blocks

[133 A] Friends Are Like Flowers set; Bashful Blue, Certainly Celery, and Confetti White card stock; Apricot Appeal, Basic Black, Brocade Blue, Certainly Celery, Pretty in Pink, and Regal Rose Classic Stampin' Pads; linen thread; Apricot grosgrain ribbon; Clear buttons; Stampin' Dimensionals; watercolor brush

[133 B] Build a Blossom, Everyday Flexible Phrases, Classic Alphabet, Newsprint Alphabet, and Pure & Simple Alphabet Lower and Upper sets; Bashful Blue and Regal Rose card stock; White vellum card stock; Pockets & Pieces, Assortment 1; Bashful Blue and Regal Rose Craft Stampin' Pads; Ballet Blue Stampin' Write journaler; Soft Subtles buttons; Soft Subtles II eyelets; Light Blue gingham ribbon; linen thread; Stampin' Dimensionals; Write Me a Memory Journaling Fonts CD, Volume II; Daisy, 1-3/8" Circle, and 1-3/8" Square punches; Crafters' Tool Kit

[134 A] Spring Garden and Much Appreciated sets; Fine Lace background stamp; Confetti White, More Mustard, and Old Olive card stock; Always Artichoke, Bravo Burgundy, Elegant Eggplant, More Mustard, and Old Olive Classic Stampin' Pads; Mustard grosgrain ribbon; Stampin' Dimensionals

[134 B] Spring Garden set; Canvas background stamp; Not Quite Navy and Sahara Sand card stock; Night of Navy, Not Quite Navy, and Old Olive Classic Stampin' Pads; Rich Regals buttons; linen thread; 1/16" and 1-3/8" Circle punches; sanding blocks

[134 C] Watercolor Garden set; Bravo Burgundy and Old Olive card stock; watercolor paper; Bravo Burgundy and Old Olive Classic Stampin' Pads; Watercolor Wonder crayons; Gold cord; Stampin' Dimensionals

[135 A] Gorgeous Grapevine and Sincere Salutations sets; Bravo Burgundy, Confetti White, and Old Olive card stock; Bravo Burgundy and Old Olive Craft Stampin' Pads; Wine 3/8" organdy ribbon; sewing machine and thread

[135 B] Autumn Leaf Prints set; Weathered background stamp; Old Olive and Sahara Sand card stock; watercolor paper; Earths mulberry paper; Bravo Burgundy, More Mustard, Old Olive, and Sahara Sand Classic Stampin' Pads; Timber Brown StazOn pad; Earth Elements eyelets; Natural hemp twine; Crafters' Tool Kit; watercolor brush

[135 C] Autumn Leaf Prints set; Bravo Burgundy and Sahara Sand card stock; Bravo Burgundy Classic Stampin' Pad; Sahara Sand Stampin' Write marker; Top Boss pad; Gold Detail embossing powder; Gold cord; Stampin' Dimensionals; watercolor brush

[136 A] Natural Beauty set; Fine Lace background stamp; Always Artichoke, Mellow Moss, Naturals Ivory, Ruby Red, and Very Vanilla card stock; Always Artichoke, Basic Black, Chocolate Chip, Close to Cocoa, Going Gray, Mellow Moss, and Ruby Red Classic Stampin' Pads; Aged Copper Hodgepodge Hardware; Moss gingham ribbon; Stampin' Dimensionals

[136 B] Ageless Adornment set; Always Artichoke, Chocolate Chip, Kraft, Mellow Moss, Naturals Ivory, Ruby Red card stock; Always Artichoke, Basic Black, Close to Cocoa, and Ruby Red Classic Stampin' Pads; Vintage brads; Stampin' Dimensionals; watercolor brush

[137 A] Sweet & Sassy, Quick Thinking, Classic Alphabet, and Newsprint Alphabet sets; Mellow Moss and Naturals Ivory card stock; Always Artichoke, Certainly Celery, Chocolate Chip, and Ruby Red Craft Stampin' Pads; Moss gingham ribbon; Chocolate grosgrain ribbon; Antique Brass Hodgepodge Hardware; Stampin' Dimensionals

[137 B] Sweet & Sassy and It's Your Birthday sets; Crosshatch background stamp; Mellow Moss, Naturals Ivory, and Ruby Red card stock; Always Artichoke, Basic Black, Mellow Moss, and Ruby Red Classic Stampin' Pads; Antique Brass Hodgepodge Hardware; Black gingham ribbon

[137 C] Close to Nature and Sincere Salutations sets; Always Artichoke, Chocolate Chip, Kraft, Mellow Moss, Naturals Ivory, and Ruby Red card stock; Always Artichoke, Basic Black, Close to Cocoa, and Ruby Red Classic Stampin' Pads; Antique Brass Hodgepodge Hardware; linen thread; 1/16" Circle and1-1/4" Square punches; watercolor brush

[138 A] Wild Fowl and Sincere Salutations sets; Canvas background stamp; Always Artichoke, Naturals Ivory, and So Saffron card stock; Always Artichoke, Bashful Blue, Close to Cocoa, Creamy Caramel, Going Gray, More Mustard, and So Saffron Classic Stampin' Pads; Timber Brown StazOn pad; watercolor brush

[138 B] Wild Fowl and Much Appreciated sets; Weathered background stamp; Always Artichoke, Kraft, So Saffron, and Very Vanilla card stock; Always Artichoke Classic Stampin' Pad; Vintage brads; Earth Tones Fancy Fibers; linen thread; Stampin' Dimensionals; 1/8" Circle punch

[138 C] Fantastic Foliage and Everyday Flexible Phrases sets; Always Artichoke, Kraft, and Naturals Ivory card stock; Always Artichoke, Pumpkin Pie, and So Saffron Classic Stampin' Pads; Always Artichoke Classic refill; Natural hemp twine; Gold eyelets; Crafters' Tool Kit; watercolor brush

[139 A] Drawing on Nature and Wonderful Words II sets; Floral background stamp; Always Artichoke, Naturals Ivory, and So Saffron card stock; Always Artichoke, Basic Black, Bordering Blue, Creamy Caramel, Pumpkin Pie, Ruby Red, Sahara Sand, and So Saffron Classic Stampin' Pads; Ivory 3/8" organdy ribbon; watercolor brush

[139 B] Fresh Fruits, Wonderful Words II, and Alphabits sets; French Script background stamp; Always Artichoke, Confetti White, Kraft, and So Saffron card stock; Always Artichoke, Basic Black, Mellow Moss, More Mustard, Old Olive, and Ruby Red Classic Stampin' Pads; Barely Banana Craft refill; linen thread; Stampin' Dimensionals; stipple brush

[140 B] Pines, Everyday Flexible Phrases, and Pure & Simple Alphabet Upper sets; Chocolate Chip, Handsome Hunter, Kraft, and Ruby Red card stock; Pockets & Pieces, Assortment 1; Whisper White & Very Vanilla tag sheets; Basic Black Craft Stampin' Pad; Black brads; Black gingham ribbon; linen thread; Stampin' Dimensionals; Slit punch; 1/16" and 1/2" Circle punches

[141 A] Lovely As a Tree set; Chocolate Chip and Very Vanilla card stock; Chocolate Chip, Close to Cocoa, Green Galore, and Handsome Hunter Classic Stampin' Pads; Ivory 3/8" organdy ribbon; linen thread; watercolor brush

[141 B] In the Wild and Stencil Alphabet sets; Canvas background stamp; Heart of Africa wheel; Chocolate Chip, Handsome Hunter, Kraft, Ruby Red, and Very Vanilla card stock; Handsome Hunter and Ruby Red Classic Stampin' Pads; Chocolate Chip Classic Stampin' Around cartridge; Vintage brads; Chocolate grosgrain ribbon; Stampin' Dimensionals; 1/16" and 1-1/4" Circle punches

[142 A] Bold Butterfly and Letterpress Alphabet sets; Flitting By jumbo wheel; Certainly Celery, Kraft, Lavender Lace, Regal Rose, So Saffron, and Whisper White card stock; Lavender Lace, Regal Rose, and So Saffron Craft Stampin' Pads; Certainly Celery Stampin' Around cartridge; Basic Black Stampin' Write journaler; Antique Brass Hodgepodge Hardware; Stampin' Dimensionals; sewing machine and thread

[142 B] Bold Butterfly and Expressive Flexible Phrases sets; Certainly Celery and Whisper White card stock; Soft Subtles Pillar boxes & tags; Certainly Celery, Lavender Lace, Regal Rose, and So Saffron Classic Stampin' Pads; Silver eyelets; Rose grosgrain ribbon; Stampin' Dimensionals; Crafters' Tool Kit; sewing machine and thread

[143 A] Ladybug Picnic and Much Appreciated sets; Certainly Celery, Confetti White, Regal Rose, and So Saffron card stock; Basic Black, Certainly Celery, and Real Red Classic Stampin' Pads; Celery grosgrain ribbon; Silver brads; Stampin' Dimensionals; Slit punch; 1/8" Circle punch; watercolor brush

[143 B] Winged Things and Tiny Talk sets; Wings & Things wheel; Certainly Celery, Confetti White, and Lavender Lace card stock; Confetti White & Kraft tag sheets; Barely Banana, Certainly Celery, Lavender Lace, and Regal Rose Classic Stampin' Pads; Jet Black StazOn pad; Certainly Celery Stampin' Around cartridge; linen thread; Rose grosgrain ribbon; Celery wide organdy ribbon; Dazzling Diamonds Stampin' Glitter; Stampin' Dimensionals; watercolor brush; sewing machine and thread; staple

[144 A] Fintastic set; Green Galore, Lovely Lilac, and Tempting Turquoise card stock; watercolor paper; Basic Brown, Blush Blossom, Green Galore, Lovely Lilac, Pixie Pink, Pumpkin Pie, and Tempting Turquoise Classic Stampin' Pads; Turquoise grosgrain ribbon; Stampin' Dimensionals; watercolor brush; 1/8" Circle punch

[144 B] Aquaria and Expressive Flexible Phrases sets; Simple Stripes background stamp; Apricot Appeal, Confetti White, Green Galore, and Lovely Lilac card stock; Basic Black, Green Galore, Lovely Lilac, Only Orange, and Tempting Turquoise Classic Stampin' Pads; Apple Green grosgrain ribbon; Natural hemp twine; linen thread; 1/16" Circle punch; watercolor brush

[144 C] Aquaria and Classic Alphabet sets; Apricot Appeal, Confetti White, Lovely Lilac, and Tempting Turquoise card stock; Apricot Appeal, Lovely Lilac, and Tempting Turquoise Classic Stampin' Pads; Basic Black Stampin' Write journaler; twill tape; Silver brads; Stampin' Dimensionals; 1/16" Circle punch

[145 A] Cute As a Bug set; Geometric background stamp; Apricot Appeal, Confetti White, and Lovely Lilac card stock; Apricot Appeal, Basic Brown, Green Galore, and Lovely Lilac Classic Stampin' Pads; Bold Brights II eyelets; Apple Green grosgrain ribbon; Crafters' Tool Kit; watercolor brush; crochet thread

[145 B] Fishy Friends and Quick Thinking sets; Fishy wheel; Apricot Appeal, Confetti White, and Tempting Turquoise card stock; Apricot Appeal, Basic Brown, and Tempting Turquoise Classic Stampin' Pads; Tempting Turquoise Stampin' Around cartridge; Apricot grosgrain ribbon; Stampin' Dimensionals; watercolor brush

[145 C] Fishy Friends and Everyday Flexible Phrases sets; Green Galore, Lovely Lilac, Tempting Turquoise, and Whisper White card stock; Bold Brights Mini Gable boxes & tags; Chocolate Chip, Green Galore, Lovely Lilac, and Tempting Turquoise Classic Stampin' Pads; White Square Aluminum Metal Edge tags; Apple Green grosgrain ribbon; Stampin' Dimensionals; Crafters' Tool Kit; watercolor brush; crochet thread

[146 A] Noble Deer and Everyday Flexible Phrases sets; Canvas background stamp; Chocolate Chip, Confetti White, Kraft, Mellow Moss, and Ruby Red card stock; Bashful Blue, Basic Black, Chocolate Chip, Glorious Green, More Mustard, and Ruby Red Classic Stampin' Pads; Vintage brads; Stampin' Dimensionals; 1/16" Circle punch

[146 B] Angler and It's Your Birthday sets; Chocolate Chip, Confetti White, Kraft, and Ruby Red card stock; Bashful Blue, Basic Black, Chocolate Chip, Close to Cocoa, Creamy Caramel, Glorious Green, Going Gray, More Mustard, and Really Rust Classic Stampin' Pads; linen thread; Vintage brads; twill tape; Stampin' Dimensionals; 1/16" Circle punch

[147 A] Bareback set; Chocolate Chip, Confetti White, Kraft, Mellow Moss, and Ruby Red card stock; Chocolate Chip, Close to Cocoa, and Ruby Red Classic Stampin' Pads; Aged Copper Hodgepodge Hardware; Caramel gingham ribbon; Stampin' Dimensionals

[147 B] Bareback and Expressive Flexible Phrases sets; Chocolate Chip, Mellow Moss, Ruby Red, and Very Vanilla card stock; Pockets & Pieces, Assortment 1; Chocolate Chip and Close to Cocoa Classic Stampin' pads; Caramel and Moss gingham ribbon; Horizontal Slot punch

[147 C] Expressive Flexible Phrases and Wonderful Weaves sets; Farmyard jumbo wheel; Chocolate Chip, Confetti White, Kraft, and Mellow Moss card stock; Bashful Blue, Brocade Blue, Certainly Celery, Chocolate Chip, Going Gray, Mellow Moss, Regal Rose, and Real Red Classic Stampin' Pads; Basic Black Stampin' Around jumbo cartridge; Vintage brads; Natural hemp twine; Stampin' Dimensionals;1/16" Circle punch; watercolor brush

[148 A] The Cat's Meow set; Old Olive and Pumpkin Pie card stock; watercolor paper; Always Artichoke, Brocade Blue, Creamy Caramel, Going Gray, Old Olive, and Pumpkin Pie Classic Stampin' Pads; Jet Black StazOn pad; French Blue grosgrain ribbon; Stampin' Dimensionals; 1/8" Circle punch; watercolor brush; sewing machine and thread

[148 B] Ruff Day set; Ruff Play wheel; Brocade Blue, Confetti White, and Pumpkin Pie card stock; Earth Elements mini gable boxes & tags; Basic Black, Brocade Blue, Chocolate Chip, Close to Cocoa, and Going Gray Classic Stampin' Pads; Old Olive Stampin' Around cartridge; White Square Aluminum Metal Edge tag; Silver brad; linen thread; Stampin' Dimensionals; watercolor brush; 1/16" Circle punch

[149 A] Going Buggy and Sassy Sayings I sets; Chocolate Chip, Old Olive, Pumpkin Pie, and Very Vanilla card stock; Basic Black Classic Stampin' Pad; Brocade Blue, Old Olive, and Pumpkin Pie Stampin' Write markers; French Blue grosgrain ribbon; Vintage brads; Stampin' Dimensionals; 1/16" Circle punch

[149 B] Going Buggy, Expressive Flexible Phrases, and Tidy Alphabet sets; Hot to Dot wheel; Brocade Blue, Chocolate Chip, Old Olive, and Very Vanilla card stock; Confetti White & Kraft tag sheets; Brocade Blue, Chocolate Chip, and Old Olive Craft Stampin' Pads; Old Olive Stampin' Around cartridge; Pewter Hodgepodge Hardware; Chocolate grosgrain ribbon; Light Blue gingham ribbon; White Circle Aluminum Metal Edge tags; Stampin' Dimensionals; 1/8" and 1/2" Circle punches; sewing machine and thread; staple

[150 A] Travel Post, Collage Numbers, and Collage Alphabet sets; Houndstooth background stamp; Always Artichoke, Bravo Burgundy, Chocolate Chip, and Pretty in Pink card stock; Heirloom Timeworn Collection paper; Always Artichoke, Basic Black, Bravo Burgundy, Close to Cocoa, and Creamy Caramel Craft Stampin' Pads; Basic Black Stampin' Write journaler; Black gingham ribbon; Chocolate grosgrain ribbon; Natural hemp twine; Aged Copper Hodgepodge Hardware; Stampin' Dimensionals; brayer

[150 B] Fire Brigade and Expressive Flexible Phrases sets; Canvas background stamp; Always Artichoke, Bravo Burgundy, Confetti White, and Creamy Caramel card stock; Basic Black, Bravo Burgundy, Chocolate Chip, Creamy Caramel, and More Mustard Classic Stampin' Pads; Natural hemp twine; Stampin' Dimensionals; watercolor brush

[151 A] Office Ephemera and Collage Alphabet sets; Ephemera background stamp; Always Artichoke, Bravo Burgundy, Creamy Caramel, and Very Vanilla card stock; Weathered Timeworn Collection paper; Always Artichoke, Basic Black, Bravo Burgundy, Chocolate Chip, and Creamy Caramel Craft Stampin' Pads; Basic Black Stampin' Write journaler; Aged Copper Hodgepodge Hardware; Chocolate grosgrain ribbon; linen thread; twill tape; Stampin' Dimensionals; 1/16" Circle punch

[151 B] On Gossamer Wings set; Fine Lace background stamp; Always Artichoke, Bravo Burgundy, and Confetti White card stock; Regals mulberry paper; Always Artichoke, Bravo Burgundy, Creamy Caramel, and More Mustard Classic Stampin' Pads; Rich Regals eyelets; White grosgrain ribbon; Crafters' Tool Kit; watercolor brush; stamping sponges

[152 A] Set Sail set; Brilliant Blue, Confetti White, Mellow Moss, and Real Red card stock; Brilliant Blue Classic Stampin' Pad; Jet Black StazOn pad; Basic eyelets; Natural hemp twine; Stampin' Dimensionals; Watercolor Wonder crayons; watercolor brush; Crafters' Tool Kit

[152 B] Netherlands and Brighter Tomorrow sets; Brilliant Blue, Confetti White, Real Red, and So Saffron card stock; Basic Black and Real Red Craft Stampin' Pads; Watercolor Wonder crayons; Red gingham ribbon; Bold Brights buttons; watercolor brush; sanding blocks

[153 A] The Back Nine and It's Your Birthday sets; Always Artichoke, Confetti White, and Mellow Moss card stock; Always Artichoke, Close to Cocoa, Going Gray, Old Olive, and Summer Sun Classic Stampin' Pads; Jet Black StazOn pad; Soft Subtles I eyelets; Earths Fancy Fibers; linen thread; Stampin' Dimensionals; Crafters' Tool Kit; watercolor brush

[153 B] Classic Pickups, Everyday Flexible Phrases, and Quick Thinking sets; Confetti White, Real Red, and So Saffron card stock; Basic Black and So Saffron Classic Stampin' Pads; Watercolor Wonder crayons; Stainless Steel Metal Magic tags, Assortment 1; Silver brads; Natural hemp twine; Stampin' Dimensionals; Crafters' Tool Kit; watercolor brush; sanding blocks

[153 C] Classic Pickups, Everyday Flexible Phrases, and Expressive Flexible Phrases sets; Crosshatch background stamp; Always Artichoke, Confetti White, and Mellow Moss card stock; Confetti White & Kraft tag sheets; Always Artichoke, Creamy Caramel, Going Gray, and Old Olive Classic Stampin' Pads; Jet Black StazOn pad; linen thread; Vintage brads; Stampin' Dimensionals; watercolor brush

[154 A] Stardust set; Confetti White, More Mustard, and Not Quite Navy card stock; Basic Black and Not Quite Navy Craft Stampin' Pads; Watercolor Wonder crayons; Gold cord; watercolor brush

[154 B] Balmy Breezes, It's a Date, Everyday Flexible Phrases, and Expressive Flexible Phrases sets; More Mustard, Naturals Ivory, and Ruby Red card stock; Confetti White & Kraft tag sheets; Basic Black, Chocolate Chip, More Mustard, and Real Red Classic Stampin' Pads; Close to Cocoa and Night of Navy Craft Stampin' Pads; Natural hemp twine; linen thread; Rich Regals eyelets; Crafters' Tool Kit

[154 C] Balmy Breezes, Collage Alphabet, and Collage Alphabet Numbers sets; On Safari background stamp; Kraft, Not Quite Navy, and Ruby Red card stock; Whisper White & Very Vanilla tag sheets; Basic Black, Chocolate Chip, More Mustard, Not Quite Navy, and Ruby Red Craft Stampin' Pads; Basic Black Stampin' Write journaler; Rich Regals and Squares eyelets; Pewter Hodgepodge Hardware; Natural hemp twine; linen thread; Regals Fancy Fibers; twill tape; Stampin' Dimensionals; Crafters' Tool Kit; sanding blocks

[155 A] Land That I Love set; Confetti Cream, Kraft, and Not Quite Navy card stock; Creamy Caramel and More Mustard Classic Stampin' Pads; Bravo Burgundy, Chocolate Chip, Night of Navy, and Ruby Red Stampin' Write markers; Vintage brads; twill tape; Stampin' Dimensionals; Crafters' Tool Kit; brayer

[155 B] Land That I Love set; Kraft, More Mustard, Naturals Ivory, and Not Quite Navy card stock; Rustic Timeworn Collection paper; More Mustard and Not Quite Navy Craft Stampin' Pads; Basic Black Stampin' Write journaler; Antique Brass Hodgepodge Hardware; Mustard grosgrain ribbon

[155 C] Star-Spangled Banner and Wonderful Words sets; Kraft, Naturals Ivory, Not Quite Navy, and Ruby Red card stock; Basic Brown and Night of Navy Classic Stampin' Pads; Stampin' Pastels; Natural hemp twine; Stampin' Dimensionals; 1/8" Circle punch; blender pen

[156 A] See with the Heart, Everyday Flexible Phrases, It's a Date, Classic Alphabet, and Classic Alphabet Numbers sets; Mellow Moss, Not Quite Navy, Ruby Red, and Very Vanilla card stock; Regals mulberry paper; Basic Black, Chocolate Chip, Not Quite Navy, Pretty in Pink, and Ruby Red Craft Stampin' Pads; Basic Black Stampin' Write journaler; Vintage brads; twill tape; Black gingham ribbon; watercolor brush

[156 B] Thinking of Father set; Canvas and Print Pattern background stamps; Mellow Moss, Not Quite Navy, and Very Vanilla card stock; Pockets & Pieces boxes and tags, Assortment 1; Mellow Moss and Not Quite Navy Classic Stampin' Pads; twill tape; Rich Regals eyelets; linen thread; Crafters' Tool Kit; watercolor brush; staple

[157 A] Knobbly Gnomes and Expressive Everyday Phrases; Print Pattern background stamp; Naturals Ivory, Ruby Red, and Very Vanilla card stock; Confetti White & Kraft and Earth Elements tag sheets; Always Artichoke, Close to Cocoa, Going Gray, Not Quite Navy, Ruby Red, and Summer Sun Classic Stampin' Pads; Jet Black StazOn pad; Moss gingham ribbon; Soft Subtles I eyelets; Stampin' Dimensionals; Crafters' Tool Kit; watercolor brush

[157 B] A Quiet Life and Everyday Flexible Phrases sets; Floral background stamp; Bordering Blue, Mellow Moss, Not Quite Navy, Ruby Red, and Very Vanilla card stock; Pockets & Pieces, Assortment 1; Basic Black, Mellow Moss, Not Quite Navy, Pretty in Pink, and Ruby Red Classic Stampin' Pads; Jet Black StazOn pad; 1/8" Circle punch; Moss gingham ribbon; Vintage brads; watercolor brush

[157 C] A Quiet Life set and Expressive Flexible Phrases sets; Mellow Moss, Naturals Ivory, Not Quite Navy, and Ruby Red card stock; Pockets & Pieces, Assortment 1; Basic Black and Not Quite Navy Classic Stampin' Pads; Black gingham ribbon; Rich Regals eyelets; Natural hemp twine; 1/2" Circle punch; Stampin' Dimensionals; Crafters' Tool Kit

[158 A] Toile Blossoms and All-Year Cheer I sets; Brocade Blue and Confetti White card stock; Regals mulberry paper; Always Artichoke, Bravo Burgundy, Brocade Blue, and More Mustard Classic Stampin' Pads; Jet Black StazOn pad; Burgundy 7/8" organdy ribbon; Stampin' Dimensionals; 1/16" Circle punch; watercolor brush; crochet thread

[158 B] Mostly Flowers and Wonderful Words II sets; French Script background stamp; Bravo Burgundy and Kraft card stock; Brights mulberry paper; Ballet Blue, Bravo Burgundy, Creamy Caramel, and Whisper White Craft Stampin' Pads; Taupe grosgrain ribbon; Vintage brads

[159 A] Gentler Times and Everyday Flexible Phrases sets; Bravo Burgundy, Confetti White, and Kraft card stock; Whisper White & Vanilla tag sheets; Whisper White Craft Stampin' Pad; Basic Black and Bravo Burgundy Classic Stampin' Pads; Ivory 3/8" organdy ribbon; linen thread; Rich Regals eyelets; Stampin' Dimensionals; watercolor brush; Crafters' Tool Kit

[159 B] Memory of the Heart, Classic Alphabet, and Collage Alphabet sets; Brocade Blue, Bravo Burgundy, Confetti White, and Kraft card stock; Confetti White & Kraft tag sheets; Pockets & Pieces boxes & tags, Assortment 1; Always Artichoke, Basic Black, Bravo Burgundy, Brocade Blue, Creamy Caramel, More Mustard, and Summer Sun Craft Stampin' Pads; Jet Black StazOn pad; Basic Black Stampin' Write journaler; Ivory 7/8" organdy ribbon; linen thread; Stampin' Dimensionals; Crafters' Tool Kit; watercolor brush

[160 A] Artifacts, Headline Alphabet, and Wonderful Words II set; Size It Up wheel; Always Artichoke, Creamy Caramel, and Elegant Eggplant card stock; Weathered Timeworn Collection paper; Creamy Caramel, Elegant Eggplant, and White Craft Stampin' Pads; Basic Black Stampin' Around cartridge; Basic Black Stampin' Write journaler; Eggplant grosgrain ribbon; Metallic eyelets; Antique Brass Hodgepodge Hardware; twill tape; Stampin' Dimensionals; Crafters' Tool Kit

[160 B] Stippled Stencils and All-Year Cheer I sets; Always Artichoke, Confetti Cream, Elegant Eggplant, and Kraft card stock; Always Artichoke and Elegant Eggplant Classic Stampin' Pads; Vintage brads; stamping sponges

[161 A] Elegant Ornaments and All-Year Cheer I sets; Always Artichoke, Confetti Cream, and Elegant Eggplant card stock; Always Artichoke and Creamy Caramel Classic Stampin' Pads; Linen Magic Mesh; Neutrals buttons; Natural hemp twine; linen thread; Stampin' Dimensionals; Crystal Effects

[161 B] Aged to Perfection set; Always Artichoke, Kraft, and Very Vanilla card stock; Saddle Stitch book kit, Assortment 5; Heirloom Timeworn Collection paper; Always Artichoke Classic Stampin' Pads; Antique Brass Hodgepodge Hardware; Chocolate and Taupe grosgrain ribbon; Moss gingham ribbon; linen thread; Stampin' Dimensionals; 1/16" Circle punch

[162 A] Kanji and Oriental Brushstrokes sets; Always Artichoke, Confetti White, and Sahara Sand card stock; Always Artichoke, Apricot Appeal, Basic Black, Old Olive, and Tempting Turquoise Classic Stampin' Pads; linen thread; Stampin' Dimensionals; watercolor brush

[162 B] Oriental Brushstrokes and Kanji sets; Apricot Appeal, Confetti White, Elegant Eggplant, and Sahara Sand card stock; Apricot Appeal, Bashful Blue, Basic Brown, Bordering Blue, Elegant Eggplant, and Old Olive Classic Stampin' Pads; Copper cord; Stampin' Dimensionals; 1/16" Circle punch; watercolor brush

[162 C] Ancient Asia set; Bamboo II background stamp; Elegant Eggplant, Pumpkin Pie, and Sahara Sand card stock; Regals mulberry paper; Elegant Eggplant and Pumpkin Pie Classic Stampin' Pads; Timber Brown StazOn pad; Stampin' Dimensionals; Wire Works; watercolor brush; bleach

[163 A] Frame & Flourishes, Everyday Flexible Phrases, and Newsprint Alphabet sets; Chocolate Chip, Elegant Eggplant, and Very Vanilla card stock; Cambridge Designer Series paper; Chocolate Chip Craft Stampin' Pad; White Circles Aluminum Metal Edge tags; Taupe grosgrain ribbon; Squares eyelets; twill tape; linen thread; Stampin' Dimensionals; Crafters' Tool Kit; 1/16" Circle punch

[163 B] Frame & Flourishes and Elegant Greetings sets; Naturals Ivory card stock; Cambridge Designer Series paper; Elegant Eggplant Classic Stampin' Pad; Ivory 3/8" organdy ribbon; Rectangle punch; watercolor brush

[163 C] Frame & Flourishes, Elegant Beginnings, and Classic Caps sets; Naturals Ivory and Perfect Plum card stock; Cambridge Designer Series paper; Regals mulberry paper; Elegant Eggplant and Perfect Plum Craft Stampin' Pads; Basic Black Stampin' Write journaler; Pewter Hodgepodge Hardware; Eggplant grosgrain ribbon; Stampin' Dimensionals

[164 A] Flora & Fauna and Everyday Flexible Phrases sets; Bashful Blue, Certainly Celery, Chocolate Chip, and Confetti White card stock; Earths mulberry paper; Bashful Blue, Basic Brown, and Certainly Celery Classic Stampin' Pads; Light Blue gingham ribbon; Vintage brads; linen thread; Stampin' Dimensionals; 1/16" Circle punch; watercolor brush

[164 B] Flora & Fauna and Newsprint Alphabet sets; Bashful Blue, Certainly Celery, Chocolate Chip, and Confetti White card stock; White vellum card stock; Basic Black Classic Stampin' Pad; Bashful Blue, Certainly Celery, Chocoate Chip, and Whisper White Craft Stampin' Pads; Basic Black Stampin' Write journaler; Neutrals buttons; Wire Works; French Blue grosgrain ribbon; Ivory 3/8" organdy ribbon; Stampin' Dimensionals; 1/16" Circle punch; sewing machine and thread; watercolor brush

[164 C] Flora & Fauna, Everyday Flexible Phrases, Alphabits, and Stencil Alphabet sets; Houndstooth background stamp; Bashful Blue, Certainly Celery, Chocolate Chip, Close to Cocoa, and Confetti Cream card stock; Bashful Blue, Basic Black, Certainly Celery, and Chocolate Chip Classic Stampin' Pads; Chocolate Chip Craft Stampin' Pad; Antique Brass Hodgepodge Hardware; Chocolate grosgrain and Light Blue gingham ribbon; linen thread; twill tape; 1/8" Circle punch; watercolor brush

[165 A] Fine Frames, Everyday Flexible Phrases, and Burst into Bloom sets; Bashful Blue, Certainly Celery, Chocolate Chip, and Confetti White card stock; Ballet Blue, Certainly Celery, and Chocolate Chip Classic Stampin' Pads; linen thread; Vintage brads; Stampin' Dimensionals; 1/16" Circle punch

[165 B] Borders Mini, Stencil Alphabet, and Everyday Flexible Phrases sets; Bashful Blue, Certainly Celery, and Confetti White card stock; Bashful Blue and Chocolate Chip Classic Stampin' Pads; Basic eyelets; linen thread; Stampin' Dimensionals; Crafters' Tool Kit

[165 C] Around & About, Everyday Flexible Phrases, and Simple Type Aphabet sets; Bashful Blue, Chocolate Chip, Certainly Celery, and Confetti White card stock; Chocolate Chip Classic Stampin' Pad; Vintage brads

[165 D] Around & About and Sweet & Sassy sets; Bashful Blue and Confetti White card stock; Confetti White & Kraft Party Favor boxes & tags; Basic Brown, Bashful Blue, Chocolate Chip, and Certainly Celery Classic Stampin' Pads; Caramel gingham ribbon; Vintage brads; Stampin' Dimensionals; 1/8" Circle punch; watercolor brush

[166 A] Itty Bitty Backgrounds, Perfect Petals, and Sincere Salutations sets; Chocolate Chip, Close to Cocoa, and Very Vanilla card stock; Chocolate Chip, Close to Cocoa, and Rose Red Classic Stampin' Pads; Caramel gingham ribbon; linen thread; Stampin' Dimensionals; thread and needle

[166 B] Stars & Swirls and All-Year Cheer I sets; Canvas background stamp; Close to Cocoa, Regal Rose, and Very Vanilla card stock; Chocolate Chip, Creamy Caramel, Mellow Moss, and Regal Rose Classic Stampin' Pads; Chocolate grosgrain ribbon, linen thread; Stampin' Dimensionals; 1/8" and 1/2" Circle punches

[166 C] Background Basics and Mini Messages sets; Chocolate Chip, Mellow Moss, Regal Rose, and Very Vanilla card stock; Chocolate Chip, Creamy Caramel, Mellow Moss, and Regal Rose Classic Stampin' Pads; Rose grosgrain ribbon; Stampin' Dimensionals; 1-1/4" Square punch

[167 A] Beyond the Basics and Nice & Easy Notes sets; Mellow Moss, Regal Rose, and Very Vanilla card stock; Basic Brown, Mellow Moss, and Regal Rose Classic Stampin' Pads; Small Flowers eyelets; Ivory 3/8" organdy ribbon; Stampin' Dimensionals; Crafters' Tool Kit; watercolor brush

[167 B] Petite Patterns, Happy Hearts, and All-Year Cheer III sets; Chocolate Chip, Regal Rose, and Very Vanilla card stock; Chocolate Chip, Mellow Moss, and Regal Rose Classic Stampin' Pads; Close to Cocoa Craft Stampin' Pad; Subtles Fancy Fibers; Stampin' Dimensionals

[167 C] Fresh Fillers set; Mellow Moss and Very Vanilla card stock; Pockets & Pieces, Assortment 1; Creamy Caramel Craft Stampin' Pad; Chocolate Chip, Mellow Moss, and Regal Rose Stampin' Write markers; Chocolate grosgrain ribbon; Silver brads; Crafters' Tool Kit; 1/8" Circle punch

[168 A] Border Builders and Expressive Flexible Phrases sets; Apricot Appeal, Cameo Coral, Certainly Celery, and Whisper White card stock; Apricot Appeal, Cameo Coral, and Certainly Celery Classic Stampin' Pads; linen thread; Stampin' Dimensionals; Crafters' Tool Kit; sewing machine and thread

[168 B] Smorgasborders, Alphabits, and Simple Type Alphabet sets; Apricot Appeal, Cameo Coral, Certainly Celery, and Whisper White card stock; Cameo Coral Craft Stampin' Pad; Apricot Appeal, Cameo Coral, and Certainly Celery Stampin' Write markers; Basic Black Stampin' Write journaler; Rose grosgrain ribbon; linen thread; Stampin' Dimensionals; 1/8" Circle punch

[168 C] Itty Bitty Borders and Everyday Flexible Phrases sets; Apricot Appeal, Cameo Coral, Certainly Celery, and Sage Shadow card stock; Confetti White & Kraft tag sheets; Apricot Appeal, Basic Black, Cameo Coral, Certainly Celery, and Sage Shadow Classic Stampin' Pads; Apricot Appeal Stampin' Write marker; Silver brads; Black gingham ribbon; Stampin' Dimensionals; watercolor brush

[169 A] Great Shapes, Expressive Flexible Phrases, and Sweet & Sassy sets; Apricot Appeal, Certainly Celery, and Whisper White card stock; White vellum card stock; Cameo Coral and Certainly Celery Classic Stampin' Pads; Apricot grosgrain ribbon; Silver brads; Stampin' Dimensionals; sanding blocks

[169 B] Everyday Flexible Phrases and Whimsical Alphabet Lower sets; By Definition background stamp; Square Pegs jumbo wheel; Apricot Appeal, Cameo Coral, Certainly Celery, Sage Shadow, and Whisper White card stock; Basic Black and Cameo Coral Craft Stampin' Pads; Certainly Celery Classic ink refill; Uninked jumbo cartridge; White grosgrain ribbon; Natural hemp twine; Stampin' Dimensionals; Write Me a Memory Journaling Fonts, Volume II; window sheets; 1/16" and 1/8" Circle punches

[170 A] Lexicon of Love, Wonderful Weaves, Alphabits, and Newsprint Alphabet sets; Bashful Blue, Bravo Burgundy, Mellow Moss, and Whisper White card stock; Always Artichoke, Bashful Blue, and Bravo Burgundy Craft Stampin' Pads; Aged Copper Hodgepodge Hardware; Burgundy grosgrain ribbon; window sheets; Stampin' Dimensionals; Write Me a Memory Journaling Fonts CD, Volume II

[170 B] Lexicon of Love and Heartfelt Thanks sets; Print Pattern background stamp; Bashful Blue, Certainly Celery, and Whisper White card stock; Bashful Blue and Certainly Celery Classic Stampin' Pads; Celery and Bluebird grosgrain ribbons; Stampin' Dimensionals

[170 C] Wonderful Weaves, Expressive Flexible Phrases, and Artifacts sets; Size It Up wheel; Always Artichoke, Bravo Burgundy, and Very Vanilla card stock; Always Artichoke, Creamy Caramel, and Bravo Burgundy Classic Stampin' Pads; Always Artichoke Stampin' Around cartridge; Caramel gingham ribbon; Aged Copper Hodgepodge Hardware; Stampin' Dimensionals; Slit punch; Word Window punch; stamping sponges

[171 A] Label Classics, Love without End, and Quick Thinking sets; Always Artichoke, Bashful Blue, Certainly Celery, and Whisper White card stock; Always Artichoke, Bashful Blue, and Certainly Celery Classic Stampin' Pads; Celery grosgrain ribbon; Silver brads; Stampin' Dimensionals

[171 B] Label Classics, Expressive Flexible Phrases, Happy Hearts, and Newsprint Alphabet sets; Always Artichoke, Bravo Burgundy, Certainly Celery, and Whisper White card stock; Always Artichoke, Basic Black, Bravo Burgundy, and Certainly Celery Craft Stampin' Pads; Rich Regals eyelets; Vintage brads; Natural hemp twine; linen thread; 1/2" Circle punch; Crafters' Tool Kit

[171 C] Little Pieces, Label Classics, Expressive Flexible Phrases, On the Edge Alphabet Upper, and Headline Alphabet sets; Always Artichoke, Bashful Blue, Certainly Celery, and Whisper White card stock; Always Artichoke, Bashful Blue, and Certainly Celery Craft Stampin' Pads; Celery grosgrain ribbon; Light Blue gingham ribbon; window sheets; Stampin' Dimensionals; Write Me a Memory Journaling Fonts CD, Volume II; 1/2" Circle punch

[171 D] Little Pieces and Headline Alphabet sets; Bashful Blue, Certainly Celery, and Whisper White card stock; Bashful Blue and Certainly Celery Classic Stampin' Pads; Celery grosgrain ribbon; Stampin' Dimensionals; 1/2" Circle punch; sewing machine and thread

[172 A] Simple Shapes and Celebrate in Style sets; Close to Cocoa, More Mustard, Naturals Ivory, and Ruby Red card stock; Basic Black, Close to Cocoa, Creamy Caramel, Going Gray, Mellow Moss, More Mustard, and Ruby Red Classic Stampin' Pads; Antique Brass Hodgepodge Hardware; Natural hemp twine; Stampin' Dimensionals; watercolor brush

[172 B] Birthday Best and By Design sets; Close to Cocoa, More Mustard, Naturals Ivory, and Ruby Red card stock; Soft Subtles Pillar boxes & tags; Basic Black, Close to Cocoa, Mellow Moss, and More Mustard Classic Stampin' Pads; Taupe grosgrain ribbon; Earth Elements eyelets; Wire Works; Stampin' Dimensionals; Crafters' Tool Kit; 1/8" Circle punch; watercolor brush

[172 C] Shape-Ups and Fun Filled sets; Close to Cocoa, More Mustard, Naturals Ivory, and Ruby Red card stock; Close to Cocoa and More Mustard Classic Stampin' Pads; Close to Cocoa, More Mustard, Mellow Moss, and Ruby Red Stampin' Write markers; Spring Moss grosgrain ribbon; Vintage brads; Stampin' Dimensionals; 1/8" Circle punch

[173 A] Fun with Shapes and Phrase Starters II sets; More Mustard, Naturals Ivory, and Ruby Red card stock; Basic Black, Close to Cocoa, More Mustard, and Ruby Red Craft Stampin' Pads; Basic Black Stampin' Write journaler; VersaMark pad; Crystal Clear Stampin' Emboss powder; Natural hemp twine; Crafters' Tool Kit

[173 B] Fun with Shapes and Simple Sayings II sets; Mellow Moss, Naturals Ivory, and Ruby Red card stock; Basic Black Classic Stampin' Pad; Close to Cocoa, Mellow Moss, and Ruby Red Craft Stampin' Pads; Earth Elements buttons; Natural hemp twine; Soft Subtles I eyelets; Stampin' Dimensionals; Crafters' Tool Kit

[173 C] Simply Circles set; Mellow Moss, Naturals Ivory, and Ruby Red card stock; White vellum card stock; Mellow Moss, More Mustard, and Ruby Red Classic Stampin' Pads; Spring Moss grosgrain ribbon

[174 A] Everyday Flexible Phrases and All Natural sets; Fine Lace and Word by Word background stamps; Ruby Red and Always Artichoke card stock; Confetti White & Kraft Pillar boxes & tags; Aged Copper Hodgepodge Hardware; twill tape; linen thread; Stampin' Dimensionals; 1/8" Circle punch

[178 A] Sincere Salutations and Happy Hearts sets; Always Artichoke, Brocade Blue, More Mustard, and Rose Red card stock; Always Artichoke, Brocade Blue, More Mustard, and Rose Red Classic Stampin' Pads; Natural hemp twine; French Blue grosgrain ribbon; Silver eyelets; White Square Aluminum Metal Edge tags; Stampin' Dimensionals; Crafters' Tool Kit

[178 B] Much Appreciated and Petal Prints sets; Always Artichoke, Kraft, and Rose Red card stock; watercolor paper; White mulberry paper; Always Artichoke Classic Stampin' Pad; Always Artichoke, Creamy Caramel, and Rose Red Stampin' Write markers; Vintage brads; Moss gingham ribbon; linen thread; Stampin' Dimensionals; Crafters' Tool Kit; sewing machine and thread

[178 C] Alphabits, Buds & Blossoms, and Everyday Flexible Phrases sets; Always Artichoke, Brocade Blue, Ruby Red, and Whisper White card stock; White vellum card stock; Brocade Blue, Creamy Caramel, and Ruby Red Classic Stampin' Pads; Clear buttons; Taupe grosgrain ribbon; Silver brads; Stampin' Dimensionals; 1/4" Square punch; sewing machine and thread

[179 A] All About U set; By Definition background stamp; Brocade Blue, Confetti White, Kraft, and Rose Red card stock; Always Artichoke, Brocade Blue, and Creamy Caramel Classic Stampin' Pads; Always Artichoke, Brocade Blue, More Mustard, and Rose Red Stampin' Write markers; Antique Brass Hodgepodge Hardware; White grosgrain ribbon; Crafters' Tool Kit; 1/8" Circle punch; 1-1/4" Square punch; brayer

[179 B] All about U set; Always Artichoke, Brocade Blue, Rose Red, and Whisper White card stock; Always Artichoke and Brocade Blue Classic Stampin' Pads; Taupe grosgrain ribbon; Stampin' Dimensionals; Crafters' Tool Kit

[179 C] It's a Date and Expressive Flexible Phrases sets; Always Artichoke, Brocade Blue, Confetti White, Creamy Caramel, Kraft, and More Mustard card stock; Always Artichoke, Close to Cocoa, and More Mustard Craft Stampin' Pads; Basic Black Stampin' Write journaler; Chocolate grosgrain ribbon; linen thread; Antique Brass Hodgepodge Hardware; Stampin' Dimensionals; 1/16", 1/4", and 1/2" Circle punches

[180 A] All-Year Cheer I and In Full Bloom sets; Canvas background stamp; Brocade Blue, Confetti White, Mellow Moss, and Ruby Red card stock; Basic Black, Brocade Blue, Mellow Moss, Ruby Red, and Summer Sun Classic Stampin' Pads; Vintage brads; Natural hemp twine; Stampin' Dimensionals; 1/16" Circle punch

[180 B] All-Year Cheer II and Shapes & Shadows sets; Confetti White, Mellow Moss, and Ruby Red card stock; Whisper White Craft Stampin' Pad; Ruby Red Classic Stampin' Pad; Silver brads; linen thread; Stampin' Dimensionals

[181 A] All-Year Cheer III, Fine Frames, and Happy Hearts sets; Canvas background stamp; Brocade Blue, Confetti White, Ruby Red, and Sahara Sand card stock; Brocade Blue and Ruby Red Classic Stampin' Pads; Red grosgrain ribbon; White Square Aluminum Metal Edge tags; linen thread; Crafters' Tool Kit; brayer

[181 B] Cheery Chat and Little Pieces sets; Brocade Blue, Confetti White, and Ruby Red card stock; Brocade Blue and Ruby Red Classic Stampin' Pads; Brocade Blue Stampin' Write marker; Rich Regals buttons; Light Blue gingham ribbon; Stampin' Dimensionals; 1/2" Circle punch

[182 A] Wonderful Words and All the Best sets; Bashful Blue, Confetti White, and Ruby Red card stock; Chocolate Chip, Old Olive, and Ruby Red Classic Stampin' Pads; linen thread; 1/16" and 1/4" Circle punches

[182 B] Simple Sayings II and Sparkling Season sets; Certainly Celery, Ruby Red, and Whisper White card stock; Chocolate Chip Craft Stampin' Pad; Certainly Celery, Chocolate Chip, and Ruby Red Stampin' Write markers; linen thread; Vintage brads; Stampin' Dimensionals; 1/16" Circle Punch

[182 C] Wonderful Words II and Sweet Seasons sets; Apricot Appeal, Bashful Blue, Certainly Celery, and Confetti White card stock; Apricot Appeal, Bashful Blue, Basic Brown, Chocolate Chip, Close to Cocoa, Going Gray, and Ruby Red Classic Stampin' Pads; Natural hemp twine; Brights Magic Mesh; Stampin' Dimensionals; watercolor brush

[183 A] Quick Thinking and Just Beakause sets; Apricot Appeal, Chocolate Chip, Ruby Red, and Whisper White card stock; Chocolate Chip and Ruby Red Classic Stampin' Pads; linen thread; Earth Elements buttons; Stampin' Dimensionals; 1/16" Circle Punch

[183 B] Tiny Talk and Birthday Best sets; Apricot Appeal, Bashful Blue, Chocolate Chip, and Confetti White card stock; Pockets & Pieces, Assortment 2; Apricot Appeal, Bashful Blue, Basic Brown, and Certainly Celery Classic Stampin' Pads; Celery grosgrain ribbon; Wire Works; Stampin' Dimensionals; watercolor brush

[183 C] Vogue Verses and Buds & Blossoms sets; Bashful Blue, Certainly Celery, and Whisper White card stock; Apricot Appeal, Certainly Celery, Chocolate Chip, and Ruby Red Classic Stampin' Pads; Stainless Steel Metal Magic tags, Assortment I; Chocolate grosgrain ribbon; linen thread; Stampin' Dimensionals; Crafters' Tool Kit

[184 A] Sassy Sayings I and Petal Pushers sets; Almost Amethyst, Bashful Blue, Certainly Celery, and Whisper White card stock; White vellum card stock; Almost Amethyst, Bashful Blue, Certainly Celery, and Elegant Eggplant Classic Stampin' Pads; Light Blue gingham ribbon; Stampin' Dimensionals

[184 B] Sassy Sayings II and Fun Filled sets; Almost Amethyst, Certainly Celery, Elegant Eggplant, and Whisper White card stock; Almost Amethyst and Elegant Eggplant Classic Stampin' Pads; Certainly Celery Stampin' Write marker; Eggplant grosgrain ribbon; Silver brads; 1/8" Circle punch

[184 C] Words of Wisdom and Flower Garden sets; Almost Amethyst, Bashful Blue, and Confetti White card stock; White mulberry paper; Bashful Blue, Basic Black, Certainly Celery, Close to Cocoa, and Lavender Lace Classic Stampin' Pads; Soft Subtles II eyelets; Natural hemp twine; White 3/8" organdy ribbon; Crafters' Tool Kit; watercolor brush

[185 A] Sweet & Sassy and Brighter Tomorrow sets; Almost Amethyst, Certainly Celery, Elegant Eggplant, and Whisper White card stock; Certainly Celery and Elegant Eggplant Classic Stampin' Pads; Natural hemp twine; Black gingham ribbon; Silver eyelets; Stampin' Dimensionals; Crafters' Tool Kit

[185 B] Elegant Greetings and Petal Prints sets; Canvas background stamp; Almost Amethyst, Bashful Blue, and Whisper White card stock; Whisper White & Very Vanilla tag sheets; Almost Amethyst Classic Stampin' Pad; Almost Amethyst, Bashful Blue, and Certainly Celery Stampin' Write markers; Silver eyelets; Soft Subtles buttons; linen thread; White 3/8" organdy ribbon; Stampin' Dimensionals; Crafters' Tool Kit

[186 A] Versatile Verses and Little Pieces sets; Barely Banana, Certainly Celery, Pixie Pink, and Whisper White card stock; Barely Banana, Certainly Celery, Pixie Pink, and Summer Sun Classic Stampin' Pads; Celery grosgrain ribbon; Stampin' Dimensionals

[186 B] Curvy Verses and Friends Are Like Flowers sets; Barely Banana, Confetti White, and Pixie Pink card stock; Barely Banana, Basic Black, Certainly Celery, Orchid Opulence, and Pixie Pink Classic Stampin' Pads; Light Pink gingham ribbon; Stampin' Dimensionals; 1/8" Circle punch; watercolor brush

[187 A] It's Your Birthday and Fun Filled sets; Barely Banana, Certainly Celery, Pixie Pink, and Whisper White card stock; Basic Black, Barely Banana, Certainly Celery, Pink Passion, and Pixie Pink Classic Stampin' Pads; Stampin' Dimensionals

[187 B] It's Your Birthday and Mini Medleys sets; Barely Banana, Certainly Celery, and Whisper White card stock; Certainly Celery and Pink Passion Classic Stampin' Pads; Celery grosgrain ribbon; Soft Subtles I eyelets; Crafters' Tool Kit; crochet thread

[187 C] Elegant Inspirations and Mostly Flowers sets; Fine Lace background set; Barely Banana, Certainly Celery, and Whisper White card stock; Always Artichoke Classic Stampin' Pad; VersaMark pad; Gold Glory Stampin' Emboss powder; Ivory 3/8" organdy ribbon; Stampin' Dimensionals

[188 A] Handmade with Love set; Chocolate Chip, Kraft, Mellow Moss, Ruby Red, and Very Vanilla card stock; Chocolate Chip, Mellow Moss, and Ruby Red Stampin' Write markers; Vintage brads; Black gingham ribbon; Stampin' Dimensionals; 1/4" Circle punch

[188 B] Handmade with Love II set; Kraft, Ruby Red, and Very Vanilla card stock; Chocolate Chip and Ruby Red Classic Stampin' Pads; linen thread; Stampin' Dimensionals; 1/16" Circle punch

[188 C] Business Memos set; By Definition, Canvas, and Word by Word background stamps; Chocolate Chip, Confetti White, Kraft, and Ruby Red card stock; Soft Subtles Mini Gable boxes & tags; Chocolate Chip, Creamy Caramel, and Ruby Red Classic Stampin' Pads; Chocolate grosgrain ribbon; Aged Copper Hodgepodge Hardware, Stampin' Dimensionals

[189 A] Word Play and Classic Alphabet sets; By Definition background stamp; Chocolate Chip, Kraft, Mellow Moss, Ruby Red, and Very Vanilla card stock; Basic Black, Chocolate Chip, and Ruby Craft Stampin' Pads; Natural hemp twine; Basic eyelets; Stainless Steel Metal Magic tags, Assortment II; Stampin' Dimensionals; Crafters' Tool Kit; watercolor brush

[189 B] Para Ti and Petal Pushers sets; Confetti White, Kraft, Mellow Moss, and Ruby Red card stock; Close to Cocoa, Mellow Moss, and Ruby Red Classic Stampin' Pads; Natural hemp twine; Stampin' Dimensionals

[190 A] Friend to Friend and Little Pieces sets; Geometric background stamp; Chocolate Chip, More Mustard, Old Olive, Rose Red, and Very Vanilla card stock; More Mustard, Old Olive, and Rose Red Classic Stampin' Pads; linen thread; Chocolate grosgrain ribbon; linen thread; Stampin' Dimensionals; 1/2" Circle punch; staples

[190 B] Season's Greetings and Sparkling Season sets; Chocolate Chip, More Mustard, Old Olive, Rose Red, and Very Vanilla card stock; Chocolate Chip, More Mustard, and Old Olive Classic Stampin' Pads; Chocolate grosgrain ribbon; linen thread; Stampin' Dimensionals; Crafters' Tool Kit; 1/8" Circle punch

[191 A] Let's Party, Everyday Flexible Phrases, Day-to-Day Flexible Phrases, and Expressive Flexible Phrases sets; Kraft, Old Olive, Rose Red, and Whisper White card stock; Chocolate Chip, Old Olive, and Rose Red Classic Stampin' Pads; Whisper White Craft Stampin' Pad; Chocolate Chip and More Mustard Stampin' Write markers; Mustard grosgrain ribbon; Silver eyelets; Natural hemp twine; Aged Copper Hodgepodge Hardware Kit; Stampin' Dimensionals; Crafters' Tool Kit

[191 B] Expressive Flexible Phrases and Shapes & Shadows sets; Kraft, Old Olive, and Rose Red card stock; Old Olive and Rose Red Classic Stampin' Pads; Neutrals buttons; Vellum Square Aluminum Metal Edge tags; Silver brads; Black gingham ribbon; linen thread; twill tape; Stampin' Dimensionals; Crafters' Tool Kit

[193 A] Journaling Fun, Sweet & Sassy, and Tidy Alphabet sets; Canvas background stamp; Ballet Blue, Kraft, Mellow Moss, and Real Red card stock; Ballet Blue, Close to Cocoa, Mellow Moss, and Real Red Craft Stampin' Pads; Basic Black Stampin' Write journaler; Silver eyelets; Silver brads; Natural hemp twine; Red gingham ribbon; Crafters' Tool Kit; sewing machine and thread

[193 B] Journaling Fun, Petal Pushers, and Pure & Simple Alphabet Upper and Lower sets; Ballet Blue, Kraft, Mellow Moss, and Real Red card stock; Ballet Blue, Brilliant Blue, Mellow Moss, and Real Red Craft Stampin' Pads; Basic Black Stampin' Write journaler; Silver eyelets; Moss gingham ribbon; twill tape; Natural hemp twine; window sheets; Stampin' Dimensionals; Crafters' Tool Kit

[203 A] Drawing on Nature and Wonderful Words sets; Simple Stripes background stamp; Barely Banana, Close to Cocoa, Confetti White, and Mellow Moss card stock; White vellum card stock; Basic Black, Close to Cocoa, Mellow Moss, and Summer Sun Craft Stampin' Pads; Basic Black Stampin' Write journaler; Natural hemp twine; 1/16" Circle punch; Stampin' Dimensionals; watercolor brush

[203 B] A Little Love set; Certainly Celery, Chocolate Chip, Kraft, Naturals Ivory, and Ruby Red card stock; Basic Black Classic Stampin' Pad; Certainly Celery, Creamy Caramel, and Ruby Red Stampin' Write markers; White Circle Aluminum Metal Edge tag; Black gingham ribbon; Chocolate grosgrain ribbon; Silver brad; Stampin' Dimensionals; mini envelope template; 1/8" and 1-1/4" Circle punches; sanding block; sewing machine and thread

[204 A] Great Shapes, Expressive Everyday Phrases, Classic Alphabet, and Headline Alphabet sets; Brocade Blue, Chocolate Chip, and Old Olive Craft Stampin' Pads; Bluebird grosgrain ribbon; Aged Copper Hodgepodge Hardware; linen album

[206 A] Aged to Perfection, Label Classics, and Sincere Salutations sets; Bordering Blue and Very Vanilla card stock; Confetti White & Kraft Mini Gable boxes & tags; Oxford Designer Series paper; Always Artichoke and Bordering Blue Classic Stampin' Pads; Natural hemp twine; Soft Subtles I eyelets; Crafters' Tool Kit

[206 B] Aged to Perfection and Everyday Flexible Phrases sets; Bordering Blue, Mellow Moss, and Naturals Ivory card stock; Oxford Designer Series paper and vellum; Night of Navy Craft Stampin' Pad; Antique Brass Hodgepodge Hardware; Moss gingham ribbon; linen thread; Stampin' Dimensionals; 1/8" Circle punch; watercolor brush

[208 A] Whimsical Upper and Lower Alphabet sets; Brocade Blue, Close to Cocoa, Night of Navy, and Whisper White card stock; Quick Strips I; Night of Navy Craft Stampin' Pad; Basic Black Stampin' Write journaler; Aged Copper Hodgepodge Hardware; Taupe grosgrain ribbon; Write Me a Memory Journaling Fonts CD, Volume II

[208 B] Letterpress Alphabet, Tidy Alphabet, and Simple Type Numbers sets; Quick Strips II; More Mustard, Old Olive, and Rose Red card stock; Whisper White & Very Vanilla tag sheets; More Mustard, Old Olive, and Rose Red Craft Stampin' Pads; Silver brads; Natural hemp twine; Stampin' Dimensionals; Write Me a Memory Journaling Fonts CD, Volume II; sewing machine and thread

[208 C] Alphadots set; I'm Here–Boy Simply Scrappin' Kit; Bashful Blue Craft Stampin' Pad; Basic Black Stampin' Write journaler; White vellum card stock; Silver brads; White 3/8" organdy ribbon; Stampin' Dimensionals

[209 A] Whimsical Alphabet set; In Full Bloom Simply Scrappin' Kit; Sage Shadow Craft Stampin' Pad; Basic Black Stampin' Write journaler; linen thread; Stampin' Dimensionals; 1/16" Circle punch

[209 B] Classic Alphabet and Letterpress Numbers sets; Summer Sketches Simply Scrappin' Kit; Natural hemp twine; Antique Brass Hodgepodge Hardware; Stampin' Dimensionals

[209 C] Newsprint Alphabet set; Vintage Keepsakes Simply Scrappin' Kit; Mellow Moss Craft Stampin' Pad; Antique Brass Hodgepodge Hardware; Moss gingham ribbon; Cream grosgrain ribbon; twill tape; window sheets; 1/4" Circle punch; Write Me a Memory Journaling Fonts CD, Volume II

[210 A] Expressive Flexible Phrases and Headline Alphabet sets; He's Too Cool Simply Scrappin' Kit; Always Artichoke and Not Quite Navy Craft Stampin' Pads; Basic Black Stampin' Write journaler; Spring Moss grosgrain ribbon; Stampin' Dimensionals; 1/8" Circle punch

[210 B] Newsprint Alphabet set; She's Too Cool Simply Scrappin' Kit; Natural hemp twine; linen thread; White eyelets; Apricot grosgrain ribbon; Stampin' Dimensionals; window sheets; Write Me a Memory Journaling Fonts CD, Volume II; Crafters' Tool Kit

[210 C] Classic Alphabet and Expressive Flexible Phrases sets; Sparkling Holiday Simply Scrappin' Kit; Close to Cocoa, Not Quite Navy, and Real Red Craft Stampin' Pads; Red grosgrain ribbon; Stampin' Dimensionals; paper clips; sewing machine and thread

[211 A] Classic Alphabet set; Toy Box Simply Scrappin' Kit; Basic Black Stampin' Write journaler; Not Quite Navy Craft Stampin' Pad; Spring Moss grosgrain ribbon; Stampin' Dimensionals; 1/8" Circle punch

[211 B] Simple Type Alphabet set; Buttons, Bows & Twinkletoes Simply Scrappin' Kit; Regal Rose Craft Stampin' Pad; Basic Black Stampin' Write journaler; Black and Light Pink gingham ribbon; Cream grosgrain ribbon; Bold Brights II and Soft Subtles I eyelets; Crafters' Tool Kit

[211 C] Newsprint Alphabet set; Polka Dot Party Simply Scrappin' Kit; Ballet Blue, Only Orange, and Regal Rose Craft Stampin' Pads; Basic Black Stampin' Write journaler; Apple Green and Rose grosgrain ribbon

[212 A] Pocket Full of Posies and Everyday Flexible Phrases sets; Naturals Ivory and So Saffron card stock; Soft Subtles Favor boxes & tags; Basic Black, So Saffron, and Rose Red Classic Stampin' Pads; Moss grosgrain ribbon; linen thread; Stampin' Dimensionals; 1/16" Circle punch

[212 B] Quick Thinking, Expressive Flexible Phrases, and Pocket Full of Posies sets; Certainly Celery and Very Vanilla card stock; Soft Subtles and Whisper White & Very Vanilla Bloomin' boxes & tags; Bashful Blue, Certainly Celery, and Regal Rose Classic Stampin' Pads; Celery grosgrain ribbon; Stampin' Dimensionals; sewing machine and thread

[212 C] Sweet & Sassy and Expressive Flexible Phrases sets; Earth Elements Petal cards & tags; Close to Cocoa, Confetti White, and Very Vanilla card stock; White Circle Aluminum Metal Edge tags; Cameo Coral and Old Olive Classic Stampin' Pads; Silver brads; linen thread; Taupe grosgrain ribbon; Stampin' Dimensionals; 1/16" Circle punch; Crafters' Tool Kit

[212 D] Petal Pushers set; Certainly Celery, So Saffron, and Very Vanilla card stock; Confetti White & Kraft Pillar boxes & tags; Bashful Blue and Certainly Celery Classic Stampin' Pads; Pewter Hodgepodge Hardware; Light Blue gingham ribbon; 1/8" and 1/2" Circle punches

[212 E] Winged Things set; Wings & Things wheel; Bashful Blue, Confetti White, and Pretty in Pink card stock; Basic Black, Pretty in Pink, Barely Banana and Bashful Blue Classic Stampin' Pads; Certainly Celery Stampin' Around cartridge; Soft Subtles Mini Gable boxes & tags; Dazzling Diamonds glitter; linen thread; Vintage brads; Stampin' Dimensionals; watercolor brush

[213 A] Expressive Flexible Phrases, Happy Hearts, Mini Medleys, and Wonderful Weaves sets; Naturals Ivory and Very Vanilla card stock; Soft Subtles Mini Gable boxes & tags; Pockets & Pieces, Assortment 1; Brocade Blue, Old Olive, Rose Red, and So Saffron Classic Stampin' Pads; Spring Moss grosgrain ribbon; Antique Brass Hodgepodge Hardware; Stampin' Dimensionals; sewing machine and thread

[213 B] Little Pieces, Expressive Flexible Phrases, and Bold Alphabet sets; Soft Subtles Purse boxes & tags; Bashful Blue, Old Olive, and Pretty in Pink Classic Stampin' Pads; Dazzling Diamonds Stampin' Glitter; linen thread; Celery grosgrain ribbon

[213 C] Everyday Flexible Phrases and Sweet & Sassy sets; Word by Word background stamp; Bashful Blue and Whisper White card stock; Pockets & Pieces, Assortment 2; Ballet Blue and Old Olive Classic Stampin' Pads; Vintage brads; Celery, French Blue, and Taupe grosgrain ribbons; Stampin' Dimensionals; 1/8" Circle punch

[213 D] Love without End and Everyday Flexible Phrases sets; Bashful Blue, So Saffron, and Very Vanilla card stock; Pockets & Pieces, Assortment 1; Bashful Blue, Chocolate Chip, and So Saffron Classic Stampin' Pads; Chocolate grosgrain ribbon; Silver brads; Stampin' Dimensionals; 1/2" Circle and 1/4" Square punches

[214 A] Everyday Flexible Phrases, Classic Numbers, Letterpress Alphabet, and Stencil Alphabet sets; Chocolate Chip, Rose Red, Sahara Sand, and Whisper White card stock; Saddle Stitch Book Kit, Assortment 7; Close to Cocoa, Old Olive, and Rose Red Classic Stampin' Pads; Chocolate grosgrain ribbon; Antique Brass Hodgepodge Hardware; sewing machine and thread

[214 B] Natural Beauty set; Print Pattern background stamp; Always Artichoke, Close to Cocoa, and Confetti White card stock; Always Artichoke and Close to Cocoa Classic Stampin' Pads; Pewter Hodgepodge Hardware; Taupe grosgrain ribbon; Moss gingham ribbon; Crafters' Tool Kit; 1/8" Circle punch; staple

[214 C] Love without End, Wonderful Words, and Everyday Flexible Phrases sets; Barely Banana, and Confetti White card stock; Soft Subtles tag sheets; Barely Banana, Bashful Blue, Basic Black, and Mellow Moss Classic Stampin' Pads; linen thread; 1/8" Circle punch; Stampin' Dimensionals

[214 D] In Full Bloom set; Soft Subtles tag sheets; Barely Banana, Bashful Blue, and Basic Black Classic Stampin' Pads; watercolor brush; linen thread; Bluebird grosgrain ribbon

[214 E] It's Your Birthday and Flower Filled sets; Soft Subtles tag sheets; Bashful Blue and Mellow Moss Classic Stampin' Pads; Natural hemp twine; Light Blue gingham ribbon; Crafters' Tool Kit

[215 A] Little Pieces and Everyday Flexible Phrases sets; Almost Amethyst, Pretty in Pink, and Whisper White card stock; Almost Amethyst and Rose Red Classic Stampin' Pads; Jet Black StazOn pad; Stainless Steel Metal Magic tags, Assortment 1; Light Pink gingham ribbon; linen thread; Stampin' Dimensionals

[215 B] Heartfelt Thanks set; Watercolor Joy wheel; Almost Amethyst, Pretty in Pink, Rose Red, and Whisper White card stock; Almost Amethyst and Rose Red Classic Stampin' Pads; Light Pink grosgrain ribbon; linen thread; White Square Aluminum Metal Edge tags; Large Corner Rounder punch; 1/8" Circle punch

[216 A] Petal Pushers set; Always Artichoke, Bravo Burgundy, and Kraft card stock; Always Artichoke, Bravo Burgundy, Chocolate Chip, and More Mustard Classic Stampin' Pads; Vintage brads; checkbook cover

[216 B] Aged to Perfection and Artifacts sets; Print Pattern background stamp; Always Artichoke and Kraft card stock; Heirloom Timeworn Collection paper; Always Artichoke, Chocolate Chip, and Creamy Caramel Classic Stampin' Pads; checkbook cover; sewing machine and thread

[216 C] Shapes & Shadows and Pure & Simple Alphabet Lower sets; More Mustard, Old Olive, and Ruby Red Classic Stampin' Pads; puzzles and envelopes

[216 D] Going Buggy and Tidy Alphabet sets; Whisper White tag sheets; Earth Elements tag sheets; Chocolate Chip, Really Rust, and Old Olive Classic Stampin' Pads; Chocolate grosgrain ribbon; Natural hemp twine; Silver eyelets; Stampin' Dimensionals; memo cube; Crafters' Tool Kit

[216 E] Happiest of Holidays set; Swirling Stars wheel; Confetti White, Mellow Moss, and Ruby Red card stock; Accordion Book Kit, Assortment 4; wrapping paper; Real Red Classic Stampin' Pad; Ruby Red Stampin' Around cartridge; Spring Moss grosgrain ribbon; linen thread; Pewter Hodgepodge Hardware; Stampin' Dimensionals

[216 F] Fun Filled set; Creamy Caramel, Lavender Lace, Rose Red, and Whisper White card stock; Creamy Caramel, Lavender Lace, Lovely Lilac, and Rose Red Classic Stampin' Pads; Jet Black StazOn pad; Caramel gingham ribbon; window sheets; 1/8" Circle punch

[216 G] Wonderful Weaves, Mini Messages, and Newsprint Alphabet sets; Bashful Blue, Old Olive, Ruby Red, and Whisper White card stock; Pockets & Pieces, Assortment 2; Bashful Blue, Old Olive, and Ruby Red Craft Stampin' Pads; Earth Elements buttons; Natural hemp twine; linen thread; Stampin' Dimensionals; 1/4" Square punch

[216 H] Autumn Leaf Prints, Classic Alphabet, and Everyday Flexible Phrases sets; Canvas background stamp; Always Artichoke, Kraft, Ruby Red, and Whisper White card stock; 6" x 6" Days to Remember desktop calendar; Pockets & Pieces, Assortment 1; Creamy Caramel, Ruby Red and Chocolate Chip Craft Stampin' Pads; Close to Cocoa Stampin' Write journaler; Creamy Caramel Stampin' Write marker; Caramel gingham ribbon; Aged Copper Hodgepodge Hardware; Stampin' Dimensionals

[217 A] Do the Hula and Everyday Flexible Phrases sets; Tempting Turquoise and Whisper White card stock; Almost Amethyst, Apricot Appeal, Gable Green, Ruby Red, and Tempting Turquoise Classic Stampin' Pads; Kraft Gable box; Eggplant and Turquoise grosgrain ribbon

[217 B] Cheery Chat and Going Buggy sets; Only Orange and Whisper White card stock; Basic Black, Green Galore, Lovely Lilac, Only Orange, and Tempting Turquoise Craft Stampin' Pads; White gift sack; Tangerine grosgrain ribbon

[217 C] Everyday Flexible Phrases, Expressive Flexible Phrases, All about U, and Headline Alphabet sets; Canvas background stamp; Apricot Appeal, Confetti White, and Regal Rose card stock; door hanger; Apricot Appeal and Regal Rose Classic Stampin' Pads; Light Pink gingham ribbon; Rose grosgrain ribbon; Clear buttons; Stampin' Dimensionals; white thread

[217 D] Expressive Everyday Flexible Phrases, All about U, and Headline Alphabet sets; Print Pattern background stamp; large bookmark; Always Artichoke, Bravo Burgundy, and Chocolate Chip Craft Stampin' Pads; Creamy Caramel Classic Stampin' Pad; Aged Copper Hodgepodge Hardware; Caramel gingham ribbon; Burgundy grosgrain ribbon; Stampin' Dimensionals

[217 E] All about U set; Canvas background stamp; Apricot Appeal and Whisper White card stock; door hanger pouch; Apricot Appeal and Regal Rose Craft Stampin' Pads; Rose grosgrain ribbon; Stampin' Dimensionals; paper clip

[217 F] Sweet Talk set; Confetti White & Kraft tag sheets; Basic Black, Lavender Lace, and Pretty in Pink Classic Stampin' Pads; crochet thread; Small organdy bags; brayer

[217 G] All-Year Cheer I, Sweet & Sassy, and Wonderful Weaves sets; Confetti White & Kraft Purse boxes & tags; Apricot Appeal, Basic Black, and Lavender Lace Classic Stampin' Pads; Vintage brads; Natural hemp twine; Delphinium grosgrain ribbon; Stampin' Dimensionals; Medium Flat cellophane bags; watercolor brush

[219 A] Buds & Blossoms, Letterpress Alphabet, and Expressive Flexible Phrases sets; Certainly Celery, Chocolate Chip, Kraft, and Tempting Turquoise card stock; Basic Black, Creamy Caramel; Certainly Celery, Chocolate Chip, Kraft, and Tempting Turquoise Craft Stampin' Pads; Natural hemp twine; Chocolate grosgrain ribbon; Silver eyelets; Basic Black Stampin' Write journaler; Stampin' Dimensionals; Plaidmaker templates; brayer; sewing machine and thread; staple

[221 A] Artifacts and Expressive Flexible Phrases sets; Canvas background stamp; Always Artichoke, Bravo Burgundy, and Very Vanilla card stock; Bravo Burgundy and Creamy Caramel Classic Stampin' Pads; Natural hemp twine; Stampin' Dimensionals; stamping sponges

[221 B] Burst into Bloom and Everyday Flexible Phrases sets; Certainly Celery, Lavender Lace, Regal Rose, and Very Vanilla card stock; Whisper White & Very Vanilla tag sheets; Certainly Celery and Regal Rose Classic Stampin' Pads; White Craft Stampin' Pad; Wire Works; Light Orchid grosgrain ribbon; Soft Subtles buttons; Stampin' Dimensionals; 1-1/4" Circle and Slit punches

[222 A] Petal Pushers and Sassy Sayings II sets; Pretty in Pink, Regal Rose, Rose Red, and Whisper White card stock; Basic Black Classic Stampin' Pad; Cotton Candy Spectrum pad; Rose grosgrain ribbon; Stampin' Dimensionals

[222 B] All-Year Cheer II and Bold Butterfly sets; Gable Green, Lavender Lace, Pretty in Pink, and Whisper White card stock; Lavender Lace Classic Stampin' Pad; VersaMark pad; Crystal Clear Stampin' Emboss powder; Silver brad; Light Pink gingham ribbon; 1/4" and 1/2" Circle punches

[223 A] Pretty Princess set; Confetti White, Gable Green, Lavender Lace, and Pretty in Pink card stock; Basic Black, Gable Green, and Regal Rose Classic Stampin' pads; Delphinium grosgrain ribbon; Stampin' Dimensionals; Watercolor pencils; watercolor brush

[223 B] Friends Are Like Flowers set; Bashful Blue, Certainly Celery, and Confetti White card stock; Barely Banana, Bashful Blue, Basic Black, Certainly Celery, and Pixie Pink Classic Stampin' Pads; White Square Aluminum Metal Edge tags; Light Blue gingham ribbon; Silver brads; Stampin' Dimensionals; watercolor brush

[225 A] Just Beakause and Newsprint Alphabet sets; Island wheel; Barely Banana, Certainly Celery, Orchid Opulence, Pink Passion, and Whisper White card stock; Barely Banana, Basic Black, Certainly Celery, Orchid Opulence, and Pink Passion Craft Stampin Pads; Basic Black Stampin' Write journaler; Whisper White Craft Stampin' Around cartridge; White Square Aluminum Metal Edge tags; Silver brads; linen thread; Stampin' Dimensionals; 1/4" and 1/2" Circle punches

[225 B] Smitten and Everyday Flexible Phrases sets; All Heart wheel; Old Olive, Almost Amethyst, and Regal Rose card stock; Earth Elements Pillar boxes & tags; Old Olive and Lavender Lace Classic Stampin' Pads; Old Olive Classic Stampin' cartridge; Rose grosgrain ribbon; Silver eyelets; Wire Works; Crafters' Tool Kit; Stampin' Dimensionals; 1/16" Circle punch

[227 A] Shapes & Shadows and Everyday Flexible Phrases sets; Certainly Celery, Naturals Ivory, and Ruby Red card stock; Certainly Celery Craft Stampin' Pad; Ruby Red Classic Stampin' Pad; Silver brads; linen thread; Shapes & Shadows Classy Brass template; 1/16" Circle punch

[230 A] Merry set; Always Artichoke, Confetti White, Mellow Moss, and Ruby Red card stock; Always Artichoke and Ruby Red Classic Stampin' Pads; Moss gingham ribbon; Wire Works; 1/16" Circle punch; Stampin' Dimensionals

[230 B] Happy Hearts and Alphabits sets; Brocade Blue and Whisper White card stock; Earth Elements tag sheets; Basic Black and Ruby Red Classic Stampin' Pads; Earth Elements button; Black gingham ribbon; linen thread; Stampin' Dimensionals; 1/4" Square punch

[230 C] Baby Talk set; Ballet Blue, Bashful Blue, Confetti White, and Kraft card stock; Ballet Blue, Bashful Blue, Basic Black, and Creamy Caramel Classic Stampin' Pads; Brights beads; linen thread; Crystal Effects; Stampin' Dimensionals; watercolor brush

[230 D] Sweet & Sassy set; Almost Amethyst, Regal Rose, and Whisper White card stock; Regal Rose Classic Stampin' Pad; Light Pink gingham ribbon; micro beads; Stampin' Dimensionals; 1-3/8" Square punch

[230 E] Mini Medleys set; By Definition background stamp; Ruby Red card stock; Confetti White & Kraft tag sheets; Ruby Red Classic Stampin' Pad; Jet Black StazOn pad; Clear button; Black gingham ribbon; linen thread; White Square Aluminum Metal Edge tags; Silver brads; 1/4" Circle punch

[231 A] Fun with Shapes and Everyday Flexible Phrases sets; Confetti Cream, Mellow Moss, and Real Red card stock; Mellow Moss and Real Red Classic Stampin' Pads; VersaMark pad; White Square Brass Metal Edge tags; Pearl Ex powder, Assortment III; Gold cord; twill tape

[231 B] Bundle Up and Everyday Flexible Phrases sets; Kraft, Not Quite Navy, Old Olive, and Whisper White card stock; Always Artichoke, Chocolate Chip, Close to Cocoa, Not Quite Navy, and Old Olive Classic Stampin' Pads; White Craft Stampin' Pad; Stampin' Dimensionals; linen thread; 1/8" Circle punch; watercolor brush

[231 C] Gladsome Garden and Everyday Flexible Phrases sets; Basic Black and Regal Rose card stock; Basic Black and Regal Rose Classic Stampin' Pads; Black Magic Mesh; Vintage brad; White Round Aluminum Metal Edge tag; Light Pink gingham ribbon; Stampin' Dimensionals

[231 D] Everyday Flexible Phrases and Merry sets; Bashful Blue, Mellow Moss, and Very Vanilla card stock; Bashful Blue and Chocolate Chip Classic Stampin' Pads; twill tape; Antique Brass Hodgepodge Hardware

PROPRIETARY RIGHTS IN TRADEMARKS AND COPYRIGHTS

The contents of this catalog are protected by federal trademark and copyright registrations. Reproduction of the catalog or any portion thereof is strictly prohibited. Purchasers of Stampin' Up! products are authorized to sell hand-stamped artwork made with our copyrighted designs only in accordance with Stampin' Up!'s angel policy, a copy of which can be found on the Stampin' Up! Web site at www.stampinup. com, or obtained from a Stampin' Up! demonstrator. Permission is not granted to mechanically reproduce stamped images.

ORDERING

All products in this catalog may be purchased only through a Stampin' Up! demonstrator. Demonstrators are independent contractors and are not employees of Stampin' Up! To help your demonstrator ensure accuracy in taking your order, always include item number, description, and price of each item ordered. Your demonstrator will provide you with two copies of your order. Please retain these copies for your personal records. You have a right to cancel order within 3 days of placing it. Ask your demonstrator for more details.

DELIVERY

We ship through the best carrier available. Product is usually shipped to deliver within seven business days from the date the order is received by the company. Stampin' Up! shall not be liable for any delay in shipment that is caused in whole or in part by circumstances beyond Stampin' Up!'s control.

GUARANTEE

We guarantee products to be free from manufacturing defects for a period of 90 days after the shipping date. Missing items, incorrect shipments, and defective or damaged merchandise must be reported to your demonstrator within 90 days of the shipping date. This guarantee does not cover merchandise damaged through accident or misuse. If you should require assistance, please contact your demonstrator.

EXCHANGES & REFUNDS

New, unused merchandise may be exchanged at no charge within 90 days of the shipping date. The merchandise must be in the current catalog and in original shipping condition. Stamps that have been assembled cannot be exchanged. Sorry, we do not offer cash refunds. The customer is responsible for return shipping charges. If you should require assistance, please contact your demonstrator.

LIMITATIONS

Stampin' Up! reserves the right to issue a refund or substitute merchandise of similar quality and value for items that are discontinued or out of stock. The decision to discontinue merchandise and the choice of whether to issue a refund or substitution belongs solely to Stampin' Up! The items sold are craft items, and your results may vary from the examples shown. Also, actual stamps may vary somewhat in size from the images shown in this catalog, and this difference in size shall not be deemed a manufacturing defect.

Information about properties of certain products (such as acid content, lignin content, and other properties affecting a product's performance or suitability for a particular use) is supplied by the product manufacturers and/or suppliers. Stampin' Up! relies on this information and does not conduct independent tests to verify the accuracy of the information supplied by product manufacturers and suppliers.

TRADEMARK OWNERSHIP

Fluid Chalk is a trademark and Option Pad, Color Box, Petal Point, and Top Boss are registered trademarks of Clearsnap, Inc. Dotto, Empressor, Painty, Stamp-a-ma-jig, and ZIG are registered trademarks of EK Success. Lumiere is a registered trademark of Jacquard products manufactured by Rupert, Gibbon & Spider, Inc. Magic Mesh is a trademark of Magic Mesh by Avant Card, LLC. uni-ball is a registered trademark of Mitsubishi Pencil Co. Coluzzle is a registered trademark of Provo Craft and Novelty, Inc. Aqua Painter, Color Caddy, Fancy Fibers, Flexible Phrases, Forget-Me-Not Keeper, Hodgepodge Hardware, Metal Magic, Plaidmaker, Quick Strips, SNAIL Adhesive, Stampin' Carry, the boxed logo of the words Stampin' Memories, The Tearing Edge, and Watercolor Wonder crayons are trademarks of Stampin' Up!, Inc. Bold Brights, Color Coach, Classy Brass, Definitely Decorative, Earth Elements, Embossing Buddy, Rich Regals, Simply Scrappin', Soft Subtles, Stampin' Around, Stampin' Dimensionals, Stampin' Emboss, Stampin' Ink, Stampin' Kids, Stampin' Memories, Stampin' Mist, Stampin' Pads, Stampin' Pastels, Stampin' Scrub, Stampin' Spot, Stampin' Up! and the boxed logo of the words Stampin' Up!, Stampin' Write, Two-Step Stampin', and Write Me a Memory are registered trademarks of Stampin' Up!, Inc. StazOn and VersaMarker are trademarks and Encore!, Kaleidacolor, and VersaMark are registered trademarks of Tsukineko, Inc.

Stampin' Up!
12907 South 3600 West
Riverton, UT 84065
www.stampinup.com

stampin' up!

Make Stampin' Up! Part of Your Family

Just as Stampin' Up! demonstrators provide their customers with one-stop shopping and individualized service, Stampin' Up! provides its demonstrators with the opportunity to meet their individual goals. Whether you'd like to earn money to pay for your stamping supplies, create a full- or part-time career, or simply get a discount on your stamping supplies, Stampin' Up! will help you do it.

With an investment of $199, you'll receive stamp sets, accessories, and business supplies to help you get started. Valued at $355, the starter kit is a terrific value. Once you purchase the starter kit, you'll become a member of the Stampin' Up! family, which entitles you to these benefits:

- A monthly magazine packed with business tips and project ideas.

- Access to our Demonstrator Web Site, where you'll find forms, flyers, tips, and hundreds of project ideas.

- The chance to attend any of the exciting Stampin' Up! events, such as our annual convention and regional conferences.

Take advantage of the opportunity to bring the benefits of Stampin' Up! into your family. Whatever your goals, Stampin' Up! can help you succeed. Contact your demonstrator and find out how you can join us today!

256